KU-489-688

THE
BRITISH ISLES

University of Liverpool

Withdrawn from stock

Also by G. H. Dury

MAP INTERPRETATION
THE CHANNEL ISLANDS
THE FACE OF THE EARTH
THE EAST MIDLANDS AND THE PEAK
GENERAL THEORY OF MEANDERING VALLEYS
ESSAYS IN GEOMORPHOLOGY (*Editor*)

University of Liverpool
Withdrawn from stock

G. H. DURY

M A, PH D, FGS

McCaughey Professor of Geography,
The University of Sydney, Australia

The British Isles

A SYSTEMATIC AND REGIONAL GEOGRAPHY

THIRD EDITION

HEINEMANN
LONDON

Heinemann Educational Books Ltd
LONDON   MELBOURNE   TORONTO
SINGAPORE AUCKLAND
CAPE TOWN   IBADAN
HONG KONG

© G. H. DURY 1961, 1963, 1965

FIRST PUBLISHED 1961
REPRINTED 1961
SECOND EDITION 1963
REPRINTED 1964
THIRD EDITION 1965

PUBLISHED BY
HEINEMANN EDUCATIONAL BOOKS LTD
48 CHARLES STREET, LONDON W1
PRINTED IN GREAT BRITAIN FOR THE PUBLISHERS BY
ROBERT MACLEHOSE AND COMPANY LIMITED
THE UNIVERSITY PRESS, GLASGOW

R105091

Contents

PART ONE

PART TWO

v

List of Diagrams and Maps

List of Plates

Acknowledgments

I AM deeply grateful for the considerable help I have received in assembling material and in writing. A number of friends have kindly commented on the text in manuscript. Public bodies who have supplied information include the British Iron and Steel Federation; the British Petroleum Company, Ltd.; the British Transport Commission; the Central Electricity Authority; the Central Office of Information; the Central Statistics Office, Dublin; Lloyd's Register of Shipping; London County Council; the Ministry of Agriculture and Ministry of Commerce, Northern Ireland; the Ministry of Housing and Local Government; the National Coal Board; the National Forestry Commission; the North of Scotland Hydro-Electricity Board; the Port of London Authority; and the United Kingdom Atomic Energy Authority. Many town clerks, public relations officers, and chambers of commerce have also been liberal with material.

The following figures are based upon Ordnance Survey maps with the sanction of the Controller of H.M. Stationery Office (Crown Copyright reserved): 27, 105, 120, 123 (based on the O.S. 1 : 63,360 Map); 85, 112, 140, 142, 148, 153 (based on the O.S. 1 : 25,000 Map); and 30, 86, 87, 92, 107, 110, 121, 122, 132, 152, 157 (based on the O.S. 1 : 10,560 Map). Figures 28 and 133 are based, by permission, on the 1 : 63,360 Map of the Geological Survey of England and Wales. Figure 21 is based, by permission, on the 1 : 63,360 Map of the Soil Survey of England and Wales, and Figure 98 on the corresponding Map of the Soil Survey of Scotland.

I should like to record especial gratitude to those who organised and undertook the sample land-use surveys. The relevant material was communicated by Miss M. McCririck (Figure 86); Mrs. M. Jones (Figure 87); Miss J. Roberts (Figure 92); Miss D. H. E. Watson (Figure 107); Mr. F. S. Hudson (Figure 110); Mr. R. O. Smith (Figures 121a, 121b); Miss E. M. Born (Figure 122); Mr. W. G. S. Edwards (Figure 132); Mr. G. Hones (Figure 152); and Mr. R. H. C. Carr-Gregg (Figure 157). These, their helpers, and additional correspondents whose information is incorporated in the text instead of in illustrations, were most generous with time and energy, and extremely kind in acceding to my requests to make the surveys. Mr. P. T. Wheeler, with equal kindness, has allowed me to use, in Figure 94, information which he has collected in a survey of crofting.

Photographs have been supplied by the following, who retain the copyright: Aerofilms Ltd. (Plates 1–4, 10, 32, 34, 38, 43, 46, 51, 62, 63, 66); The Belfast Telegraph (Plate 24); Brighton Corporation (Plate 3); the British Iron and Steel Federation (Plate 17); the British Council (Plate 5); the British Motor Corporation (Plate 54); the British Petroleum Co., Ltd. (Plates 39, 40); the British Travel and Holiday Association (Plates 30, 33, 35, 41, 45, 59, 61); the Caterpillar Tractor Co., Ltd. (Plate 11); the Central Electricity Generating Board (Plate 53); Colin Cuff (Plate 22); Crawley Development Corporation (Plate 23); the English Steel Corporation, Ltd. (Plate 18); the Esso Petroleum Co., Ltd. (Plate 20); Imperial Chemical Industries, Ltd. (Plate 13); the International Wool Secretariat (Plates 36, 50); the Irish Tourist Bureau (Plates 26–28); Kemsley Newspapers, Ltd. (Plate 19); the National Coal Board (Plate 14); the North of Scotland Hydro-Electricity Board (Plate 37); the Northern Ireland Government Office (Plate 25); Paul Popper (Plate 71); Photoflight Ltd. (Plates 9, 16, 47–49, 52, 55–57, 64, 67, 69, 70, 72); Sylvia Hall (Plate 65); and the United Kingdom Atomic Energy Authority (Plate 15).

Brian T. Bunting, of Birkbeck College (University of London), kindly undertook the indexing.

Preface to Third Edition

IN revising for this edition, I have wherever possible incorporated the suggestions which correspondents have helpfully made. Since part of the preliminary report on the 1961 census is alone available at the time of revision, it is not possible to change statistics of industrial employment, or the maps drawn from these statistics, which still relate to the returns of 1951. Data on population, however, have been altered in accordance with the 1961 records. Sample maps of land use, summaries of land use for regions, and general maps of agricultural distributions have not been altered, since they already related to the conditions of the late 1950s—for the most part, to the period 1957–1959, but other economic data have, wherever possible, been brought into the 1960s. For help with revision I am indebted to Barry W. Higman.

Department of Geography   G. H. DURY
The University of Sydney
Sydney, NSW, Australia

PART ONE

CHAPTER 1

Livelihood and Land Use

IN the British Isles, 57 million people live in an area of 120,000 square miles. The average density of population—some 470 per square mile —is very high. For what the comparison is worth, this figure may be set against the densities of 769 per square mile in Belgium, 642 per square mile in Japan, and 520 per square mile in Western Germany. England as a whole is far more densely peopled than are the other parts of the British Isles, with an average of 860 people to the square mile, against 330 in Wales, 270 in Northern Ireland, 175 in Scotland, and 110 in the Irish Republic.

A density of 470 per square mile is equivalent to one person for every 6,600 square yards—i.e. one to a plot of land about 300 ft. long and 200 ft. wide, roughly 1½ acres in extent. But such an average plot would include land of varying quality, for the land of the British Isles varies greatly both in its nature and in the use to which it is put. Not much more than half the total area is improved farmland. The average extent of improved farmland per head of population is but 4,000 square yards—equivalent to a plot 300 ft. long and only 120 ft. wide, rather less than 1 acre in area. Now in the cool rainy climate of the British Isles, and in the rather high latitudes in which the islands lie, there can be no question of producing from so little land enough food for so many people. Even if the standard of living fell to incredibly low levels, the British Isles could not support their present population by the unaided means of their own agricultural resources.

The high density of population sets a problem of land use and of livelihood. Within the British Isles it implies a pressure on land, a pressure reflected both in competition for space and in intensive cultivation. Externally, a high standard of living and a high density of population imply a vigorous overseas trade, which in its turn depends on a great industrial output. It is no exaggeration to say that the economy and the standard of living of the U.K. are maintained by external trade far more directly than are those of any other nation. The manifest dangers of such a condition reveal themselves

1

fully in time of war, as when during the Napoleonic and the two
World Wars a hostile blockade was imposed; they can also be
severe in times of peace, as when world trade slumped during the
Great Depression of the 1930s. In the later part of 1956 and during
the early months of 1957, the rationing of petrol followed the blocking
of the Suez Canal—a purely political matter. But it is pointless to
deplore the dependence of the U.K. or of the Irish Republic on
external trade. This dependence is a fact which must be recognised
and accepted.

The present geographical status of the British Isles, and the nature
of the geographical problem which they present, are indicated by
summary statistics of employment, land use, and oversea trade. The
relevant figures, showing the dominant occupations of the people,
the chief goods produced and the chief services rendered, the
significance of external trade in the economy, and the distribution
of land among various categories of use, give a factual basis to the
general statement that the British Isles are highly industrialised,
intensively cultivated, and deeply committed to production for
export.

LABOUR FORCE AND NATIONAL PRODUCT

FIG. 1. Employment in the United Kingdom and in the Irish Republic

As Fig. 1 shows, half the people in the United Kingdom are at
work.[1] By far the largest group works in manufacturing, which takes
over one-third of the entire labour force. When workers in mines
and quarries are added to those in manufacturing, the combined
total of people directly employed in industry nears two-fifths of all
workers. A further 1 in 5 is engaged in transport, communication,
or distribution—that is, in moving people, goods, and mail, or in

[1] The term *at work* is used here to mean *in paid employment*. Housewives are
excluded, for census purposes, from the categories of people in paid employment.

transmitting messages. One in four is needed to supply the great range of professional, financial, administrative and defensive services which a complex industrial society demands; included in this group are doctors, bankers, professional scientists, civil servants, and members of the armed forces. Already more than 80% of the whole labour force has been accounted for.[1] More than half of those remaining work in building and construction, or in supplying gas, water or electricity. Agriculture, forestry and fishing combined employ fewer than 1 in 20 of all workers in the U.K.

FIG. 2. Percentage origin of national product,
United Kingdom and Irish Republic

A generally similar distribution appears in Fig. 2, which shows the origin of the national product. The figures from which this diagram is constructed are for the *net* national product—that is, for values added during manufacture or processing and for services rendered. They represent the contributions made by the various groups of activity, after allowance has been made for costs of working and of materials. The grouping has been changed slightly from that used in Fig. 1, so as to bring together manufacture, mining and quarrying, and building and construction. These account for well over two-fifths of the net national product. Buying and selling of goods, carriage of goods, mail and passengers, and the transmission of messages account for another quarter. Agriculture, forestry and fishing yield but a twentieth of the net product, mostly from agriculture. Both in its contribution to the net product, and in its demands on the labour force, manufacture predominates, and in both respects agriculture occupies a minor place.

The diagrams for the Irish Republic (Figs. 1 and 2) immediately reveal a number of striking differences from the United Kingdom. Agriculture, forestry and fishing take one-third of the labour force of the Republic, whereas in the U.K. the two last-named make small demands for workers. Farms in the Irish Republic take proportionally as many workers as do factories in the U.K.—a fundamental

[1] Both the diagram and the text refer to a time of little unemployment.

contrast in economy. Manufacturing in the Republic employs but one worker in seven, and transport, communication and distribution have as great a need for labour as has industry.

Agriculture makes the greatest single contribution to the net national product of the Irish Republic, but is less dominant than in its demand for workers: with two-fifths of the labour force it provides but one-third of the total net product, whereas manufacture with one worker in seven accounts for a quarter of the product. Worker for worker, agriculture in the Republic is only half as productive as manufacture, whereas the agriculture of the U.K. can be described as running at a pitch of industrial efficiency.

EXTERNAL TRADE

The United Kingdom in 1962 imported goods at the rate of some £88 per head of its population.[1] Exports of goods ran at about £77 per head.[1] Food, beverages, and tobacco accounted for some 35% by value of imports into the U.K. in 1960, and raw materials for some 20%. Although some items in the first group can hardly be called essential, one-third of the meat and two-thirds of the flour consumed in the U.K. are imported. Industry and transport depend on external supplies as heavily as the people depend on imported food: wool, cotton, timber and ores are prominent in the list of imports, and large quantities of oil are also brought in (Fig. 3).

FIG. 3. Percentage comparison of the import and export trades of the United Kingdom by value

Manufactured goods dominate the export trade of the U.K. In the early 1960s they provided more than 80% of exports by value. Machinery, vehicles and aircraft alone accounted for two-fifths of the total.

[1] These figures refer only to visible trade: see Chap. 9.

The volume of external trade per head of population in the Irish Republic is less than that of the U.K., with exports in 1962 at some £56 per head, and imports some £91 per head. But the nature of trade differs very strongly from that of the U.K. Of imports into the Republic, 52% by value consist of manufactured goods, while two-thirds of exports by value are provided by live cattle and food-stuffs (Fig 4). The contrast in the economies of the two nations is brought out as clearly in the records of trade as by statistics of employment and of production.

FIG. 4. Percentage comparison of the export and import trades of the Irish Republic, by value

LAND USE

Since the economy of the whole of the U.K. is dominated by manufacturing industry, its component countries may suitably be grouped together in a summary account of the labour force, national product, and trade. Such a grouping is further justified by the political fact that goods passing through the ports of the U.K. are subject to a single system of regulations—for purposes of trade, prohibitions, subsidies, and tariffs, the U.K. is a single unit. But when land use is discussed, it becomes desirable to separate England, Wales, Scotland and Northern Ireland from one another. As can be seen from Fig. 5, there are pronounced differences between them in the uses to which their land is put, and in the relative extent of the major categories of land use.

Two-thirds of the land of England is improved farmland, despite the demands for space made by towns, roads, and railways. Tillage[1] takes more than one-third of the total area, improved grassland[1]

[1] Tillage excludes rotation; grass improved grassland includes both rotation and permanent grass.

rather less than one-third. Rough grazing is limited in extent, amounting to little more than one-tenth of the whole, and one-fifth of the country is put to non-agricultural uses.

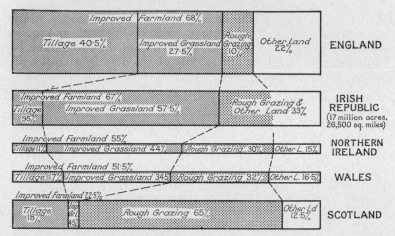

FIG. 5. Summaries of land use, by countries

Northern Ireland and the Irish Republic resemble one another in the distribution of their land among categories of use. The proportion of improved farmland in Ireland as a whole is almost identical with that in England—namely, about two-thirds. Tillage, however, takes a far smaller share in the land of Ireland than in that of England, for while more than half of Ireland is in improved grass, only one-eighth is in tillage. Rough grazing[1] is proportionally twice as extensive as in England, amounting to no less than one-fifth of the total land area. Industry, towns, roads and railways are far less common in Ireland than in England, and the proportion of non-agricultural land in Ireland is no larger than one-eighth of the total area.

In Wales (Fig. 5) improved farmland is reduced to little over half of the land area, and tillage in this country amounts to less than a fifth of the whole—a figure similar to Scotland's. Rough grazing in Wales is correspondingly extensive, covering nearly the entire country. Non-agricultural land is about as extensive as tillage.

Figures for Scotland show a still smaller proportion of agriculturally productive land. Rough grazing is by far the most extensive kind of use (Fig. 5), taking well over half of the entire area. Farmland is confined to less than one-quarter; it is restricted mainly at

[1] Separate figures for rough grazing are not available for Northern Ireland, and the fraction of the total area allocated to this category in the six northern counties is estimated.

the expense of grass, for the proportion of land in tillage is not much lower in Scotland than in Wales or in Ireland. Non-agricultural land amounts to one-fifth of Scotland; but whereas in England this category mostly represents the works of man, in Scotland it includes a great deal of bare rock.

CONCLUSION

Differences between one portion and another of the British Isles are already making themselves apparent, even in summary statistics for whole countries. These summaries are bound to obscure the contrasts which occur within each of the countries—that is to say, between the regions into which each country can be subdivided. Regional character and regional differences are however reserved to a later section of the book. This chapter has attempted neither detailed description nor explanation: it is meant merely to present in very general terms some leading facts about the present geographical condition of the British Isles.

This short account is both the starting-point and the objective of the chapters which follow. There has been nothing inevitable in the developments which have brought the British Isles to their existing geographical state—nothing, that is to say, except the fact that those developments took the course which they did. In so far as this book is an enquiry into present-day geography, it must therefore attempt to be both informative and explanatory. It must seek to show the nature of the land and of the climate of the British Isles, and to indicate the ways in which the use made of the land by man has changed. Only by taking into account the resources of the land, and the way in which those resources have been exploited through the centuries, can one hope to understand the geography of the British Isles today.

CHAPTER 2

The Nature of the Land

THE physical environment provides, as it were, much of a country's working capital, fixed assets, and reserves. But the people are in no way obliged to exploit any particular part or property of their environment, and given elements of the environment can have different worth at different times.

A few examples will readily illustrate these principles. In Roman days, the surplus economic wealth of the British Isles was provided by food and raw materials—grain from the limestone uplands of the south and tin and lead from the mountains. During the Middle Ages fortunes were made from sheep, many of which grazed on the Cotswolds where the land had once been tilled, and where much is again under the plough today. When industry made its first beginnings, wood served for fuel and running water supplied power, so that forests and streams—instead of coalfields and seaports—influenced the location of manufacturing. The south coast of England was the sunniest part of the British Isles many centuries ago, just as it is today, but its climate did not acquire a cash value in the resort trade until quite recent times. Whereas the physical environment is, for most practical purposes, a stable one, the relationship between people and their surroundings is selective and inconstant. Changes in that relationship accompany changes in economy and in culture.

At all times, the environment sets practical limits on what people can do—limits of possibility, limits of commonsense, and limits of cost. Mineral resources are limited to certain districts; climate (among other factors) prevents the growing of wheat in the Scottish Highlands; tropical fruits could be grown in the British Isles in hot-houses, but only at great expense. Cost exerts a powerful influence on production in the competitive world of the present day. Competition tends, in a general way, to confine manufacture to those districts where it can show a profit—districts where geographical advantages are greatest. But since production of food or of goods is promoted by the need to make a living, and not primarily by the facts of the environment, one must expect the physical environment to prove favourable in some places and in some ways, but to be adverse in others.

8

Adjustment to environment is most easily studied where people depend directly on the resources of the land. Very many people in the British Isles work in industry, and their dependence on the land is indirect. To this extent the influence of the physical environment on their lives is remote. On the other hand, the leading industries of the British Isles, subject to severe international competition, need to make the most of natural resources as well as of technical skill. They demand a huge and ever-growing range of raw materials. If industry is to be maintained and expanded, the resources of the British Isles must be increasingly exploited. Advantage will be taken of elements in the environment which have hitherto been neglected or little used—compare the rising output of domestic iron-ore, the recently-built hydro-electric stations in the rainy highlands, and the working of domestic oil and natural gas. Although a high state of economic development means, in one sense, a certain freedom from or command over the environment, in another sense it makes for closer links with it, complex though those links may be.

In the British Isles there is obviously some kind of association between the distribution of people, crops and livestock on the one hand, and the qualities of landforms, soils and climate on the other. Significantly enough, the geographical contrasts between various parts of the British land have intensified themselves in the last hundred years. It seems that the mode of adjustment between man and land is better defined today than it was a century ago. A given association may, however, reflect a complicated relationship between people and their surroundings. The connection of sheep-grazing and sparse population with certain upland districts, for instance, is by no means as simple as it looks at first sight. Even when they seem self-explanatory, existing distributions are usually the result of centuries of development. It is, moreover, impossible to say exactly how the environment produces an effect on the people. Men do not migrate from upland districts simply because the land is high, any more than they settle on coalfields simply because coal is found there. The influence of the environment works at several removes. The best that can be done is to define and contrast the different qualities of different environments, and to describe the adjustments to them which have actually been made.

TIME-SCALES

In tracing the physical evolution of the British Isles, it is necessary to use more than one time-scale. On the scale of historical time, which is graduated in years and centuries, the physical environment appears to change very slowly indeed. The present distributions of people and of economic activity have come into being during the last two centuries—far too short a period for the physical environment to have changed. Even in the last two thousand years, changes in climate and in the form of the ground have been but slight.

The events of the Ice Age and of prehistory are measured on a coarser scale, which is divided by centuries and has a total length of nearly a million years. On this scale climatic change seems rapid, including as it does the repeated waxing and waning of ice sheets, but the evolution of the land-surface still appears slow. It is true that during the last million years the *details* of landform have been modified in many areas, but the sum total of change has amounted chiefly to a re-touching of the already-existing surface.

The scale of geological time is marked in millions of years. On it are recorded, in apparently rapid succession, profound and repeated changes in the physique of the British Isles, and the formation and deformation of the rocks which compose the land itself.

PHYSIQUE: HIGHLAND BRITAIN

The first part of the geological record relates to Highland Britain—the blocks of high ground, broken and fringed by patches of lowland, which constitute the north and west (Fig. 6). Most of the ground here stands above 1000 ft. Its rocks are mainly of Primary age (See Appendix 1). Their sedimentary formations have been generally hardened, while in some districts crystalline rocks—both igneous and metamorphic— are widespread. Although some parts of the highlands have been severely dissected by rivers or deeply grooved by ice, Highland Britain is mainly plateau country. The chief physical units are rigid crustal blocks, which rise steeply from the adjacent lowlands or from the surrounding seas. Only in Central Ireland do rocks of Primary age come to the surface in a broad lowland, and even this part is more conveniently treated with the highlands than with the lowlands. Highland Britain, then, includes Southwest England, Wales, Ireland, the Lake District and the Pennines, the Southern Uplands and the Scottish Highlands.

A great deal of Highland Britain consists of the remnants of fold mountains. Two main episodes of folding occurred, separated by a vast interval of time. Each was followed by uplift and severe denudation. By the time that the fold-mountain system had been worn down, its rocks had become rigid; they were broken into blocks by faulting on a large scale, some blocks foundering and others rising. It is the latter which form the upstanding massifs visible today.

The Caledonides

The first of the two episodes of folding was responsible for the

FIG. 6. Physique of the British Isles

structural grain of much of Highland Britain. As can be seen on the most general geological map, the structures and outcrops in many highland areas run from northeast to southwest. This trend, emphasised by successive earth-movements, belongs to the former fold-mountains known as the *Caledonides*.

The Caledonian mountain-building began some 500 million years ago. A huge strip of the earth's crust slowly sank, forming a sedimentary basin called a geosyncline. Subsidence was intermittent but prolonged, and in the course of 150 million years the centre of the basin was depressed to a depth of miles. Great thicknesses of sediment were brought in from either side; a long and complex sequence of deposition, crumpling and uplift converted the weak sediments to firm rock and the vast basin to a system of high fold mountains.

The Hebrides and the Atlantic fringe of the Northern Highlands of Scotland represent the rigid margin of the basin; that is, they are part of the foreland against which the rocks in the geosyncline were folded. Northwest Ireland, the rest of the Northern Highlands of Scotland, and the Scottish Highlands south of the Great Glen were included in the flank of the folded belt itself. Their rocks are greatly disturbed and much altered; heat and pressure, operating powerfully on a regional scale, have metamorphosed them into schists and gneisses—foliated crystalline rocks. Large bodies of igneous rock, originally emplaced in the deep roots of the folded belt, have been laid bare by erosion. Nearly all the rocks of this northwestern flank of the Caledonides are highly resistant to denudation, and valleys have been cut on lines of faulting rather than on belts of weak rock (Plate 1).

The central area of the old geosyncline is well illustrated in the Southern Uplands, the core of the Lake District, the Isle of Man, the Mourne Mountains, a large part of Wales, and the Wicklow Mountains. Here are found enormous thicknesses of sediments belonging chiefly to the Cambrian, Ordovician, and Silurian systems (Appendix 1). Most of the total bulk consists of fine-grained sediment, originally laid down as mud, and now hardened into shale or compressed into slate. Among the sediments occur the deposits of volcanoes which, strung along the axis of the geosyncline, extruded lava and showered down dust. The fine-grained sediments weather into rounded landforms, and their scenery is rarely spectacular even when the ground is high, but the lavas give rise to majestic craggy country, as in the centre of the Lake District and on Snowdon (Plates 6, 32).

Between the northwestern and the central subdivisions of the Caledonides lies a strip, some 35 miles wide, where the crust has been depressed between faults. In Scotland this strip is represented by the Midland Valley, but in Ireland it is largely hidden beneath the basalts of Antrim.

Little can be said about the southeastern flank of the Caledonides in the British area, for it is largely buried by later sediments. Structurally it is likely to have resembled Norway, where rocks formed in the geosyncline are crumpled and thrust southeastwards against the rigid foreland of the Baltic Shield.

Desert Sedimentation and Marine Transgression

When the Caledonides were uplifted, they bordered a lowland

where the climate was dry. It is quite possible that the mountains themselves were responsible for the dryness. Sediment carried down from mountains on the northwest accumulated, in the British area, in wide but shallow lakes, forming conglomerates, sandstones and marls with a characteristic reddish or purplish colour. These are the rocks of the Old Red Sandstone, which now appear on the fringe of older rocks on the sites of the lake-basins—along the shores of the Moray Firth, on the flanks of the Midland Valley, and along the southern Welsh Border. In this last area the thick, weak marls have been much eroded, and the terrain developed on them seems to belong to Lowland rather than to Highland Britain. In Southwest England and in the south of Ireland sediments were laid down not on land but in the sea, forming the Devonian rocks from which the whole system takes its name. They lack the bright colours of the Old Red Sandstone, being generally pale in tint and dull in tone.

By the end of Devonian times the once-lofty Caledonides had been worn down. Thirty million years of denudation had reduced them to low levels. In the British area, as in some other parts of the world, there followed a phase of subsidence. The land gently sank and was overspread by the sea and by new marine sediments. To such a marine invasion the name *transgression* is given; this transgression was that of the Carboniferous sea, in which the rocks of the Carboniferous system were formed.

Thick deposits of limestone first accumulated off the shores of the sinking land. The resulting formation is the Carboniferous Limestone, whose thick well-jointed rocks are widely exposed at the surface in the North Pennines and in the Derbyshire Dome (Plate 44). Their bare surfaces and craggy edges are unmistakable, and their underground caverns are still not fully explored. A wide expanse of Carboniferous Limestone in Central Ireland stands at a low level, and is almost wholly concealed by glacial deposits and peat. It fails therefore to display the typical features of limestone country, but these reappear round the margins of the South Wales Coalfield and in the Mendips.

Uplift of the land to the northwest caused great rivers to bring down huge loads of coarse sand. The formation of limestone ceased. Great deltas spread outwards from the shore, depositing the Millstone Grit, which now comes to the surface at the very margins of the coalfields and underlies the whole of the dark moorland of the Central Pennines. Like the Carboniferous Limestone, the Millstone Grit is generally resistant and forms high ground.

Intermittent subsidence was typical of the Millstone Grit deltas, and continued during the formation of the succeeding Coal Measures. The deltas by this time had become muddy rather than sandy, and had been colonised by flourishing associations of swamp-plants. Thick layers of peat accumulated. Every subsidence depressed the peat, which was then buried by mud or sand over which the plants spread once more. Compression changed the peat to coal, the mud to shale, and the sand to sandstone.

Without the Coal Measures, Britain might have taken a very small part in the industrial revolution and would certainly not have led it. The distribution of coalfields has of course profoundly affected the location of industry, and thereby the regional pattern of geography. The peat of the coal seams was formed at the margins of the land of Coal Measure times, so that deposits of coal now occur on the flanks of the massifs by which that land is represented. This means that some of the largest coalfields straddle the boundary between Highland and Lowland Britain, and the regional boundaries drawn round them do not coincide with the break between high ground and low—particularly on the flanks of the Pennines. Some of the coal originally formed has been destroyed by erosion, being stripped away from uplifted areas, as for instance between the Lancashire and the Yorks., Derby and Notts. coalfields. Elsewhere the seams have been carried down by subsidence and deeply buried beneath later sediments, as beneath the Lancs.-Cheshire Plain.

The Carboniferous period was not free from crustal disturbance. In addition to the sinking of the basins where coal was formed, there were volcanic outbursts in the Midland Valley of Scotland. These added more lava and dust to the volcanic rocks formed in the same area in the earlier Devonian period. Today the lavas give rise to the craggy shapes of the Renfrew Hills, the Ochils, the Campsie Fells, and the Sidlaws.

The Altaides

Carboniferous times ended with an episode of mountain-building, the second of those mentioned above. The new mountains were the Altaides. Like the older Caledonides, they began with thick sedimentation in a geosyncline. Most of the British area, however, lay outside the margins of the great depressed basin and of the folded belt, acting as a foreland where crustal movements were not general but localised. The Pennines were asymmetrically uplifted, and domes were formed at their southern end and in the Lake District. Southern Ireland, South Wales, and England south of the Bristol-London line were incorporated in the mountain arcs of the Altaides, which looped across Central Europe, running westwards through the Ardennes, Northwest France and the south of Britain. The east-west grain is still prominent where the denuded remnants of the fold mountains are exposed, and in Southwest England can be seen some of the igneous rocks which invaded the mountain roots. The folded rocks, now set firm in rigid blocks, have been broken across by subsidence, so that inlets of the sea occur between the south of Ireland and South Wales, and between the latter and Southwest England. East of the Exe, beneath the Channel, and beneath the Paris Basin, the remnants of the Altaides have foundered; where there is land today, they lie concealed by a cover of later sediments.

PHYSIQUE: LOWLAND BRITAIN

Renewed Sedimentation in Deserts

Just as the formation of the Caledonides was succeeded by a long period of dry climate, so did the rise of the Altaides introduce the desert conditions in which the rocks of the Permian and Triassic systems were laid down. These are often grouped together as the Permo-Trias. They consist of red sandstones, thick marls, breccias, pebble beds and salt deposits which were laid down by winds and torrents, or accumulated in drying lakes, as sands, muds, scree, gravel and evaporites. In Permo-Triassic times crustal dimples formed in parts of the British area, presumably where blocks were foundering, and provided the enclosed basins in which thick sedimentation took place.

A number of these basins are roughly oval in plan. The best-defined is that which underlies the Lancs.-Cheshire Plain, with its ends formed by the scalloped edges of the Pennines and of the Welsh Massif. Here the Coal Measures which underlie the Permo-Trias have been depressed by thousands of feet, and the faulted northeastern edge of the basin is clearly displayed. A whole complex of coalescent basins occurs in the Midland Triangle, amid the small upstanding blocks of the coalfields and of Charnwood Forest. At the angles of the Triangle the Permo-Trias merges with the Lancs.-Cheshire Plain through the Midland Gate, runs northward through the Trent valley and the Vale of York to the mouth of the Tees, and projects southwards along the Lower Severn towards the Plain of Somerset. All this is essentially lowland country, contrasting very strongly in height, texture of relief, and soil with the adjacent parts of Highland Britain. The boundary between the two divisions is in many places formed by the exhumed edges of the massifs, for the Permo-Trias is generally weak and has been deeply eroded. Only on the eastern side of the Pennines, where the crust has been tilted rather than broken, does the Permo-Trias dip gently off the older rocks.

It seems likely that the Irish Sea is underlain by a second complex of basins filled with Permo-Trias, for rocks belonging to this group occur in northeast Ireland and project as tongues into the valleys of the Conway, Clwyd, and Eden. In these three valleys the desert sediments accumulated in long narrow depressions bounded by huge faults which have subsequently been stripped out by erosion. The Vale of Taunton between Exmoor and the Quantocks is also due to faulting, and is also partly filled by Permo-Trias.

The margins of Lowland Britain correspond generally to the lower boundary of the Permo-Trias, and in places they coincide with marked structural breaks. Highland Britain, beyond the margins, is an area of massifs and of plateau country. Lowland Britain, within the margins, is an area of plains, wide vales, low plateaus and scarplands.

Jurassic Scarplands

Adjoining the Midland Triangle and the vale country between Nottingham and Middlesbrough is the belt of Jurassic scarpland. Its rocks are marine sediments—clays, limestones and sandstones. The clays are weak, and have been eroded into broad strips of lowland, while the limestones and sandstones are strong, and rise in cuestas[1] with their scarps for the most part facing west or north-west. There is no single line of scarp, for the succession of Jurassic rocks is very varied. Furthermore, the strong formations vary in thickness, so that in some places they form high ground whereas in others the terrain is composed of low, irregular, broken hills. Thick sandstones form a bold cuesta in the North York Moors, rising to more than 1000 ft. and leading down to the Vale of Pickering by a dissected back-slope.[1] About the head of the Humber the rocks thin out and are concealed by younger sediments; but Jurassic limestones appear in Lincoln Edge, with overlying clays to the east in the Witham valley. In the Leicestershire Wolds and the Northamptonshire Uplands the country is strongly dissected and is largely covered by boulder clay, so that the relief is confused; but strong limestones thicken towards the southeast, giving rise to the dissected plateaus of the North Oxfordshire Hills and of the Cotswolds (Plate 56). Here the scarp-face is high, prominent, and continuous, and the crest of the cuesta rises again to 1000 ft. The outcrop of Jurassic rocks swings southwards across the Mendips, continues through the irregular hilly country on the eastern border of the Somerset Plain, and reappears on the Dorset coast where it laps round the Hampshire Basin.

[1] *Cuesta* is the only available term for a belt of hills developed, by erosion, on a dipping formation of sedimentary rocks. It includes two elements: (*a*) the scarp, scarp-face, or escarpment—strictly synonymous expressions—and (*b*) the back-slope. If the back-slope coincides with the surface of a strong formation, it can be called the *dip-slope*; but since true dip-slopes are uncommon, the term back-slope is used throughout the following text.

In the Fenlands the solid rocks are obscured by peat and silt, but thick Jurassic clays appear again in the Great Ouse Valley, forming a wide vale which extends southwestwards for more than a hundred miles. The Jurassic clays are covered in places by glacial deposits, but these too consist mainly of clay. The whole belt is one of lowland, except where a formation of limestone occurs to form hills running SW-NE across the line of the Cherwell.

Cretaceous Scarplands

East and southeast of the Jurassic belt comes the outcrop of Cretaceous rocks, dominated by the prominent cuesta formed by the Chalk. The Chalk scarpland begins at Flamborough Head, at the extremity of the Yorkshire Wolds. Swinging round to the south, it obscures the thin Jurassic rocks near the head of the Humber, and then swings away again in the Lincolnshire Wolds, a belt of low hills where the Chalk is covered by glacial deposits. Beyond the Wash, again, boulder clay is widespread, and very little Chalk appears at the surface, but the underlying Greensand forms a scarp which overlooks the Fens. Bold, continuous scarps are magnificently developed on the faces of the Chilterns and the Berkshire Downs, which rise to even crests at about 800 ft. and descend in backslopes dissected by numerous dry valleys. From place to place the Greensand protrudes from beneath the Chalk, varying in importance because it varies in thickness, and indeed vanishing altogether in some localities. At the eastern edge of Salisbury Plain, the Chalk outcrop is deeply indented where upfolds have been eroded. In the same area the Greensand becomes really thick, and forms an outfacing scarp as bold as that of the Chalk itself. In the dissected, tabular Blackdown Hills it is the Greensand which forms the high ground. The Chalk thins out here, but thickens again round the southern rim of the Hampshire Basin.

Salisbury Plain forms a node from which the Chalk outcrops run southwestwards, northeastwards, and eastwards. The Plain itself is an area of gentle uplift. Farther east, in the Weald, the strongly uplifted Chalk has been eroded away (Plate 2), revealing the alternating strong and weak formations in the Wealden series, which have been dissected into infacing cuestas and concentric vales.

Tertiary Basins

To the north of the Weald lies the London Basin; to the south of Salisbury Plain lies the Hampshire Basin. The former is a funnel-shaped structural depression, which received muddy and sandy sediments during Tertiary times. The muds formed the London Clay which is now widely exposed at the surface. Sandy and gravelly sediments appear from beneath the London Clay in North Kent, and relics of quite thick sands above the clay occur in the Bagshot district. The Hampshire Basin is almost encircled by a rim of Chalk. It subsided persistently in Tertiary times, receiving mud, like the London Basin, but subsequently being filled with the widespread sands which today form the geological basis of the New Forest.

ORIGINS OF THE PRESENT LANDSCAPE

Much of the present land-surface has been produced by a sequence of erosion which began when the floor of the Chalk Sea was elevated. Like the Carboniferous Sea, the Chalk Sea was transgressive. Its northern and western limits are uncertain; it may have lapped against the margins of Wales, the Pennines, the Southern Uplands, the Scottish Highlands, and the blocks of Irish hills, or it may have passed right over them. In either case, transgression ended with uplift in the west. This uplift, exposing the Chalk as new land, initiated new rivers which drained across Great Britain from west to east.

The crustal movements which caused the uplift were accompanied by volcanic outbursts. In northeast Ireland floods of basaltic lava poured from fissures, spreading far outwards in thick, gently-sloping sheets. The remains of these sheets, strongly eroded round the edges, now underlie the basalt plateau of Antrim. In the area of the Inner Hebrides were central volcanoes—i.e. volcanoes with localised vents which erupted streams of lava and formed conical mountains. Their ruins now appear in Skye, Mull, and Arran. In southeastern England there was movement of another kind. The subsidence of the London and Hampshire Basins was accompanied by the rise of the Wealden area, and also by compression from the south. Short, offset folds were formed, running in a sheaf from the east of the Weald to the borders of the West Country. Streams ran down the flanks of the rising Weald, and additional streams flowed southwards across the site of the Hampshire Basin.

The consequent streams flowing down the various slopes of the new land (Fig. 7) were certain to be dismembered by capture. They flowed across outcrops of contrasted strength, on which they were superimposed—in places at least—from the cover of Chalk. In the Scottish Highlands the drainage has become largely adjusted to the lines of structural weakness in the ancient rocks. On the eastern side of the Pennines, many of the headstreams have been collected by the subsequent Ouse and Trent, which worked along the unresistant outcrop of Permo-Trias. The former Dee-Trent has almost vanished from the Midland Triangle. Its headwaters have been captured to

1. View southwestwards along the fault-guided Great Glen. The Ben Nevis group rises to more than 4,000 feet, clear above a broad summit-surface about 3,000 feet high.

2. Scarp-face of the South Downs. Most of the visible part of the backslope is in permanent grass, the scarp is in rough grazing, and the vale country below is in mixed farmland and wood.

3. Great Orme's Head, North Wales. Old cliffs cut in flexured
Carboniferous Limestone overtop a raised beach.

4. Coastal marshes of the Blackwater Estuary, Essex. Reclaimed
land, in pasture, lies behind a low sea-wall.

FIG. 7. Some early elements in the drainage of Great Britain. Trunk streams flowing from west to east are reconstructed consequents

the Irish Sea, its lower part beheaded; the upper Severn, a former tributary, has been diverted by glaciation to the Bristol Channel, and much of the former Soar reversed to form the Warwickshire Avon. The Kennet-Thames now flows in its lower reaches far south of its old line, having been displaced by lobes of the ice-sheet. In the Wealden area, subsequent streams extending themselves along belts of weak rock have developed at the expense of the original consequents.

Changes of Sea-level

River-development has been influenced not only by the changes of plan which have accompanied capture and glacial diversion, but also by changes of sea-level. For at least a million years, and possibly for very much longer, sea-level has been falling intermittently. The effects of intermittent falls in level are most clearly illustrated by the high ground of the north and west, where, whatever the complications introduced by the cutting of valleys by rivers or by glaciers, the land of the massifs can be seen to ascend in steps. The broad upland surfaces which are so extensive in some districts are erosional in origin. They represent platforms cut across the underlying rocks, either by wave-action on the shore or by running water on land. Dissected plateau country is very widespread indeed. It is moreover not confined to the highlands, for the even crests and backslopes of the Jurassic and Chalk cuestas are also remains of erosional platforms related to high base-levels.

Periods of stable base-level enabled the platforms to be cut: periods of falling base-level caused the rivers to be rejuvenated. All the rivers of the British Isles have undergone rejuvenation, so that they are sharply incised into the plateaus and flow in terraced valleys across the low ground.

The Ice Age

The sequence of intermittent rejuvenation goes back far into Tertiary times, long pre-dating the Ice Age. Glaciation, setting in when base-level stood about 300 feet above its present mark, introduced complications.

Down to about 300 feet the great steps of the erosional platforms are well-marked. Halts in the fall of the sea at this and higher levels were long enough for large areas to be reduced to gently-sloping, continuous plateau surfaces. When the great ice-sheets formed, their waxings and wanings made the level of the sea fall and rise by turns. The lower parts of valleys were deepened when sea-level fell, and infilled when it rose again. But because the movements of glacial times were superimposed on the general tendency for base-level to fall, the net effect has been to produce valleys in which terrace deposits record old flood-plains at successively lower heights. The changes of the Ice Age were too rapid to permit the cutting of platforms across strong rocks, but from the weaker outcrops a great deal of material was removed; in all cases terraces are the rule rather than the exception.

Around the shores of the British Isles, raised beach deposits are widely distributed. In the south they belong to times when sea-level stood higher than it does today; but the last movement has been one of submergence, for the mouths of all valleys have been drowned by the rising sea (Plates 3, 4). In the north-west the land has risen, having been relieved of its former load of ice, and has carried the beaches up with it.

Whatever its ultimate cause, the Ice Age began with a lowering of air temperature and an increase in snowfall. Snow-fields and glaciers established themselves on the high ground of the British Isles; the valley-heads became corries and the valleys glacier troughs. Peaks and ridges rising above the glaciers were shattered by frost. The typical features of glaciated highland are best developed on the highest land of all, which broadly speaking is based on the most resistant rocks (Fig. 6). Those parts of the massifs which are underlain by fine-grained sediments or by rocks of Carboniferous age fail to exhibit the full range of glacial features, partly because of the nature of their material and partly because they were entirely covered by the ice-cap. The Southern Uplands, the Pennines, and Central Wales are especially deficient in corries, arêtes and ribbon lakes, although their principal valleys have been converted into deep grooves.

The ice spread over Lowland Britain as far south as the Cotswolds, crossed the Northampton Uplands and the clay belt to the south, and passed over the Chalk country east of the Chilterns. East Anglia and Lincolnshire were deeply buried by the united fringes of the sheets which spread from northern Britain and from Scandinavia. When the ice finally melted away, the lowland on which it had rested was mantled with sand, gravel, and boulder clay. Parts of this cover have been stripped off, but large spreads still remain in East Anglia, the eastern Midlands, the low ground on the east of the Pennines, and the Lancs.-Cheshire Plain (Fig. 6). Most of Ireland is covered by glacial drift, which is also extensive on the flanks of the Lake District and the Southern Uplands, in the Midland Valley of Scotland, and along the eastern margins of the Scottish Highlands. Tongues of drift run up the valleys in these areas between the steep, rocky walls of the glaciated troughs.

A most severe climate of the tundra type affected the lands south of the ice-edge. The ground was deeply frozen. When the topsoil melted in summer, it tended to sludge downslope and to form spreads of the dirty rubble called *head*. Only in the southeast was the climate dry enough for dust-storms to deposit the loess which appears on geological maps as brickearth.

The chief types of post-glacial deposit are alluvium, peat, and the material of present-day beaches. It is impossible to give an account of beaches except at great length, and they will not be treated here. The formation and distribution of peat fall more readily into the following chapter than into this. The alluvium of present flood-plains is restricted to the valley floors, and is more widely developed in the lowlands than in the highlands. In the Fens and in the Somerset Levels, large inlets of the sea have been enclosed by beach-bars and filled with peat and silt, so that sizable areas have been added to the land; on the eastern side of Romney Marsh shingle ridges are still being added, extending seaward the remarkable cusp of low-lying ground which has been formed during the last two thousand years.

Superficial deposits of glacial débris, head, brickearth, terrace material, alluvium, and peat are of high geographical importance wherever they occur. Although in places they greatly modify the form of the ground, their significance lies less in this fact than in the profound influence which they have on the quality of the soils which are developed on them.

APPENDIX

THE GEOLOGICAL TIME-SCALE

Era	System	Approximate age (in millions of years)
Tertiary	Recent*	
	Pleistocene*	
	Pliocene	
	Miocene	
	Oligocene	
	Eocene	
		55
Secondary	Cretaceous	
		100
	Jurassic (including Rhaetic)	
		150
	Triassic	
		180
Primary	Permian	
		225
	Carboniferous	
		275
	Devonian	
		305
	Silurian	
		345
	Ordovician	
		390
	Cambrian	
		475
	pre-Cambrian	
	possibly extending back to 3,000 or 4,000 million years ago	

* The Recent and Pleistocene systems are sometimes grouped together under the title *Quaternary*.

CHAPTER 3

Climate, Vegetation, and Soils

THE British Isles lie between 50° and 61°N., on the western side of a great landmass, and within the belt of prevailing westerlies. Their climate is dominated by marine influences and is rainy and equable. Within the limits of the general climatic type—maritime, temperate, with no dry season and with summers only moderately warm—there is, however, room for considerable variation between one region and another.

Because the British Isles lie so far from the equator, the length of daylight which they experience is much greater in summer than in winter. There is also a marked seasonal range in the height above the horizon of the noonday sun. But although, in these latitudes, temperature must vary from season to season, the seasonal range is far less than latitude alone would suggest. The ocean to the west, and the westerlies which transport its influences over the British land, ensure that seasonal contrasts in temperature are minimised.

FIG. 8. Eastward increase in mean annual range of temperature

23

Fig. 8 shows how the annual temperature range—the difference between the mean temperatures of the warmest and of the coldest months—increases from Britain eastwards across the European mainland; it also shows that the increase in range is due mainly to the winter cold, which increases in intensity towards the interior of the landmass. Conversely, the low annual ranges in Britain result mainly from the mildness of British winters. Whereas in summer the air over Britain is no more than 2°F. cooler than the average for the latitude, in winter it is some 30°F. warmer.

OCEANIC INFLUENCES

The supply of heat to the overlying air in winter is one of the most notable of all the oceanic influences on British climate. The ultimate source of the heat is, of course, the sun. The proximate source is the North Atlantic Drift. This rather shallow skin of surface water, light because it is warm, is driven north-eastward across the ocean by the westerly winds. It forms part of the Gulf Stream system, which begins where Florida Current pours vast quantities of remarkably warm water into the circulation of the North Atlantic. In its journey across that ocean the water loses part of its heat, but retains enough to keep the ocean surface west of the British Isles warm in winter. During the winter months water which has been heated in far lower latitudes is arriving in the North Atlantic. Furthermore, the ocean surface becomes warmer or cooler, according to season, far more slowly than does a land surface in similar latitudes. The maximum surface temperature off the British coasts is reached in August, or even as late as September. Thus, when winter comes, there is much heat available to warm the air of the westerlies, and the seasonal fall of air temperature over Britain is slow and slight.

The moderating effect of the ocean on air temperature is stronger in winter than in summer (Fig. 9). When the surface water is cooler than the air above it—as frequently happens during the summer months—the air tends to lose its heat to the water. The lowest layers of air are chilled and become denser by contraction, and the chilled air tends to remain at low levels. The surface water expands because it is warmed, and remains on the surface of the ocean. Unless the air is turbulent, little of it can be cooled, for little heat is exchanged. Opposite conditions apply in winter. The air in winter is likely to be cooler than the surface water, so that heat passes from water to air. Air at low levels is warmed and expands and rises, carrying oceanic heat with it, while the chilled surface water contracts and sinks, to be replaced by unchilled water from below. This convectional overturning both of water and of air leads to a vigorous exchange of heat.

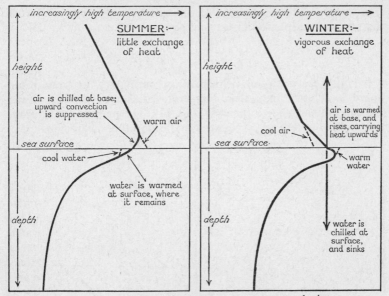

FIG. 9. Effect of sea on air temperature, summer and winter

The westerlies which bring the air over the land exist mainly as a kind of statistical abstraction. There are indeed times when the British Isles are traversed by a powerful westerly airstream, but wind-direction is typically variable at all stations (Fig. 10). Only when the resultant wind-direction is determined by cancelling winds

FIG. 10. Wind-roses for selected stations; net transport of air

from opposite directions against one another does it become clear that the net transport of air is from the west.

TEMPERATURE

It is this eastward flow which brings warmth to the western seaboard in winter, and raises temperatures there above the figures recorded inland and to the east (Fig. 11). The map of sea-level isotherms for January reveals in striking fashion that mean temperature

FIG. 11. Sea-level isotherms for January and July; mean annual range of temperature; length of frost-free period

in mid-winter is a function of location rather than of latitude. The isotherm of 44°F. runs through the western peninsulas of Ireland, and that of 43° crosses the peninsulas of Wales. Even on the east, where the shallow North Sea is cooler in January than is the deep Atlantic, the coastlands are slightly warmer than the inland areas behind them. The course of the 40° isotherm as a whole records the effect of the chilling of air over land in winter.

The sea-level isotherms for July (Fig. 11) run broadly from east to west, the highest mean temperatures occurring in the south and the lowest in the north. But although the effects of location are weaker in this month than in January, they can still be made out. The 62° isotherm closes round southern England, and the 60° line loops northward over the land and southward towards the sea.

Mean annual ranges (Fig. 11) also reveal the difference between coastal and inland locations. Ranges, below 15°F. on the western coastlands of Ireland, rise to more than 22° in East Anglia and the London Basin. Both in Ireland and in Great Britain the greatest ranges occur well to the east of centre—another illustration of the effects of the westerlies in moderating climate. Mean *daily* ranges, however, increase generally from the coasts inland, running at some 10° or less near the sea and rising to 14° or so in the interior districts.

With the small annual ranges of temperature recorded at all stations in the British Isles goes a slow and smooth change in the mean temperature from month to month. At most places July is the warmest month and January the coldest. A certain time-lag is to be expected between the greatest noonday height of the sun and the peak of the temperature-curve, for incoming solar radiation continues to exceed outgoing radiation for some time after midsummer day. The influence of the ocean so increases the time-lag that, at such stations as Falmouth in Cornwall and Valentia in Kerry, August is slightly warmer than July, and at many places in the west there is very little difference in the average temperature of the two months. Similarly, maritime stations in the west are very little, if at all, warmer in February than in January.

The delayed rise of the temperature-curve for western stations in the early months of the year makes nonsense of the statement that Cornwall has early springs. Climatically speaking, spring there is late. Winters, however, are very mild, so that plants in low-lying and sheltered localities can grow throughout the winter season, or can start their spring growth very early in the calendar year.

Frost

Situation with respect to the sea has much influence on the likelihood of frost. Coastal districts have the longest frost-free period

B2

(Fig. 11), which lasts on the average for 9 months in the western extremities of Ireland, Southwest England, Pembrokeshire, Anglesey and the Lleyn Peninsula. Along the Channel coast the duration is reduced to some 7 months, and northwards along the east coast to about 6 months, but places near the shore are everywhere less liable to frost than are nearby places inland. In Wales the effect of high ground reduces the frost-free period to less than five months; in the northern Pennines and the Southern Uplands it falls below 4, and in the Grampians to less than 3.

Actual Temperature

The map in Fig. 11 refers to actual frosts—that is, to actual records of temperatures of 32°F or below. In this it differs from the isothermal maps already given, which are constructed from temperatures reduced to sea level. Sea-level figures are necessary to reveal the influences of latitude and of inland or coastal location, for isotherms of actual temperatures look very much like maps of relief, whereas sea-level isotherms arrange themselves in simple patterns. But as soon as temperature is considered in relation to wild plant-life, to cultivated crops, or to the keeping of livestock, actual figures are required.

The change of temperature with height is far more rapid than the change with latitude or with distance from the sea. On the Channel coast, for instance, the mean annual *sea-level* temperature is about 51°F, while in the centre of the Scottish Highlands it is about 47°F—that is, a difference of 600 miles in latitude produces a difference in mean temperature of 4°F. But mean temperature falls about 1°F for every 300 feet of height, so that a rise of 2,400 feet—less than half a mile—lowers the mean temperature by 8°F. In other words, from the Channel to the Highlands the mean temperature falls about 2,500 times as rapidly with height as it does with distance.

This very rapid fall of temperature with height emphasises the contrasts between highland and lowland, especially since the most extensive lowlands of the British Isles lie in the south while the highest ground occurs in the north. There is a very great actual difference between, say, Ipswich, with an annual mean of 50°F, and the summit of Ben Nevis where the annual mean is slightly below freezing point. The contrast is as great as that between Ipswich and the coast of southern Greenland, less than 100 miles from the edge of an ice-cap.

Detailed maps of actual temperature are bound to resemble maps of relief. The generalised representations in two parts of Fig. 12 emphasise, in a general way, the manner in which air-temperature is modified by height. In January, mean actual temperatures of less than 32° are recorded for all the highest summits, from the Peak to the north of Scotland. On the high plateaus of Wales, the mean monthly figure is in the neighbourhood of 35°. The eastern part of the English Plain records actual means of some 37°, while patches of the western Plain approach 40°. In July, when actual means on the low ground of central and southern England run above 60°, the figure for much of the Southern Uplands is 54° or below, and means lower than 50° occur widely in the Grampians and north of the Great Glen. The highly-fragmented uplands of Ireland are

Fig. 12. Actual isotherms for January and July; mean daily duration of sunshine-hours; mornings with lying snow

faithfully reflected in the maps of actual temperatures, even though the whole island displays the effect of moderating oceanic influences.

Sunshine

The maps of actual temperature and of the duration of the frost-free period should be read in conjunction with the map (Fig. 12) of the duration of sunshine. Naturally enough, the sunniest areas occur in the south—on the coasts of Cornwall, the Channel, and East Anglia—and it is here that many seaside resorts and market-gardens are found. But in Great Britain generally the coasts are everywhere sunnier than neighbouring inland districts, for the amount of cloud is increased by turbulence in the air over land. The frequency of cloud rapidly increases over high ground, and the duration of sunshine as rapidly diminishes. Ireland is subject to frequent cloud, and records little sunshine. Its high western rim, broken though it is, suffices to provoke heavy cloud in the damp winds which blow from the open Atlantic, and the passage of air over the moist Central Plain does little to reduce the cloud cover.

PRECIPITATION

Precipitation is the most important of all climatic elements. Without water there could be no life, and water-supply depends on precipitation. Some large towns in the British Isles suffer a shortage of water in dry years. Agriculture in some areas would benefit from

FIG. 13. Mean annual precipitation; number of rain-days

increased rainfall in the summer, when evaporation tends to dry out the soil, although the annual total is everywhere adequate. Precipitation is excessive in most of Scotland, Ireland, and Wales, the wettest areas of all receiving more than 100 inches a year.

The map of mean annual precipitation (Fig. 13) shows that the highest falls occur on the high ground of the north and west. The wettest areas lie west of the axis of high ground instead of centrally on its highest parts, as is clearly indicated in Scotland. Over the low ground, too, there is a general fall in the total from west to east: 50 inches in the Clyde Valley becomes 30 on the Firth of Forth, 40 inches on the west of the Central Plain of Ireland falls to 30 inches on the east, and the 30 inches recorded at Gloucester is significantly greater than the 25 inches at London.

This westward displacement of heavy precipitation is due simply to the prevalence of the westerly winds. If rain falls in the west it is not available for the east, and eastern districts lie in rain-shadow (Fig. 14). Similarly, the number of rain-days is greatest in the west, falling from more than 250 a year on extreme western coasts to below 175 in some parts of the east. Throughout most of the massifs the average is above 200 days a year, and very little of Ireland—which is fully exposed to the westerlies—records fewer than this, even on low ground.

FIG. 14. The rain-shadow effect in the north of England

Totals of precipitation are however not due solely to the combined influences of the westerlies and of the height of the land. Orographic precipitation is the type produced by the flow of air over high ground—in the British Isles, mainly by the ascent of the westerlies over the upland areas of the north and west. Air from the Atlantic, rising over the west-facing highlands, ascends into levels of reduced pressure where it expands and cools. Being typically moist, the maritime air frequently reaches condensation-point in cooling, becoming still more cloudy and discharging precipitation. Latent heat released during condensation often makes the rising air unstable; lifting occurs, resulting in further expansion, cooling and precipitation. Indeed, the ascent due to instability of the air itself is more powerful in causing precipitation than is the forced ascent of moving air over relief barriers. The converse of lifting is subsidence, which occurs on the eastern flanks of the highlands. The subsiding air becomes more stable; already carrying the latent heat of condensation, it is further warmed by compression, and tends to be notably warmer, drier, and less rainy than when it rose over the western slopes of the highlands. Here is the explanation of rain-shadow.

Cyclonic precipitation is brought by travelling low-pressure systems (see below). Warm air in travelling lows ascends over cold air instead of over high ground. Ascent is again accompanied by increased instability, lifting and precipitation. In the wettest areas, cyclonic precipitation serves merely to increase the total fall, but in the east and over the low ground generally it is responsible for most of the precipitation which occurs.

Convectional precipitation tends to complicate the distribution map, for thunderstorms are most frequent in inland districts. The lower Trent valley and East Anglia are the most thundery areas, with more than 15 thunderstorms a year; much of the English lowland records more than ten. These are mainly summer thunderstorms, due to the heating from below of moist air, which becomes markedly unstable and rises in the turbulent columns of thunderclouds. Thunder in the cooler months is almost entirely restricted to western districts.

Most of the precipitation which falls in the British Isles comes as rain, but snow is frequent in the north. In a general way the likelihood of snow increases from southwest to northeast, but snowfall is much affected by the distribution of relief. The map of mornings with snow lying (Fig. 12) reveals that the snowiest areas, unlike the wettest areas, lie squarely on the highest ground. In this as in other maps, the influence of the ocean is well displayed, for a low frequency of lying snow characterises most of Ireland and the entire western and southern coastlands of Great Britain.

Régimes of Precipitation

Varying combinations of orographic, cyclonic, and convectional precipitation are seen in the régimes of individual stations. Precipitation in the west is heaviest in the winter half-year, when winds are strongest and travelling lows are most vigorous, but the summer months there can by no means be called dry. An excellent example of heavy precipitation, both cyclonic and orographic, is given by the record from Loch Quoich, Inverness (Fig. 15), where the January total is over 15 inches and that of July nearly 6 inches, with the yearly average well above 100 inches. At Aberdeen the winter half-year is also the wetter, but there is a significantly greater fall in August and September than in October. At Hull August becomes the wettest single month, as it also is in London. Over a considerable part of the eastern Midlands, East Anglia, and the London Basin the summer half-year is wetter than the winter half, because thunderstorms combined with the weak summer lows bring more precipitation than do the vigorous lows which alone occur in winter. There is a faint development of a régime typical of continental rather than of oceanic stations.

FIG. 15. Rainfall régimes at selected stations

August, the main holiday month, is rainy at many stations, even in those parts of the British Isles which receive more than half their total of precipitation in the winter half-year. At Valentia, Co. Kerry—a station fully exposed to the westerlies—August is wetter than September. A secondary maximum of precipitation in August is very common. At some stations where August is the wettest single month, considerable summer thunder is experienced— e.g., at Southport—but at others, such as Dublin, summer thunder is rare. The typical raininess of August cannot be wholly due to thunderstorms, but is to be accounted for in part by the arrival of unstable maritime air.

WEATHER

In direct contrast with climate, in which short-term variations disappear with the calculation of averages, the weather of the British Isles is notoriously variable. Not only is it liable to day-to-day changes—some whole seasons are markedly wet, markedly dry, unusually cold, or unusually warm. Even though variations from season to season tend to cancel one another in figures for the whole year, the yearly total of precipitation ranges widely (Fig. 16). There is no single month which, during the last 80 years, has not been the wettest in some one year and the driest in some other.

FIG. 16. Year-by-year variations in rainfall at Oxford

Weather is produced in the air which overlies a place at a given time. Three main kinds of air flow over the British Isles—maritime tropical air from the southwest, maritime polar air from the west or northwest, and continental polar air from the European mainland in winter. Each kind arrives as an *airstream*, having acquired its original characteristics in the source region of an *air mass*.

An air mass is a large body of air, perhaps thousands of miles across. Stagnating over an expanse of land or of sea, it is cooled, warmed, dried or moistened according to the character of the underlying surface. In a very few days it can reach equilibrium, in respect of temperature and humidity, with that surface; and when it moves away from the source region as an airstream, it retains its distinctive character for some time.

Maritime air, whether maritime tropical (mT) or maritime polar (mP) air is brought in by the westerlies. Maritime tropical air is supplied to the British Isles by the Azores High; although it is typically moist it is also usually stable, so that it tends to give little precipitation. In summer it can produce warm, settled weather, and in winter it gives unseasonable warmth—as, for instance, during the winter of 1956/57. Maritime polar (mP) air is very variable. Its source regions lie over the North Atlantic and eastern Canada. When it comes from a northerly quarter, and when it arrives during the summer, it is liable to be unstable and to discharge much precipitation, as in the summer of 1958, but it can also come in from the west after a long traverse of the warm ocean, and may then be fairly stable and bring little rain to lowland areas. Continental air sometimes reaches the British Isles in summer as a warm, dry airstream, but it is more frequently experienced in winter when, as icy currents of continental polar (cP) air, it crosses the North Sea and brings bitter weather to eastern and inland districts of Great Britain. In some winters, cP air overspreads the whole of the British Isles and occasions severe and prolonged frost. Such a winter was that of 1946/47.

Travelling Lows

Airstreams of varying type are drawn, or blown, across the British Isles by temporary pressure-systems, some of which are themselves moving. Low-pressure systems tend to be both vigorous and mobile. Most of the travelling lows which cross the British Isles move from west to east or from southwest to northeast, in accordance with the general flow of the westerlies. Many of them are frontal depressions, in which the individual airstreams are separated from one another by narrow zones of transition known as fronts. Lows commonly originate on the polar front, the boundary between the westerlies on the south and cold air blowing outwards from higher latitudes on the north. A bulge on the polar front becomes enlarged into a deep re-entrant (Fig. 17) which encloses a warm sector surrounded by cold air. The whole system travels towards the east; since it can cross the British Isles in the space of one or two days, a given station can experience three distinct kinds of weather in a short time. In the forepart of the low, in advance of the warm front, polar air is drawn northwards; in winter it reaches most of Great Britain from the mainland of Europe, and may well be very cold. Cloud thickens and rain or snow falls as the warm front approaches; but as it passes there is a rise in temperature, for the warm sector is typically occupied by maritime tropical air. Precipitation in the warm sector is not often heavy, although there is much cloud; precipitation is renewed along the cold front, the passage of which is marked by a drop in temperature. If the maritime polar air behind the cold front is unstable, it is likely to give heavy showers.

FIG. 17. Pressure, fronts, weather and airstreams in a travelling low, winter

Lows are often partly or wholly occluded by the time that they reach the British Isles, the cold front having caught up the warm front, so that the air in the warm sector is raised above the ground. The weather typical of the warm sector is omitted from the sequence, and the two frontal rain-belts merge into one.

In the heart of a travelling low, whether it is occluded or not, general rain often occurs. This means that any low which traverses the British Isles is likely to supply more precipitation in the north than in the south, even when the effect of high ground in the north is left aside. Moreover, highs tend to form over the English lowlands in the latter part of winter, fending off the moving lows, forcing them to take a north-easterly path and to bring precipitation to the northwest rather than to the southeast. In both these ways the contrast between the drier and the wetter parts of Great Britain is increased.

Systems of High Pressure

Systems of high pressure are simpler than those of low pressure. Highs are stagnant systems of stable air which give little precipitation. Some bring overcast skies; if there is little cloud, highs result in warm sunny weather in summer and in sunny but frosty weather in winter. Because they are stable and inert, highs may persist for days on end.

Seasonal Weather

British weather is affected by several other types of pressure-systems, in addition to simple travelling lows and more-or-less

FIG. 18. Tracks of travelling lows for two selected months. The dotted boundaries mark the limits of persistent (or fairly persistent) high-pressure systems. The highs guided lows away from the British Isles in April 1955, but forced them to cross the British Isles in August 1956

stationary highs, all of which increase the general variability of British weather. But the number, strength, and frequency of travelling lows and stagnant highs are the chief influences upon the character of seasonal weather.

The contrast between weather dominated by travelling lows and that dominated by persistent highs has rarely been better shown than in the two summers of 1955 and 1956. In the first of these two seasons highs were dominant. They blocked the approaching lows, which moved away to the northeast (cf. Fig. 18); prolonged droughts occurred, even in the west of Ireland. By contrast, during the summer of 1956 many lows passed across the British Isles (Fig. 18). Unusually heavy rain was recorded in all parts, for large quantities of polar maritime air streamed in and frontal rain was common. Many stations recorded more than twice the average rainfall in August, and the difficulties of harvesting will long be remembered. Nevertheless, the total precipitation for the whole year of 1956 differed very little from the average, for the very wet summer was compensated by slight precipitation both in spring and in late autumn and early winter.

LOCAL CLIMATES

Just as weather varies during short periods, so does climate vary over short distances. Local climate in highland areas changes very rapidly from place to place. The contrasts are not merely those of height, although precipitation can increase with height as strikingly as temperature falls. Nor are they to be explained wholly by aspect, although contrasts in aspect are important where—as in the Scottish Highlands—climate is so generally severe that every advantageous circumstance becomes significant. In highland areas especially, and on uneven ground everywhere, cold-air drainage exerts a powerful influence on local climate. Cold air can only drain downhill when the air as a whole is still, or very nearly so, and the air can remain still only during the calm weather brought by high-pressure systems. Although calms in the British Isles are not very common, they occur often enough to encourage the drainage of cold air into certain enclosed valleys, which in consequence experience frequent fog and frost in the colder months. The Lea Valley is perhaps the most notorious example, but there is no doubt that many Welsh, Pennine, and Scottish valleys suffer in a similar way. In coastal districts, air chilled during the night can flow out to sea; sea breezes rise by day if the air is still, giving the coasts their characteristically small daily range of temperature.

VEGETATION

There is little in the British Isles that can be called natural vegetation, in the sense of spontaneous vegetation which has been little modified by man and his domestic animals. The 60% of the whole area which is classed as improved farmland can be eliminated at once from a general discussion of wild plant life. Parts of the wooded land and much of the unfenced expanses of rough grazing can be described as clothed in semi-natural vegetation—i.e., in vegetation which is spontaneous in origin but has been much modified in the course of human history.

Vegetation in the natural state is powerfully affected by climate, soils, and animals. The respective groups of influences at work are called the climatic, edaphic, and biotic; of these, the most powerful group is usually the climatic. Wild vegetation left to itself tends to develop the most complex community of plants with the largest dominant members which the climate permits. Such a community is the *climax community*, or more properly the *climatic climax*. Throughout most of England, and in parts of Wales, Scotland and Ireland, the climatic climax is deciduous summer forest. In many northern and western areas the climatic climax is northern coniferous forest, dominated by the native Scots pine but also including birch. Where drainage is especially poor, the highlands run to blanket bog which is frequently colonised by ling.

Although soils are to be separately treated below, it is impossible to refer to climax communities of plants without mentioning the variations in them which may result from variations in soil. Within the area of lowland which was once covered mainly by deciduous forest were patches of heath; these lay in highly permeable, sandy districts, where percolating water had removed the soluble matter and had produced acid soils. On the mild peat soils of fenland and on the silt of marshes grew reeds and sedges; and even in the lowlands there were some vigorously-growing peat-bogs, for instance in the Somerset Levels and on the Lancashire Plain. In all such places the vegetation tended towards an *edaphic climax*.

Biotic influences came into operation as soon as grazing by domestic animals began. Their effects are seen throughout those parts of the British Isles which are now classed as rough grazing, except on unused blanket bog. With the assistance of felling, grazing has destroyed most of the woodland which used to grow on the hillsides of Wales, the Pennines, the Lake District, the Southern Uplands and the Scottish Highlands. The hill grassland seen there today represents a *biotic climax* of vegetation.

Climatic Change

Vegetation—whether wild, semi-natural, or cultivated—is never static. It shares a dynamic quality with soils, whether natural or agricultural soils. The story of the existing vegetation of the British Isles begins with the disappearance of the great glaciers of the Ice Age. At the last glacial maximum, ice covered the highlands and spread in lobes on to the fringes of the lowlands. Beyond the ice-edge the land was subject to a very severe climate which kept the subsoil permanently frozen, and on the seasonally melted topsoil grew vegetation of the tundra kind, interspersed in places with hardy trees such as birch. This cover is called *park-tundra*. The birch spread far and wide as temperatures rose and the glaciers melted back, but its dominance did not last. Some 9,000 years ago (Fig. 19) there was a rather sudden change in climate. The British area came under continental influences, which caused precipitation to decrease and brought long spells of dry weather. The hazel spread vigorously, and pine also came in. The typical vegetation of the Boreal climatic phase was at first hazel-birch-pine forest, which was later replaced by hazel-pine forest as the birch declined. At this time elm and oak appeared. Pine alone became dominant in many parts of Ireland where it was widespread.

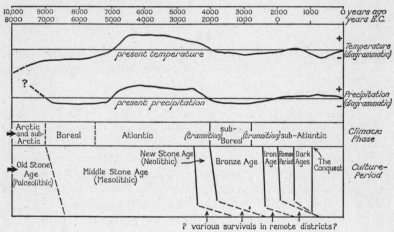

FIG. 19. Climatic trends, climatic phases, and culture-periods

The next climatic development produced the Atlantic phase, which lasted from about 5500 to 2000 B.C. and was marked by the powerful streaming of oceanic westerly air over the British Isles. Mean temperatures rose because the prevailing winds blew strongly and often from a warm sea, reaching a maximum which they have never since attained, and probably representing the peak of an interglacial. But the westerly winds brought heavy rainfall to the north and west, where blanket bog spread over much land that had formerly been wooded. On the lower slopes and in the English Lowlands, the damp-loving alder suddenly increased in importance in damp places, while mixed-oak-forest established itself elsewhere.

These highly oceanic conditions were modified in the sub-Boreal phase, which lasted from about 2000 to 750 BC. The sub-Boreal was climatically similar to the earlier Boreal, but its continental character was too weakly marked to bring back the forests typical of Boreal times. Oak and alder retained their dominance in the lowlands, but some of the bogs of the uplands dried out enough to allow birch and pine to colonise them. The re-growth of the northern forests was halted by a return to oceanic conditions in the sub-Atlantic phase, which set in about 750 BC. Increased rain again enabled the upland bogs to grow. Surviving forests on the rainy plateaus were rooted in heavily leached soils of the podsol type. Dominated by the Scots pine, they formed an outlier of the great belt of coniferous forest land which stretched across the north of Eurasia. The deciduous woodland which covered very large parts of the lowlands still contained a great deal of oak, but with enough alder and birch to justify the name of alder-birch-oak forest. Beech and hornbeam entered the southeast, the former rising to dominance in some districts where the soils were developed directly on limestone.

Forests Today

It is very many centuries since climatic conditions suitable to forests were established in the British Isles. The only large areas which would not be naturally forested today are those which are too wet because the soil drainage is very poor, those which are too dry because the soil is highly permeable, and those where there is too little soil for trees. The reduction of woodland to 5 % of the total land area is a measure of the changes wrought in the visible scene by man —a conservative measure, for much of the existing woodland is the result of deliberate planting.

If any relic of the former natural forests is to be seen, it probably lies in the shreds of oakwood which survive on the valley-sides of Southwest England, Wales, the Southern Upland , and the sheltered parts of the Scottish Highlands. There are, too, some stands of Scots pine in the Highlands, and of ash on the limestone soils of the Pennines, which may serve for samples of the once extensive native woodland. Beechwoods on the limestone soils of the Jurassic and Chalk cuestas are growing in their native localities, but are nearly everywhere so subject to management that they can hardly be called even semi-natural. The same may be said of most of the oak-woods of the lowlands, whether they are dominated by the stalked oak (*Quercus robor*), which favours damp situations, or by the durmast oak (*Q. sessiliflora*, also known as the pedunculate or sessile oak)—which is suited to well-drained soils.

The character of British forests is still changing. The Forestry Commission, established in 1919, is carrying out a programme of planting in places which are not now forested, and of improving existing woodland. Although hardwoods are planted in some of the Commission's forests, most of the newly-planted ground carries conifers—mainly spruces and larches (Plate 5). Patches of softwood are spreading across ground which has long been under rough grazing, but which before clearance supported deciduous forest. Similar planting is going on in the Irish Republic. There is no dispute that the gloomy ranks of conifers are scenically less attractive than the native hardwoods, but afforestation is being practised for economic purposes. Over 90% of the main demand from industry is for soft-wood timber, and over 90% of the timber used in the U.K. is imported. Imports in fact fall short of demand, for the main potential supplier is Canada which lies in the dollar area. There is no prospect that supplies from Europe can be increased, for reserves of timber on the Continental mainland tend to decline and consumption there to increase. The stated aim of the Forestry Commission is to rehabilitate some 2 million acres of existing woodland and to plant an additional 3 million acres, in order to supply some 30% of the normal need for timber. One million acres have already been planted in Great Britain, 40,000 in Northern Ireland, and 200,000 in the Irish Republic. The oceanic climate of the British Isles ensures rapid maturing, so that thinning can produce timber large enough for pit-props in 15 years after planting, and felling for sawtimber can begin in 20 years. Softwood forests will inevitably spread.

Rough Grazing

The land taken over for planting falls almost entirely into the class of rough grazing. It has already been stated that a great deal of the vegetation of rough hill pasture constitutes a biotic climax, the old forests having been removed by felling and kept down by grazing. Large areas of Wales, the Southern Uplands and the Scottish High-lands provide instances of the nearly complete destruction of thick forests which formerly occupied all but the broad exposed summits. The attacks were made by charcoal-burners and by sheep-graziers. Fine forests still stood in the Scottish Highlands in the late Middle Ages, on land which is now open treeless moor. They outlived the forests of the Southern Uplands because they were the more remote, but finally vanished in the great expansion of sheep-farming in the late 18th and the 19th centuries. Irish forests had almost vanished by the end of Tudor times.

The existing vegetation of unenclosed hill districts is shown in a generalised and simplified manner in Fig. 20. Subdued summits in the north and west are extensively mantled with acid peat, which also occurs at many places in the valleys. Peat—mainly of the acid type—covers a fifth of Ireland. But some of the bogs, formed under the oceanic conditions of the sub-Atlantic climatic phase, are no longer growing, being unable to expand either vertically or horizontally for lack of moisture.

On the areas shown as *peat moor*, sphagnum is common. It is usually colonised by cotton-grass, another major contributor to the formation of peat. The distribution of peat moor is patchy, for its development depends on very poor site drainage as well as on a moist climate, but large expanses of peat moorland occur in the far north of Scotland, in parts of the Grampians, in the west of the Southern Uplands and on the north Pennines. Peat moor is common in all the Irish west, and on upland everywhere in Ireland. In the southwest of the Scottish Highlands it is intermingled with Molinia moor, and in the central Pennines with Nardus-Fescue moor (see below).

Heather moor, dominated by Calluna, covers very large areas on the eastern flanks of the Scottish Highlands, fringes the Pennines, characterises the North York Moors, and occurs patchily in Wales. The heathery areas mapped in the Lake District and Southwest England are best called *heather fell*. The heather moors of Scotland are periodically burned over to promote new growth and to give shelter to grouse. Grazing destroys heather; if grazing ceases, heather takes over the mountain grasslands.

Fescue-Agrostis grassland is dominated by species of bent (agrostis) and of fescue. It is well developed in the SW of the Grampians and in parts of the NW Highlands, and fescue grassland forms a fringe all round the edges of the Welsh upland.

Molinia moor, which in Fig. 20 includes Molinia-Nardus moor, is dominated by the purple moor-grass. It occurs in small blocks at high elevations in SW England and broadly on the high platforms of Wales (Plate 6), and is intermingled with heather moor in the western half of the Southern Uplands. Molinia grows in wet sites where water does not stagnate in the soil. It thus contrasts with the matgrass, nardus, which does best where the soil is not always wet. *Nardus moor* typifies the eastern, drier, half of the Southern Uplands and fringes the low ground around Moray Firth.

much peat moor

Molinia, sedges, etc. at low levels.
Fescue-agrostis at high levels.
Arctic-alpine vegetation at higher levels.

mountain fescue
all round edges

Peat moor and
cotton-grass moor

Heather moor and
heather fell

Molinia-nardus moor
and molinia-sedge moor
(wet grass moor)

Nardus and
nardus-fescue moor
(dry grass moor)

Fescue-agrostis grassland
and mountain fescue
(acid grassland)

Arctic-Alpine vegetation

Heaths of the
New Forest type

N

0   50   100 MILES

FIG. 20. Distribution (much simplified) of uncultivated vegetation

The distributions in much of the Northern Highlands are too complex to record on Fig. 20, because the ground is very broken. Molinia moor is typical of the lower ground, Fescue-Agrostis grassland of intermediate levels, and specialised Arctic-Alpine vegetation of the highest summits. This last type is also recorded in the eastern Grampians.

The distribution map does not show the former heaths of the Breckland, where the highly-leached soils developed on glacial outwash are now mainly under planted conifers, nor does it show the small patchy heaths of the East Anglian coastland. Two districts of *Heath of the New Forest Type* are represented. That in the Hampshire Basin includes the New Forest itself; in this locality, acid soils have formed on permeable Tertiary sandstones, and heather (Calluna) and small oaks are the most noticeable plants. The heathland on the Hampshire-Surrey border is far more scattered than the map suggests. It is based on acid soils developed both on Tertiary sandstones in the London Basin and on the Lower Greensand within the Weald. Its plants include oak and birch, along with the pine which was long ago introduced and has now naturalised itself.

SOILS

Soil may be defined as that part of the mantle of weathered rock which has been transformed by the action of organisms and by the re-arrangement of its material. Its character is affected by the nature of the parent material from which it is formed, by the vegetation which grows on it, by climate, and by the length of time during which soil-forming processes have been at work. Many British soils have been greatly changed from the natural state by cultivation, whether by being disturbed, by losing nutrient materials to plants, or by the deliberate addition of fertilisers.

The parent material is provided by weathering, which breaks down the rocks. In the various developments of climate which occur in the British Isles, the end-products of weathering consist mainly of sand and of clay. The calibre of weathered material is controlled partly by the texture of the rocks which provide it; conglomerates, sandstones, gravels and sands yield gravelly and sandy rock-waste on which coarse-textured soils develop, whereas fine-grained rocks—slates, shales, clays and mudstones—weather into fine-grained waste and are transformed into clayey soils. The crystalline rocks of the massifs weather very slowly; since they have for the most part been scoured by ice, any soil lying on them is developed mainly on glacial material rather than on the rocks themselves. Large expanses of the highlands are overspread by peat, which

forms organic soils and effectively covers both the drift and the
solid rocks.

The results of soil-forming processes are as varied as the processes
themselves are complex. When the 1-inch/mile maps of the Soils
Surveys of England and Wales and of Scotland have been completed, thousands of different soils will have been located, named,
and described. The mapping carried out by the two Surveys undoubtedly represents actual distributions and real differences
between adjacent soils (Figs. 21, 98), but for the present purpose it is
sufficient to concentrate mainly on the classification of soils into
groups.

FIG. 21. Sample of soil-distribution on the Shropshire Plain. Parent materials are
glacial deposits or Triassic rocks

Very many of the soils of the British Isles fall into one of seven
soil groups, each group being recognised by its profile—i.e., by its
arrangement in section. Soils of three groups are especially widely
developed, having formed under the influence of climate and of
climatic-climax vegetation: the podsols associated with the northern
coniferous forest, the brown earths formed under deciduous summer
forest, and the blanket bog peats of wet and gently-sloping upland
areas. Soil groups developed in special conditions of soil-drainage
or of parent material include meadow soils, rendzinas, fen peat, and
raised bog. Podsols are developed in moist, cool conditions under the
influence of leaching, where water percolates downwards through

the soil and raw humus is added by the vegetation. These conditions were most widely realised under the former cover of coniferous forest, but also applied to areas in the southeast where the rock-waste was coarse and highly permeable and leaching was highly effective. Podsols occur in the Weald on part of the Lower Green-sand, on the weak sandstones in the southwest of the London Basin, and on the sandy rocks of the central Hampshire Basin. The typical podsol profile shows a clear distinction between the several horizons (layers) of the soil (Fig. 22). The topmost horizon is blackened by raw humus; below this comes a layer of coarse grey sand devoid of soluble material, and at the base an iron-stained and often well-cemented layer of *pan* rests on the weathered but otherwise unchanged parent rock.

FIG. 22. Contrasted profiles of some mature soils

Brown forest soils formed widely under the deciduous summer forest from which they received an increment of mild humus. They have been very commonly modified by cultivation and their arrangement in horizons has been disturbed. In any event their layers, even in the natural state, are never as strongly distinguished as are those of mature podsols. The humified upper part of the brown forest soil grades downwards into the lighter-toned material beneath, which in turn passes into weathered rock. The brown forest soils of the British Isles suffer leaching and lose their lime, becoming somewhat acid; but water also moves upward through them in dry seasons, so that the very powerful leaching which produces the strongly acid podsols is inhibited.

Blanket bog, an organic soil, is acid and permanently wet. It consists of little but a grossly exaggerated development of the layer of raw humus in the upper part of a podsol.

Meadow soils occur in flood-plains. Although their drainage is typically impeded, they can be rich in lime and humus. The permanently-saturated layer lies at a depth of feet below the surface (Fig. 22), so that meadow soils well repay cultivation if flooding can be prevented. Rendzinas form on limestones where the slope is great enough for rock-waste to creep constantly downhill; they are best illustrated from chalk scarps, where they are shallow, blackened with humus, and enriched with lime from beneath. Where the surface is flat, as on parts of the Chalk crests, residual material can accumulate to a depth of feet. The soil developed at such sites resembles the terra rossa (red earth) of the Mediterranean lands; the leading example is provided by the soil formed on Clay-with-Flints.

Fen peat is rich in mild humus. As agricultural material fen peat soils are very different from blanket-bog peat, as may be seen from a comparison between the Fenlands and the blanket-bogs of western Ireland. The two localities differ in climate as well as in soil, but the two sets of differences are interrelated. Fen peat forms in water-logged areas where the stagnant water is rich in lime: in the Fenland region the lime was brought in solution by rivers draining from the Jurassic limestone belt.

Where the climate is moist enough, peat will continue to grow after a basin has already been infilled by fen peat. It has done so in very many places in Ireland, especially on the Central Plain. Sphagnum is the first great contributor to raised bogs, which carry their own water-table up with them as they grow. It is typically followed by cotton-grass and bell heather (Erica), with Calluna spreading as the level of the bog rises and especially when drainage is improved by the cutting of peat. Raised bogs are uncultivated and their soils acid.

Soil groups are subdivided into soil series, according to the parent material on which they are developed. On the maps of the Soil

Surveys, soil series are named after places. Soil series will not be discussed here.

Soil series are further subdivided into soil types, on the basis of texture. For the present purpose it is enough to recognise five grades of texture—clay, clay loam, loam, sandy loam, and sand (Appendix 1). Clays and clay loams are heavy soils, tending to be cold in the sense that they warm up slowly when the air temperature rises. In addition, they are not readily permeable. Loams possess the texture most generally favourable for cultivation, although sands and sandy loams have advantages in special circumstances. Sands are loose and light, highly permeable, and liable to suffer leaching—hence their tendency to develop podsols—but some sandy loams contain enough fine material to check leaching to some extent, and are remarkably warm: their air-spaces allow warm air to raise the soil temperature. Sandy loams are in many places under the intensive cultivation of market-gardens and orchards, as for instance in the fruit-growing districts of North Kent, the Medway valley, and the southern fringe of the Hampshire Basin. Heavy fertilisation of sandy loams is repaid by early cropping (cf. Plates 7, 8).

APPENDIX 1

SOIL TEXTURE

Soils can be subdivided, according to texture, into more than 20 grades. For many practical purposes, however, it is enough to subdivide them into five grades, as follows:—

1. *Sand:* incoherent soil, which feels very gritty when rubbed between finger and thumb.
2. *Sandy loam:* soil which, although it coheres, feels gritty.
3. *Loam:* soil which can be smeared when rubbed between finger and thumb; smooth feel, no grittiness; surface of rubbed sample tears, giving broken surface.
4. *Clay loam:* soil which feels very smooth when rubbed, and can be made to take a dull sheen when buffed with thumb.
5. *Clay:* soil which is very stiff to mould, and can be made to take a high gloss.

CHAPTER 4

The Pattern of Peopling

THE present distribution of people in the British Isles is the outcome of very lengthy development. The distribution of rural population is still strongly influenced by the original founding of pioneer settlements, by early settlement-patterns, and by modifications of settlement-pattern which occurred in the distant past. Each of these topics is related to some body of knowledge which lies beyond the strict scope of geography. Many of the Dark-Age settlements, for example, were founded by immigrants from Europe, whose arrival was a manifestation of the widespread wandering of peoples. The cause of this wandering is most obscure, and may never be fully understood. The original pattern of Dark-Age settlement on the English Plain depended not only on the quality of the land, but also upon the social structure and the farming customs of the immigrants. Changes in the pattern of settlement and in the distribution of population have been linked with changes in agriculture, in industry, and in social and political habits. At all points, the geographical treatment of peopling becomes entangled with other studies. One theme, however, runs throughout the history of peopling from the earliest days up to the Conquest—the successive arrivals of new groups of settlers or invaders, and the successive defeat, displacement, or absorption of those in possession.

PREHISTORIC IMMIGRATIONS

Immigration into the British area began well before the last[1] glacial maximum of the Ice Age. The first immigrants belonged, culturally speaking, to the Old Stone Age, living as hunters on the river-terraces and tundra-lands of southern Britain. They have left no enduring mark on the visible landscape. Their successors of the Middle Stone Age are equally unrecorded on the modern map. The change from the one culture to another corresponded quite closely to a drastic change in the natural environment. The hunters of the Old Stone Age disappeared—by migration or by dying off—

[1] The word *last* is used here for convenience, for we are probably now living in an interglacial, with another glacial phase still to come.

5. Planted conifers in Thetford Chase.

6. Part of the interior plateau of Wales, at about 2,000 feet up. Subdued crests carry moorland vegetation under a cloud-laden sky.

7. Part of the Lower Greensand belt in Bedfordshire—planted conifers replacing oak-birch scrub and bracken; contrast Plate 8.

8. Part of the Lower Greensand belt in Bedfordshire, adjacent to that shown in Plate 7; market-garden land on light sandy loam.

when the great ice-caps waned, and when improving climate allowed the trees of the Boreal period to colonise large parts of the British Isles. The tundras which had fringed the ice-caps were replaced by forests, and their inhabitants were succeeded by the forest-dwellers of the Middle Stone Age, who used carpenters' tools of stone, and kept dogs to help them in the chase.

The New Stone Age

When the maritime climate of the Atlantic phase set in, the water-table in southern England rose. Its rise made possible the farming of a new group of immigrant peoples—those of the New Stone Age. These newcomers arrived in the British Isles some 4,500 years ago, bringing with them the essential achievement of their culture-period—farming. Whereas their forerunners had depended on hunting and gathering, the peoples of the New Stone Age raised crops and kept flocks and herds. To judge by the burial mounds which they constructed, the familiar long barrows, they lived in well-organised societies and practised a highly-developed religion, for none but the people of a complex society would have been able to build the barrows, and none but those with a strong religious sense would have cared to. Long barrows are especially numerous on the limestone uplands of the Cotswolds and of Salisbury Plain, where the rainy climate of the time supplied plentiful soil-moisture. These areas were the most easily farmed, for the highlands were largely. under peat, and the low-lying clay country of the Midlands and the southeast was covered by forest, marsh or fen. Farming of the New Stone Age seems to have been restricted to those parts of the limestone plateaus where shallow limestone soils occur—avoiding, for instance, tne rather heavy soils of the Clay-with-Flints. The shallow soils were the most lightly wooded and the most easily cleared, and their shallowness was no handicap to the use of the scratch plough. The small tilled plots were customarily abandoned after a few seasons' use, tillage in Britain in the New Stone Age taking the form of shifting cultivation.

There was a lag of 3,000 years between the change to a maritime climate and the immigration of farmers. This lag was due partly to the situation of the British Isles, which lay on the unknown fringe of the known world of the time. Cultural advances flowed very slowly across the mainland from the Middle East or from the shores of the Mediterranean, reaching the British Isles tardily and in a thin stream. Within the British area, the currents set weakly towards the north and west, so that technical advances and social changes tended to occur later in the highlands than in the lowlands, if ever they reached the highlands at all.

c

The Bronze Age

The New Stone Age in Britain lasted for about five centuries—
i.e., until about 4,000 years ago. It was brought to an end by a new
series of immigrations, which happened to coincide roughly with a
further change in climate. The maritime conditions of the Atlantic
phase changed to the cooler but drier conditions of the succeeding
sub-Boreal. The water-table in the permeable rocks was lowered.
The new culture-period was the Bronze Age, in which the inhabitants
of the British Isles were introduced to the use of metal. The Bronze
Age was a time of prolonged peace, permitting an increase in population and in wealth—an increase recorded in the great numbers of
round barrows. Some allowance must be made for the fact that the
Bronze Age in the British Isles lasted three times as long as the New
Stone Age, but Bronze Age barrows outnumber those of the former
period by far more than three to one. Significantly enough, in view
of the falling water-table, the round barrows are typically sited on
false crests, so that they appear on the skyline when seen from
lower levels. Habitations lay below the crests, but the Bronze Age
peoples in Britain, being mainly herders, have left little in the way of
permanent settlements. The distribution of their burial-mounds,
however, is enough to show that the limestone plateaus continued
to provide the best land and to support many of the inhabitants of
these islands.

All but the hilliest and swampiest districts were however populated
to some extent. There was a considerable population on the Atlantic
coastlands, which were connected to Brittany and Iberia by long-
established sea-routes. Among the trade-goods carried by the little
ships were fine gold ornaments made by Irish craftsmen.

The Iron Age

The next culture-period was the Iron Age. Iron-Age culture did
not reach the British Isles until about 2,500 years ago, long after
the rather difficult technique of smelting iron ore was widely known
in many parts of Europe. The nearest parts of the mainland were
quite well peopled by this time, and some of the best land was possibly
overcrowded. At about the time that iron-users invaded the British
Isles, there was a change towards more maritime conditions of climate
—the change from the sub-Boreal to the sub-Atlantic. Summers
became moist and cool, so that peat once more grew vigorously
in the highlands and killed large portions of the forest. Those small
groups of people who retained the culture of the Bronze Age, or
even of the New Stone Age, were driven into the remote and rainy
north and west. Most of the British Isles was in time occupied by the

iron-users, who once more put the limestone uplands of the south under the plough, and also farmed parts of the Pennines.

With the aid of a water-table which again stood high, and of limestone soils which were damper than they are today, tillage was practised in these areas. The plough used was still the scratch plough, with which little rectangular fields were worked in two directions. Many groups of such fields have been located on air photographs, mainly on Salisbury Plain and the neighbouring Chalkland districts. Farming was so prosperous that southern England could export surplus grain to Gaul. Minerals were exploited at a number of places—tin and copper in the Southwest, lead in the Mendips and in the Pennines.

Both farming and mining, however, were liable to interruption by war. The Iron-Age inhabitants of the British Isles were organised in shifting alliances of tribal groups, with frequent hostilities occurring between one group and another. Many commanding hilltops in the southeastern lowlands and on the fringes of the highands were heavily fortified (Fig. 23, Plate 9), the strongholds often absorbing the compounds erected during the New Stone Age. But, despite the generally disordered nature of the time, towns arose— Colchester, London and Canterbury among them—on or very near to sites which are occupied by towns today.

FIG. 23. Defended hilltops in part of Somerset; the sites have clear tactical advantages

In all the most accessible parts of the British Isles, the languages of the Iron Age were Celtic. An evolved form of Celtic speech still survives in Scotland, Ireland, and Wales, and its Cornish variety has not long been extinct. It is highly probable that Iron-Age culture and Celtic speech spread through the highlands, and especially through Ireland, by diffusion rather than by conquest, and quite likely that the diffusion was still going on long after the British tribal power in the lowlands had been overthrown. It is certain that tribal power and tribal culture survived in Highland Britain for a long time, resisting with varying success the Roman, Saxon, Scandinavian and Norman invasions.

Roman Times

Caesar's expeditions of 55 and 54 B.C. involved the destruction of a tribal fortress at Wheathampstead, near St. Albans, and an unsatisfactory treaty with the British. It was left to the emperor Claudius, in A.D. 43, to establish the new Roman province of Britannia. Forty years were necessary to subjugate the peoples of eastern and southern England and to subdue the few inhabitants of the Pennines. The advancing wave of conquest did not break until it had reached the Welsh Border and washed over the Southern Uplands of Scotland.

Behind the expanding military frontier came order of the Roman kind. The lowlands became a civil province, with a network of planned roads intersecting in planned towns. Lowland Britain was incorporated in the Roman Empire. Portions of the Roman arterial roads survive in the modern network—not all of them, however, represented by main roads today (Fig. 24). Most of the minor Roman

FIG. 24. Comparison and contrast between parts of the Roman and the present road-systems

roads have been lost, and some Roman town-sites have been abandoned. Enough remains to show that the usual routes from the mainland to Britain passed across the eastern Channel; ships made land at Dover, Lympne, Richborough, or Reculver, according to weather; roads from these ports converged on Canterbury, whence Watling Street led to London. London was a Roman metropolis, with a fortified wall enclosing a square mile of ground. Roads radiated from it to such country towns as Bath, Uriconium, York and Colchester.

The pieces of the Roman pattern which have come down to us are impressive. Arterial roads in the lowlands ran straight for long distances, well adapted to the broad features of relief. On the highland borders, where roads led to fortresses and to mines, the form of the ground exercised a sterner control. The highlands themselves, difficult to traverse and unpromising to farmers, remained for the most part in native hands.

Wealthy citizens in the province of Britannia enjoyed many of the benefits of a complex civilisation. Although the Roman towns tended to decay after about A.D. 300, the country villas flourished. Trade with the Continent was considerable: lead, copper and gold were smelted and worked for export, iron was made in the central Weald, wool was sold abroad, and kilns for the making of bricks, tiles and pottery were numerous. The mark of Roman life was heavily impressed both on the land and on the life of its half-million inhabitants.

THE DARK AGES

That mark was all but erased by the Saxon invasions of the 5th century. Roman rule in Britain was ended by threats to the Imperial capital (by that time Constantinople). The legions were withdrawn; Britain and its inhabitants lay open to attack by forest-dwellers from the northern mainland of Europe.

Piracy had long troubled the Roman administrators of the southeast coasts. Piracy soon turned to settlement when the armies departed. Saxon ships beached in creeks along the whole range of shore from the Tweed to Southampton Water. The invaders penetrated far inland, sacking settlements, killing or enslaving all those who did not flee, and establishing themselves in farming communities on sites of their own choosing.

The period of history thus begun in about A.D. 450 is known as the Dark Ages. Its title is justified by the lack of written records; the illiterate invaders, by destroying towns and villages, by overthrowing the Christian Church, and by displacing the Latin language, removed both the art of writing and the men who could practise it. Contrasting strongly with the absence of documents is the mark of the Dark Ages on the actual land. Many of the rural settlements of today were founded in the Dark Ages. The term *rural settlement*[1] must be used instead of *village*, for by no means all the pioneers were organised in compact village communities. The village was typical in Saxon England, an area comprising most of Lowland England

[1] The word *settlement* can mean either an inhabited place, the pattern made by many such places, or the process of settling, according to context.

except the southeast (Fig. 25). The unit of rural settlement in the southeast was the hamlet, as it remains to this day.

KEY

Nucleated villages common

Hamlets or single farms common, nucleated villages rare

Considerable mixture of nucleated dispersed settlement

Heavily urbanised areas

Approximate former boundary of Midland system of open fields

FIG. 25. Forms of rural settlement in England and Wales
(considerably generalised)

The name *Saxons* was given by the Romans to pirates attacking the southeastern coasts. The same word forms an element in the county-names Essex, Middlesex, and Sussex, and in the old kingdom-name Wessex. But Saxon settlement spread far to the north of these areas, for by A.D. 700 writers in Northumbria were describing their peoples as Saxon. Southeastern England was settled by Jutes; but it is not clear whether these were a distinct body of invaders, or whether the Jutish nation arose in the region itself. The third group, the Angles, gave their name to England, to the English language, and to the surviving kingdom-name East Anglia; they came from a single homeland and preserved their traditions in their new country. It is difficult to say how the ambiguous term Anglo-Saxon arose, or what led the Saxon king Alfred to speak of an Angle-race and to call his language English. The Angles, like the Saxons, settled in compact villages; and the word *Saxon* will serve as a generic title for all the Teutonic invaders, to whatever group they belonged.

The general course, and the extent, of Saxon settlement can be traced by means of place-names (cf. Fig. 26). The distribution of place-name elements shows that the Saxon settlers gained complete control over most of the lowlands. Few Celtic words survive there, either in place-names or in the English language itself. There were two main phases of pioneering settlement. In the first, the *penetration phase*, the pioneers occupied the eastern parts of the lowlands. Their advance was then checked for a time by the Celts, who, descending from their hills and mountain valleys when the Roman legions withdrew, assumed control of the western plains. Eventually the Celts were driven back, not by small groups of armed settlers, but by the armies of the kingdoms which emerged in the east. This was the *expansion phase*, during which the frontier was forced over the Pennines, up to the Welsh Border and well into the West Country.

Behind the moving frontier the numbers of settlements increased, as new immigrants arrived and as secondary settlements were made

FIG. 26. Some directions and limits of early settlement and control

by already-established communities. Whatever their form or date, Saxon settlements were everywhere carefully related to the form and quality of the ground (cf. Fig. 28). Very many of them were set in forest, part of which was cleared to provide arable land. Here was the real beginning of the clearance of the extensive woodlands— a clearance which was to continue for many centuries.

During the ninth and tenth centuries there were further attacks and invasions, those of the Danes and Norsemen. By that time the term *Saxon* had been superseded by *English*, and it was on English kingdoms that the new invaders fell. The Danes established a state which at one time stretched as far southwestwards as Watling Street. Norsemen settled the fringing islands of Scotland, the Isle of Man, and northwestern England (Fig. 26). In Ireland and in Wales, where the interior remained in Celtic hands, Norse settlements took the form of coastal towns which were strongholds, ports, and the capitals of little coastal kingdoms. On the pattern of rural settlement, however, the Scandinavian invasions had little effect, except for adding new settlements and changing existing names.

Throughout the whole of the British Isles, the form of rural settlement in the Dark Ages was related to the system of agriculture and of land-tenure. Three main types of combination can be distinguished in the Saxon areas. The simplest of these combinations was associated with the best-known element of rural settlement— the nucleated village, formed in the beginning by a number of dwellings set close together. Nucleated villages were typical of most of England except for the southeast, and remain so to this day (Fig. 25). Except in East Anglia and in some parts of the north, the village lands were held in common by the village community, and were worked in large open fields. Very many villages at the outset had two great fields, which lay fallow in alternate years. The ploughed land was worked in strips, each farmer holding a number of strips scattered through the arable (Plate 10).

In much of southeastern England, the unit of settlement was the hamlet—a small group of dwellings associated with a small, compact block of ploughland and occupied by members of a single family. The difference between the Kentish field-system and the open-field system of the Midlands had little to do with the quality of the land. The Midland system was brought from Europe by the settlers; that of Kent was either introduced in the same way, or was adopted from local Romano-British practice. The arable of the southeast came to be subdivided, so that each patch of arable was distributed among a number of farmers. The subdivision was due to the practice of gavelkind—i.e., inheritance by a number of heirs instead of by a single one. In the Midlands, where land was held by the whole village, subdivision of this kind was impossible. If village population increased, the number of strips available for ploughing could be increased either by taking in more land or by converting the existing two fields to three, but the village remained intact and its open fields survived.

Although in East Anglia the original settlements were nucleated villages, the land was worked in scattered rectangles instead of in scattered strips. It is thought that there, as in Kent, originally compact blocks were fragmented by the operation of gavelkind; but the subdivision was arrested by the Danish invasions, so that East Anglian ploughland was less fragmented than that of the southeast.

Every one of the original settlements which can be identified today has manifest physical advantages of siting. The simplest illustrations are given by nucleated villages in scarpland country. Settlement at the scarp-foot secured a supply of water from springs. The village itself lay on, or immediately next to, the belt of deep mixed soil which characteristically occurs below the scarp. This belt provided the best arable land, while the scarp-slope gave wood, the scarp-top supplied rough grazing, and the lower ground supported damp woodland with meadow alongside the rivers. Scarp-foot settlements had access to land of contrasting quality—a great advantage to self-sufficient communities. The wet meadows were cut for hay, the woodland yielded timber for building and gave pasture for pigs, while the rough grazing for sheep and cattle supplemented the fallow arable and the stubble which was left after harvest.

In different terrains, different patterns evolved. On the great spreads of boulder-clay, for instance, settlements were located on patches of glacial gravel or of river terrace. A rough circle was cut out of the surrounding forest, so that when parish boundaries were laid down they formed a cellular pattern (Fig. 27). Settlements on the

FIG. 27. Strip-like parishes on the edge of Salisbury Plain (left), running across the grain of the country; cellular parishes in clayland between Huntingdon and Oundle (right)

flanks of the Pennines avoided both the plateaus and the wet flood-plains, and typically lay near the edge of the valley-bottom. The heaviest clayland was everywhere avoided, and remained largely under forest. To this day there are large expanses of clay country without nucleated settlement, within the areas where villages are typical (Fig. 28). The forests were by no means unused, however, for in large portions of them pigs were grazed. The Wealden forests in particular were much exploited in this way by the people living on their margins.

| 0 | 1 | 2 | 3 | 4 MILES |

●● Villages   • Single dwellings   ◻ Limestone & Sandstones   ◻ Clays

FIG. 28. Relationship between forms of settlement and geological outcrops, Somerset-Dorset border

NORMAN TIMES AND THE EARLY MIDDLE AGES

Domesday Book records most of what is known about the Dark-Age settlements; but it was compiled in 1086, twenty years after the Norman Conquest, and centuries later than the foundation of many of the settlements. The rural pattern, both of habitation and of administration, had already been modified before the Conquest. The Normans, however, completed the stratification of society and the binding of cultivators to the land. They set a social pattern which was to last throughout the early Middle Ages.

The first pioneers had been free men; even when kingdoms began to emerge, the structure of society was by no means rigid, but the rise of a nobility and the threats of Scandinavian invasions combined to lower the status of the people who worked the land. The kingdom came to be owned by the king; by a kind of sub-letting, all but the king's personal holdings were administered by tenants, and a fundamental unit of administration evolved which appears in Domesday Book as the manor. Many of the manors were co-extensive with ecclesiastical parishes, for Christianity had been re-introduced and officially adopted well before the coming of the Normans. Thus to nucleated villages were added churches and the houses of local lords. In regions of hamlet settlement, such as the southeast and southwest of England, the small foci selected as centres of parishes often failed to grow as a result of their increased importance, so that very few large villages developed.

The most densely-peopled parts of England at the time of the Domesday survey lay southeast of the Jurassic scarp, with the greatest concentrations in East Anglia. By the mid-fourteenth century, three hundred years later, a second area of high density had emerged in the eastern Midlands, and it was the speech of this part of the country which prevailed over other dialects to become the direct ancestor of the English language in its present form. A slow increase in population had led to the founding of new settlements, and also to the clearing of more woodland—except where the land lay in the extensive hunting-preserves of the king. Where the land was worked in open fields, many villages had converted from two-field to three-field working, putting one-third instead of one-half of the arable into fallow each year. In general, however, the pattern of rural settlement had changed little in the three hundred years since the Conquest. Agricultural practice was set in the mould of custom, just as the structure of rural society was held rigid by the feudal system.

THE LATER MIDDLE AGES

These conservative arrangements were seriously disturbed by the disastrous epidemic of the Black Death. Entering the country in 1348, the epidemic killed at least a third of the people. Labour for the land became scarce, and the scarcity led to the decline of bondage and to the common use of hired labour. It also promoted the letting of land for rent, and the spread of sheep-grazing. These developments favoured commercial farming and commercial landlords as against feudal tenure, barter, and the discharge of customary services. So profitable did sheep-farming prove that, in the two centuries between 1350 and 1550, no fewer than a million acres were withdrawn from the arable of communal fields. Many settlements were depopulated, their inhabitants being driven out to make way for sheep (Fig. 29). Sheep and sheep-farms increased greatly in number, producing large quantities of wool, which were at first sent mainly for export and later used for the manufacture of cloth within the country.

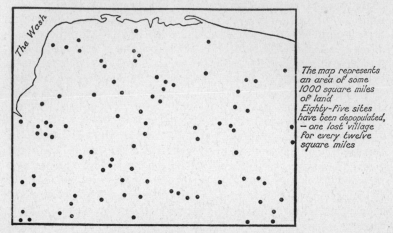

Fig. 29. Sites of lost villages in north Norfolk

POST-MEDIEVAL TIMES

Although many elements were thus removed from the pattern of rural settlement, that pattern was by no means obliterated. On the other hand, the pattern of fields was changing, even in that wide belt where large open fields were typical and where farming was most conservative. During the 16th and early 17th centuries, a 4-field system, involving one year's fallow in four, appeared and spread in the midlands. Frequently the four fields were created by the subdivision of the two open fields which already existed, but at some places additional land was taken in to make up the number.

Modification of the open fields was accompanied by enclosure of part of the cultivated land, which was removed from common holdings. Enclosure of one kind was already long-established, for the lord's house of the early Middle Ages was surrounded by the lord's estate. During Tudor times, however, there was considerable enclosure of a piecemeal kind, which took in small irregular fields—often called *closes* today—at the edges of a village (Fig. 30). Official policy and small farmers were alike hostile to enclosure, the depopulation of villages by grazing magnate having caused much alarm, and penalties were set on enclosure under Elizabeth I, encouragement being given to arable farming. Grain grown on land formerly grazed by sheep yielded heavily—a great benefit at a time of rising population; but the lesson of heavy yields was not understood, any more

FIG. 30. Pattern of enclosure-boundaries at Newnham, Northants (village buildings omitted). The very small regular enclosures are gardens; next outward come the irregular closes of late-medieval times, and then the large regular fields of Parliamentary enclosure

than the practice of enclosure was abolished or reversed. The pace of enclosure was indeed checked in those districts where the land was worked in open fields, Oxfordshire retaining one-third of its whole extent in common arable as late as 1750; but in the southeast, the southwest, and along the Welsh Border, enclosure of open land or subdivision of already enclosed land continued. Kent, and to a lesser extent East Anglia, were largely enclosed by the mid-18th century, while Herefordshire by that time had but one-fortieth of its area still in open arable fields.

THE CELTIC WEST

In most parts of the Celtic west there was never anything like the compact villages of Midland England. Most districts seem to have been characterised by a kind of hamlet settlement. The matter is not easy to investigate, for the small and loosely-grouped units of rural settlement in the Celtic areas seem to have been less stable than the Midland villages. There seems, however, to have been a marked contrast in size between the typical Midland village and the typical

hamlet of the Celtic districts; whereas the Midland villages of the
early Middle Ages had up to a hundred tenants holding land, and a
thousand acres or so under cultivation, the Celtic units of land ran
to about a hundred acres and the number of tenants to about five.
That is to say, a representative *clachan* (hamlet) in Scotland and
Ireland included some five families.

FIG. 31. Diagrammatic summary of the infield-outfield system;
progression in the outfield is from left to right

In Scotland and in Ireland the land held by a community was
typically divided into infield and outfield (Fig. 31). The infield, perhaps a quarter of the whole, was manured each year and sown with
grain. The outfield was divided into ten parts, each of which was
cropped with oats for four or five years and then left to fallow for
the remainder of the ten-year period. Sowing of part of the outfield was
preceded by the folding of stock, so that the ground could be enriched
by dung. Variations of practice occurred in a number of districts,
but the general scheme of infield-outfield was widespread.

The tilled land was divided into strips, both in the infield and in
the outfield, so that each tenant had a share in every kind of soil.
The strips were steeply ridged, giving the name of *runrig* or *rundale*
to the land so worked. The infield-outfield system, with land cultivated in runrig, lasted best in Scotland, where nearly all of the land
was still unenclosed by 1750. It seems likely that from time to time
the landlords re-consolidated the land, offsetting the subdivision
which resulted from inheritance. A similar process went on in Ireland,
where gavelkind was capable of producing a complete fragmentation

of holdings in two generations. By means of re-consolidation, the
Irish townlands were preserved until the 19th century (Fig. 32).
Wales contrasts strongly with Ireland: gavelkind in Wales tended
not only to subdivide plots of land but also to disperse settlements,

Fɪɢ. 32*a*. Two nucleated settlements in Donegal, 1834

Part of the enclosed land was in rough pasture on bog

Fɪɢ. 32*b*. The same two settlements in 1850

until it was made illegal by Henry VIII. In addition, Wales was influenced by the agricultural practice of the Marchlands, and its land was early enclosed. Southwestern England was conquered by the English before Norman times, but its rural settlements remained dominantly of the hamlet type. Like Wales, it experienced enclosure at an early date.

TOWNS

A new start had to be made with town life during the Dark Ages, and town growth was slow throughout the Middle Ages. It is difficult to realise today, when four out of every five people in Britain live in towns, how few and how small were the towns of five hundred years ago. Those of a thousand years ago were even smaller and fewer. Their location and origin are important, however, for most of them are towns today, with their centres still on the original sites.

The Roman towns were sacked either by the local inhabitants, by Celts from the west, or by the invading Saxons. Dark-Age settlers tended to avoid the sites both of towns and of villas, possibly for superstitious reasons, just as they made little use of Roman roads. The rural communities of the pioneers were organised as if towns did not exist. When towns arose once more, their growth was due to several factors which worked in a variable combination— the practice of administration, the influence of the Church, the need for defence and the need for markets.

Of the origin of some towns very little is known. London, Canterbury, Rochester and York were already centres of government, religion and trade at the time of the Scandinavian onslaughts. The danger from Danes and Norsemen provoked the foundation of strongholds—e.g., Oxford—and the fortification of existing settlements. In the territory held by Scandinavians, fortresses were also established, as already noted for the Welsh and Irish coastlands.

Places which had already grown to some size with the aid of flourishing markets were naturally selected for fortification, while the defensive works themselves gave protection to merchants and to church buildings. Thus came about, at the very outset, the interplay of more than one factor in town growth. Each town is a special case, but every site offered certain natural advantages to the founders. Durham and Shrewsbury, for example, are almost enclosed by incised meanders and were consequently easy to defend in their early days. Situation, in addition to site, was influential. Fortified towns were established on the Welsh and Scottish Borders to withhold the unruly Celts, Norman strongholds were built in Ireland. During the early Middle Ages, when local magnates became very powerful, private armies were based on walled towns throughout the land.

Because of the effects of walls and castles upon the plans of towns, defensive works and defensive sites attract much attention; but town walls lost most of their usefulness when cannon were introduced, and local strongholds lost much of theirs as the power of the monarchy increased and as feudalism decayed. The powers of central and local government and of the church were exercised principally from urban centres, but it was the function of marketing which was common to all towns of the Dark Ages and medieval times. That function is still discharged by all towns at the present day. No single feature of a town is more distinctive than the old market-place. In some towns the market-place still lies open, forming a broad stretch of street, a triangle, or a square in or near the main shopping district; in others it has been built over, carrying a guild-hall, a corn exchange, and a huddle of shops separated by narrow alleys. Although the medieval fair has degenerated into the modern fun-fair, and cattle-markets have been banished to the outskirts of many English towns, the weekly produce market still flourishes on its traditional site (cf. Plate 59).   Norwich

Town life in the Middle Ages was almost as strictly regulated as was rural life under the feudal system. Trade and craft-industry were organised and controlled by the town-based gilds, whose rise marks the elaboration of urban functions. The special status of town-dwellers encouraged migration from country to town as soon as the bonds of serfdom were loosened. Even so, nothing occurred to foreshadow the explosive growth of towns which was to accompany industrialisation during the 18th and 19th centuries. In the mid-14th century, when the population of England was perhaps two million in all, London had some 35,000 people, York 11,000, Bristol 10,000, Coventry and Plymouth each 7,000 and Norwich 6,000. In other words, the aggregate population of the six largest towns of the time was but 76,000—less than the present population of Bath. In the late 17th century London had grown to a population of half a million—a huge figure for those days: Bristol and Norwich had perhaps 35,000 each, Birmingham 15,000, and Manchester, 10,000. The rise of Bristol was associated with the town's ocean trade; that of Birmingham and Manchester marks the beginnings of manufacture. But although a quarter of England's population already lived in towns by 1700, the total for the country was no more than 5 or 5½ million, so that the inhabitants of all other towns than London numbered only 1¼ million—a figure comparable to the present population of Birmingham. The economy of the British Isles was not yet dominated by manufacture; the countryside supplied a large surplus of grain for export, as it continued to do until well into the 18th century, and the largest social groups were formed by country-dwellers (see Appendix 1).

APPENDIX

ESTIMATED CHARACTER OF THE POPULATION OF ENGLAND IN 1688

Group	Total	Arbitrary allocation to	
		Country	Town
cottagers, paupers, vagrants	1,330,000	1,115,000	215,000
labourers, outservants ..	1,275,000	1,000,000	275,000
freeholders	940,000	840,000	100,000
farmers	750,000	750,000	—
artisans and craftsmen ..	240,000	40,000	200,000
shopkeepers and tradesmen..	225,000	25,000	200,000
esquires, gentlemen, office-holders	196,000	100,000	96,000
law and clergy	122,000	61,000	61,000
liberal arts and sciences ..	75,000	—	75,000
traders and merchants ..	64,000	—	64,000
titled aristocracy	27,520	13,760	13,760
armed forces	256,000	56,000	200,000
Totals	5,500,520	4,000,760 (72.5%)	1,499,760 (27.5%)

Source (first column of figures): estimates made by King and Davenant, quoted in Ernle: *English Farming, Past and Present.*

CHAPTER 5

Agriculture from 1700

ALTHOUGH the rigid rules of feudalism in England were relaxed and modified from 1350 onwards, nothing occurred for another four centuries to transform the whole pattern of rural landscape, despite the effects of two centuries of expanding sheep-farming and of Tudor enclosures. The organisation of society which is called feudalism started to break down in the 14th century, but the manorial system— an organisation of land-tenure—persisted. During the 17th century, in which England saw two political revolutions and a civil war, the most noteworthy changes in the English countryside were the enclosure and improvement of parts of the Pennines and to the drainage of much of the Fenland; and these extensions of the available farmland, remarkable though they were, are overshadowed by the events of the 18th century.

THE AGRICULTURAL REVOLUTION

It was in the 18th century that the movement began which is called the agricultural revolution. This movement is impossible to explain but was transfiguring in its effects. Much had already been learned by individuals in Tudor and Stuart times about the possible application of new ideas to husbandry, but, in the common fields which included much of the arable land of England, experiment and change were alike impossible. Outside the belt of common fields, and in Wales, Scotland, and Ireland, farming was also notably conservative in its methods. Most farmers and all farm workers were illiterate, and agricultural science as it is now understood had not yet developed. Scientific agriculture had still to be learned by trial and error. Many successful trials were made, and their results disseminated, during the 18th century, when such improvers as Tull, Townshend, Coke and Bakewell provided farmers with the drill and horse-hoe, a scheme of crop-rotation which included courses of roots and clover, and livestock improved out of recognition by deliberate and careful breeding.

It is possible to see, in the agricultural experiments of the 18th century, a manifestation of the spirit of improvement which pervaded

18th-century thought. This spirit was responsible for many of the planned estates and reconstructed great houses which still adorn the English countryside. Even more important were its effects on farming in general, and through farming upon the location and structure of rural settlement.

Parliamentary Enclosures

As the new ideas about farming gained support, the enclosure necessary to put them into practice gained momentum. In 1750 the open-field system, in some variety or other, still survived in one out of every two English manors. During the reign of George III (1760-1820), hundreds of enclosure acts were passed, applying to 5½ million acres of land. First the open fields were enclosed and parcelled into consolidated holdings, then the common grazing-land was taken. The direct results were the redistribution of land in compact farms, a great increase in total yields, the creation of a large class of landless labourers, and a new network of field-boundaries in the districts where open fields had been (cf. Plate 64).

Enclosure undoubtedly involved much injustice and hardship, especially to smallholders, cottagers, and squatters. The main problem was one of expense: not only had legal fees and surveyors' fees to be paid, but the new fields had to be fenced. The poor sold out to the rich. Even many of the more well-to-do could not afford to build on the new farms, and the erection of farmhouses and out-buildings had to wait in many places for a generation. The process of secondary dispersion of settlement—the movement away from an existing nucleus—was deferred. This is why so many existing farm-steads date from the early or middle 19th century rather than from the time of the actual enclosures.

Eighteenth-century enclosures could only affect those parts of the country where open fields still survived. It has already been observed that Southeast England, East Anglia, Southwest England and much of Wales underwent enclosure in earlier times. Irish land remained liable to repeated subdivision and consolidation until the mid-19th century, and the island has never experienced a swift and drastic alteration of farming practice such as that which took place in England between the mid-18th and the mid-19th centuries. In parts of Scotland, on the other hand, agricultural changes were still more rapid than in England. Many of the small holdings worked on the runrig system were consolidated during the late 18th century, leases were lengthened, crop rotation was introduced, land was enclosed in fields, and lime was applied to the soil. At the same time much land was taken for large sheep-farms, which could be established all the more easily in the Highlands because the clan-structure of society was deliberately broken after the failure of the rebellion of 1745 (p. 235). The spread of sheep-farms was accompanied by emigration. Raw wool was sent to the thriving mills of the West Riding, and people moved to the rising factory towns or emigrated overseas.

From a distance of a century-and-a-half, it is possible to regard the parliamentary enclosures and their attendant distress with some detachment—the modern world has problems of its own, which divert attention from past tragedies. In their social aspects, the emergence of a labouring class, the division of rural society into farmers and labourers, and the pauperising of many countryfolk can only be condemned. These accompaniments of enclosure were not wholly compensated by the rise of a class of independent farmers, some of them secure in ownership or in long leases. Technically, however, the agricultural revolution was wholly beneficial. It enabled the country to be fed during the Napoleonic Wars, and to support the rapidly-growing towns of the early years of industrialisation.

CHANGING EXTERNAL RELATIONS

The agricultural revolution brought into existence much of the rural landscape of Great Britain as we know it today. But although it set the pattern of fields and of holdings, it did not immediately transform the aims of farming. Although the new farms were commercial undertakings from the beginning, they were still worked in order to provide basic foodstuffs. The British Isles in 1800 were still approximately self-supporting in essential foods. By 1900 a profound change had occurred, for by that time heavy reliance was being placed on farms abroad. Two main factors account for the change— the increase in population which accompanied industrialisation at home, and the spread of farming in mid-latitudes overseas. A combination of influences strengthened the commercial nature of British farming, promoted the growth of towns, and depressed the status and numbers of rural labourers.

In 1750 the population of Britain was about 5½ million. By 1801 England and Wales alone contained 9 million and by 1851, 18 million. Food shortage was already a possibility by 1800, but the pressures of wartime led both to high prices and to the reclamation and improvement of land. Agriculture flourished, the cultivated area was increased, and the country was fed. After the long war ended in 1815 at the Battle of Waterloo, the strong tariffs of the Corn Laws were imposed by a parliament dominated by landowners, in order to protect the cultivation of cereals. The Corn Laws weighed heavily on a country whose population was increasing faster than the supply of food from its farms, and became unpopular with manufacturers because they kept up the price of food and the level of wages. They survived, however, into the mid-century. The famine in Ireland forced their modification (p. 154), and in 1869 duties on imported grain were abolished, in accordance with the prevailing esteem of free trade at that time. While they lasted, the Corn Laws protected British farming from foreign competition and discouraged any tendency to replace cereals as the main kind of tillage crop.

Between 1850 and 1860 the external trade of Britain trebled in volume. In the mid-century Britain enjoyed the position—never before held and never since regained—of workshop of the world. Farm workers were attracted to the growing industrial towns by wages which were one-third or one-half as great again as those offered in the country. At first the new towns killed many of their immigrants, for they provided unbelievably hard conditions of work and of living, and suffered frequent epidemics. As public health improved, the towns were able to grow with increasing speed and to become ever more attractive to the country people.

British agriculture and agricultural workers were especially hard hit by the spread of grainfields in the New World—in the U.S.A., in Canada and in the Argentine—and by the rapid increase in British imports of grain made possible by railways and steamships. Keepers of livestock also suffered. Competition from Australian wool was already severe by 1850, and in the later half of the 19th century much land in Scotland was withdrawn from sheepwalks and put to use as deer-forest and grouse-moor. The most impressive single event was the disastrous British harvest of 1879, when it became clear—even to those who had hitherto resisted conviction—that Britain had become dependent on foreign suppliers for large imports of food grain. British farming never recovered. Between 1870 and 1890, 3 million out of 8 million acres were lost to corn production, and from 1890 onwards oversea farms sent into Britain great quantities of meat, cheese and butter.

CHANGES IN LAND-USE

Contemporary estimates make it possible to compare the land use of England and Wales in the late 17th century with the use in the early 19th century (Fig. 33). Records are available from the 1860s; the changes which they indicate (Fig. 34) culminate in the distributions mapped below.

| Tillage 23% | Pasture & Meadow 31% | Heath, Moor etc. 26% Rough grazing ←perhaps 20%→ | Woodland, Parks & Commons 15% | 5% | ENGLAND & WALES, 1688 |

←——Improved Farmland· 54%——→

Houses, Gardens and Inland Water

| Tillage 27% | Total Grassland 48·5% (includes rough grazing) | | ENGLAND & WALES, 1808 |

Corn Crops 18%   Fallow 6%   Root & Green crops 3%   Rotation grass 3%

FIG. 33. Summaries of land use in England and Wales 1688 and 1808; based on contemporary estimates

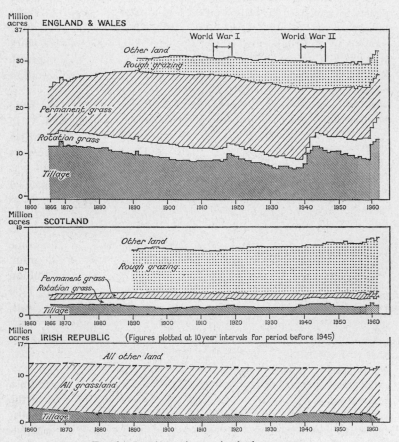

FIG. 34. Land-use changes in the last century

Changes in England and Wales

The graph for England and Wales just includes those peak years about 1870 which immediately preceded severe agricultural depression. Nearly a third of the land in 1870 was under tillage crops, and rather more than a third under grass. The marked subsequent decline in the arable acreage was at the expense of tillage crops and not of rotation grass. As the graph shows, the decline was checked but not arrested in the late 1800s, and continued well into the years of World War I. Permanent grassland, on the other hand, expanded up to 1890, at the expense both of tillage and of 'other land'—in addition to conversion of arable to grass, there was some improvement of rough grazing. But the expansion of permanent grass ceased after 1890 in the face of competition from meat-producers overseas. Some of the worst grassland was allowed to revert to rough grazing, and reversion continued right up to World War II.

After the First World War, the grassland which had been hastily ploughed-up was soon seeded down again. The decline of ploughland went so far that, in the 1930s, no more than 7 million acres were in tillage—less than half the total for 1870. Farming throughout England and Wales suffered severe depression in the 1930s—depression made still worse by the slump in trade and industry. Every effort had to be made to reduce working costs, and the loss of farm-workers to the towns was accelerated.

The great exception to the story of progressive decline was dairy-farming. During the inter-war period, this branch of farming was favoured by the impossibility of importing fresh milk, by an advertising campaign designed to increase milk-consumption, and by the high prices which dairy-farmers secured by means of collective bargaining. Dairying paid better than beef-production in England, and numbers of Welsh farms also converted to dairying.

In all this, factors quite unrelated to the physical environment can be seen at work. Direct government action to encourage certain types of farming by subsidies or by guaranteed prices, and discouragement of other types by lack of support, became familiar in the years between the wars. Tariffs, import quotas and marketing boards were freely used to carry agricultural policy into effect. When the Second World War broke out, a great campaign was launched to increase the area of tillage, in order to offset as much as possible the effects of the expected blockade, and compulsion as well as persuasion was employed. Some of the results appear strikingly in Fig. 34. The total area of tillage increased to a figure unknown for seventy years. The expansion becomes even more impressive when it is recalled that much good farmland was taken for military use—especially for airfields and training-grounds. But the total area of farmland was not increased, as the graph shows, and the extension of ploughland was secured at the expense of permanent grass. The reduction of the acreage of meadow was accompanied by a marked fall in the number of sheep.

During and after the Second World War, selected branches of farming were heavily subsidised. This fact goes far to explain the retention of tillage in the post-war period near the level of 1870. The policy of subsidising agriculture has been most beneficial in the short run, since it has meant working capital for farms which needed capital very badly. Farms in the United Kingdom today are in general efficient, productive, highly mechanised and with their buildings in good order. Yields per acre of the chief crops are between 10% and 15% above the level of the late 1930s. The number of tractors at work on farms today is more than 10 times as great as in 1938, and there has been a corresponding increase in the use of tractor-drawn implements. Labour for the land was short during wartime, and the deficiency had to be met by machines; but mechanisation has continued in the post-war period, effecting great changes in farming practice (Plate 11).

Another change with clearly visible results is the great increase in the use of chemical fertilisers, weedkillers and insecticides. All contribute to the increase in yields, and the weedkillers make standing crops look remarkably clean (their use is not common in the Irish Republic, where in some districts crops are always thick with weeds). A rapid improvement in cattle has been made possible by artificial insemination, by means of which one bull can become the sire of 10,000 calves instead of 500. It is now possible to breed desirable characteristics into large numbers of stock in a short time, and dairy-farming in particular has benefited (cf. Plates 12, 13).

The long-term effects of subsidies or other forms of assistance to agriculture are keenly debated. Successive governments have, however, been determined to keep farms in good order, both for the sake of reducing imports and as a safeguard against food-shortage in case of renewed war. Under the Agriculture Act of 1947 the principal farm products of Great Britain were assured markets at guaranteed prices, and when a change of government brought a change of policy, support continued to be given to products which failed to obtain a minimum or standard price. The current cost of such support is about £250 million a year. It is of course obvious that if agriculture is to be directed or guided to any significant extent, the price of direction or guidance must be paid.

Changes in Scotland and Northern Ireland

Much of what has been said of England and Wales applies also to Scotland. Contrasts arise, however, between England and Wales on the one hand, and Scotland on the other, from the fact that so large a proportion of Scotland's farmland is under the plough. The decline of tillage in Scotland lagged behind that in England, mainly because the great tillage crop of Scottish farms is oats, which is not so susceptible to foreign competition as are wheat and barley. Nevertheless the area under the plough in Scotland began to decrease in the late 1880s, and has remained at a relatively low level ever since, except during the two World Wars. The expansion of Scottish tillage during World War II has been largely offset by reversion to rotation grass since 1945. A slight but steady loss of farmland to rough grazing has been going on since 1900; much of this loss represents the abandonment of small, remote, unprofitable farms in the highland districts.

Figures for Northern Ireland since 1922 show a tendency for tillage to decline, and a reduction in the acreages of the leading crops—oats and potatoes. The trend was reversed during World War II, but has subsequently been resumed. In Northern Ireland, as in Great Britain, agriculture is much influenced by government policy, and at the present time prices are guaranteed and markets assured for some 70% of all farm produce.

Pre-war and Post-war Acreages, Productions, and Yields in the U.K.

The following tables make a contrast between the agriculture of the U.K. for the mid-1930s and the early 1960s. The first table shows differences in the extent of the main tillage crops, yields per acre, and numbers of stock, while the second shows the results of increased production combined with some change in volume of imports.

Item	Acreage in early 1960s as % of acreage in late 1930s	Production in early 1960s as % of production in late 1930s	Yield per acre in 1960s as % of yield per acre in 1930s
Tillage plus temporary grass ..	140	—	—
Wheat	117	185	158
Barley	403	637·5	158·5
Oats	63·5	88	139
Potatoes ..	100·5	130	121·5

*Numbers in early 1960s as % of
numbers in late 1930s*

Cattle	135
Pigs	154
Sheep	110
Poultry	145

*Home production of certain commodities as % of
total consumption*

Item	late 1930s	mid-1950s
Wheat and wheat flour	12	28
Meat	51	67
Bacon and ham	32	46
Cheese.. ..	24	38
Eggs	71	86

Changes in the Irish Republic

The graph of land-use changes in the Irish Republic begins with tillage in steep decline (Fig. 34). The reduction of tillage began in the mid-19th century, with the famine of 1845 and the mass emigration which resulted. Many holdings were abandoned as they stood, and in some of the western counties a quarter, or even a third, of the farmland fell into disuse. But tillage was also diminished by the changeover from wheat and oats—formerly grown for export to Great Britain—to livestock farming. Some of the main tillage crops display a long-term tendency to decline in importance, their extent rising abruptly during the two periods of world war but rapidly diminishing again and continuing to fall in time of peace. This group includes potatoes, oats, and turnips. Acreages under other and much less extensive crops have changed little, except in the cases of wheat and sugar beet, which have been subsidised since the early 1930s and have actually increased in extent.

Up to the partition of 1921, Northern Ireland displayed similar agricultural trends to those in the 26 counties of the Republic. The farming of the North since partition has reacted to changing conditions in a similar way to the farming of Great Britain, while, in the Republic, the land ploughed-up during the time of World War II has again gone back to grass. Were it not for the bounties on wheat and sugar beet, the total extent of tillage would be less today even than it was in the late 1930s. Resumption of pre-war trends has been so effective that agriculture in the Irish Republic displays no such contrasts as those observable in the foregoing tables for the U.K.

Changes in Livestock

Variations in land use, themselves constituting changes in the visible landscape, were associated with changes in numbers of livestock. Between the mid-19th century and the 1930s, the number of cattle in the British Isles increased by half. The increase began as a response to the competition of foreign grain. It was least marked in Scotland, where oats, the leading grain, was not primarily a cash crop, but many grain-farmers in eastern England turned to stock-fattening, and many Welsh farmers took to raising store cattle for sale in England. The collapse of grain-farming in Ireland and the turnover to cattle has already been noted. The expansion of dairy-farming in the inter-war period occurred mainly in England and on farms with access to urban markets. Wales took some share in this expansion, but Scotland very little. The Irish Republic has developed a highly successful export of fat and store cattle; it also exports butter, but its trade in dairy produce has been damaged by disputes with the U.K. Northern Ireland has developed its farming on different lines, with pigs, milk and dairy produce, and eggs the chief items of agricultural produce in that order.

At the present time there are some 14 million cattle in the British Isles, an increase of about 2 million over the figure for 1938, and the greatest total yet recorded. Between 5 and 6 million are dairy animals. In contrast with cattle farming, which has more than held its own since the mid-19th century, sheep-farming has suffered a number of setbacks. The decline of grain-growing led to a decline in the number of sheep in the arable districts of England, where they had formerly been folded on ploughland in large numbers. The total flock numbered about 30 million in 1870, declined to little more than 20 million in the 1920s, and fluctuated considerably up to 1938. There were heavy slaughterings in World War I, and again in World War II when numbers were reduced from 30 million to 22½ million. The present figure is about 26 million, representing a far from complete recovery in numbers.

AGRICULTURAL DISTRIBUTIONS

The distribution-maps (Figs. 35-43) are drawn from statistics for whole counties, except in the cases of Yorkshire, Lincolnshire, Sussex, and Suffolk, which are subdivided in the official returns. Unless county boundaries coincide with boundaries of contrasted agricultural districts, county statistics tend to obscure the agricultural variations which actually occur. The concentrations and the areas of sparsity which appear are, in consequence, all the more impressive.

Improved Farmland

Fig. 37 shows improved farmland as a fraction of the total land area. The fraction exceeds ¾ in a large block of England—the block

FIG. 35. Summary of land use in England and Wales, by regions; compare Figures 36, 72. Regions are named in Fig. 83

FIG. 36. Summary of land use, Scottish regions

lying athwart the Humber and the Wash, with a broad extension into the eastern Midlands. This first concentration links, by way of the Jurassic belt, with another highly-farmed area in the western Midlands, the Borders of the West Country, and the Welsh Border. More detailed information would show this second belt extending from Shropshire into the Lancs.-Cheshire Plain. A third concentration occurs in the east of Ireland—in a climatic setting comparable to that of the eastern English block, allowance being made for regional differences in climate.

These three parts of the British Isles include the largest and most continuous patches of improved farmland, which, simply because they are large and continuous, are reflected in the figures for whole counties. The relative extent of farmland is reduced in southern England by various means—by the woods of the southeast, by heaths, by the unimproved Chalkland of Salisbury Plain, and by the high moors of the Southwest. In parts of Wales the fraction falls below one-tenth. In the northern Midlands, farmland laps round the end of the Pennines and encroaches on their flanks, but much ground here is used for industrial purposes. In the north of England and in Scotland, the difference between the wet hilly west and the drier east with its more extensive lowland is well brought out. In very large areas of the Scottish Highlands there is no improved farmland at all, by contrast to the west of Ireland, where the highlands are broken and where no county records less than ¼ of its area as improved farmland.

FIG. 37. Farmland, cropland, and improved grassland as fractions of the total land area; relative extents of cropland and grassland

Rough Grazing

Rough grazing in Great Britain (Fig. 38) is very nearly coincident with the areas of moorland shown on Fig. 20 (see also Chap. 3). It accounts for a great deal of the Scottish Highlands, and is also extensive in the Southern Uplands, the North and Central Pennines, the Lake District and the heart of Wales. It is less widespread in Ireland than might be expected, being most common there on the broken high ground of the northern, western and southern parts of the island, but limited in extent in the lowland districts.

FIG. 38. Distributions of cropland, improved grassland, and rough grazing

9. Cadbury Camp, Somerset. A defended hilltop, on a prong of high ground overlooking the Somerset Levels.

10. Strip-pattern of surviving open fields at Laxton, Notts. Contrast the pattern of enclosure-boundaries in the surrounding area.

11. Harrowing by caterpillar tractor, Lincolnshire.

12. Free grazing by pedigree Guernsey cows, in parkland with ornamental hardwood trees in the background.

13. Grazing of pedigree Friesian cows controlled by electric fencing. The pasture is of ryegrass, sown in April after kale.

The maps of rough grazing provide negative information, since they represent a great deal of the land which is not in improved farms.

Cropland

The maps of cropland (Figs. 37–38) show a concentration in the east of England, especially in East Anglia and the Fenland. Tillage amounts to more than a quarter of the land area in most of the English Lowlands, rising to more than $\frac{1}{2}$ in the east and to more than $\frac{3}{4}$ in the heart of the Fens. It is most widespread on the drier side of Great Britain, in areas where good arable soils are most widely developed. In all highland areas tillage is limited; throughout northern England, in Scotland, and in Wales, it is much commoner on the drier eastern side than in the wetter west. The eastern and western flanks of the massifs are separated by the highland of the interior, but in Central Scotland and in Ireland, which are not thus subdivided, tillage is also most extensive in eastern districts.

Grassland

Grassland in the English lowlands is least extensive in the much-tilled regions of East Anglia and the Fens, or near the urban centres of London, the Black Country, and the industrial districts of the North Midlands (Fig. 37). In highland areas it gives way to rough grazing, but is very common indeed in Ireland. There is an obvious correlation between rainy lowland and land in grass, but some allowance has also to be made for soil-type: heavy clay soils are often put to grass in all parts of England, while much Irish grassland is developed on lime-rich glacial drift and serves the needs of cattle-producers.

As a feature of the landscape, grass is commonest in the eastern part of the Central Plain of Ireland and in the lowlands of Limerick, where it amounts to more than $\frac{3}{4}$ of all land (Fig. 37). In Ireland as a whole, only the hilly districts of the west and the Wicklow Mountains have less than half their total area under improved grass. In Great Britain, grass is most widespread in Southwest England, Southwest Wales, the borders of the West Country, and in the Welsh Borderland and its English fringe; there is an outlier of grazing land in the clay belts of Northamptonshire and Leicestershire.

Ratio of Cropland to Grassland

A comparison between the relative extents of cropland and improved grassland is made in Fig. 37. In East Anglia and the Fenland, tillage crops are twice as extensive as grass. On the eastern fringe of Scotland, in eastern England from Holderness to Kent, and in the Hampshire Basin, cropland is at least as common as grassland.

D

The relative extent of grassland increases westwards, until it becomes more than twice as common as tillage. This map once more emphasises the contrasts in farming between the drier east and the wetter west.

FIG. 39. Distributions of wheat, barley, and oats; relative extent of the chief grain crops. In Somerset, the three chief grains are roughly equal in extent

Leading Crops

Distribution-maps for the leading single crops naturally resemble, in a general way, the map of the distribution of cropland as a whole. Barley (Fig. 39) is concentrated in the east of England, where it takes more than half the area under grain in East Anglia but is not common in the Fenland. Wheat replaces barley in the Fens, and is quite widely grown throughout the English Lowland; its appearance in the southeast of Ireland is a recent development in response to the grant of a bounty. Oats is cultivated throughout the arable districts, becoming the dominant grain crop in Scotland and Wales, and would be dominant also in Ireland were it not for the bounty on wheat. The climate experienced by most farmland in Wales and Scotland prevents the ripening of either wheat or barley,

FIG. 40. Distributions of potatoes, vegetables grown for sale, orchard fruit, and small fruit. All four distributions show marked concentrations in certain areas

but oats will stand almost unbelievable conditions of damp and cold.

FIG. 41. Distributions of farm livestock; compare Figures 42, 43, 73

Two very marked areas of concentration appear on the distribution-map of land under potatoes (Fig. 40)—the Fenlands and the eastern part of Central Scotland. Since one dot on this map stands for 1,000 acres, instead of for 5,000 acres as on the maps of grain crops, Fig. 40 is therefore not comparable, dot for dot, with Figs. 38–9.[1]

[1] The change of symbol is necessary because potatoes have a much smaller total extent than any one of the three chief grains.

The two concentrations correspond to two areas on the drier side of Britain where the soils are highly productive, and where on some farms potatoes are the main cash crop. In Ireland, where the potato has lost much of its old importance, the crop is no commoner than in the western Midlands of England.

Distributions of Livestock

The distribution of cattle (Figs. 41–43, 73) is, as might be expected, very like that of improved grassland. Cattle are most common in England in the Midlands, along the Welsh Border, and in the Borders of the West Country. They are kept in considerable numbers near the flanks of the high ground in the north, on the lower western slopes of the Southern Uplands, and in the west of Central Scotland. In the Scottish Highlands they are confined mainly to the eastern side by the small extent of farmland of any kind in the west. All parts of Ireland, except the bleak uplands and the boggiest lowlands, carry many cattle, and cattle-farming is well established in Southwest England and the southwest of Wales.

In direct contrast, sheep today are concentrated chiefly in certain upland areas—the plateau country of Wales, the Central and North Pennines, the Lake District, and the Southern Uplands (Fig. 41). Minor concentrations occur in Southwest and Southeast England, on the North York Moors and the Yorkshire Wolds, and on the fringes—but only the fringes—of the Scottish Highlands. Ireland has few sheep, which are located mainly on the unproductive uplands in the northeast, southwest, and extreme west. The present distribution of sheep represents, to some extent, their displacement from the best grasslands by cattle. Sheep in Lowland England are numerous mainly where the soils are too dry and too poor to favour dairy-farming, but the animals are also used to keep down the rapidly-growing grass of summer in cattle-grazing districts. In some areas they are pastured on floodplains in summer, and on very many lowland farms are folded on arable land in the winter.

Pigs (Fig. 41) are found mainly in Lowland England, with a minor concentration in Northern Ireland. The map roughly reflects the close association between pig-keeping and dairying, skimmed milk on dairy-farms being commonly fed to pigs, which are most numerous in the great dairying districts of England.

Factors Influencing Distribution

It is clear from the distribution-maps that some kind of connection exists between quality of land and of climate on the one hand and type of farming on the other. Farming, however, is carried on for profit, and not merely in order to satisfy the principles of geography.

FIG. 42. Farm livestock in England and Wales, by regions

Farmers decide on particular crops and on types of livestock according to their own judgement of what will pay best. Their decisions are affected by government policy, by how well their neighbours do, and by their own ability. Some of the results of official policy have already been mentioned; for comparison, an instance may be given of the effect of example. In recent years a number of Lincolnshire farmers have moved into Kent, taking over land on Romney Marsh; used to arable farming in the Fenland, they put their land to tillage crops in place of the traditional sheep-pasture, and their success has done far more than subsidies to establish tillage on the Romney Marsh alluvium.

Because most farming in the British Isles is cash-farming, and because it needs to pay in the face of competition, the distribution-

FIG. 43. Farm livestock in Scotland, by regions

maps may be regarded as showing which kinds of crop and stock
pay best in particular areas *in existing circumstances*. These circumstances, as has been stressed, include political as well as geographical
facts.

CHAPTER 6

The Rise of Industry

IN the foregoing account of agricultural change, a number of references were made to industrialisation. To some extent, agricultural change and industrial change were interdependent; but the revolution in farming had already passed its peak when the first climax of industrial change had still to come. Industry was to expand so fast, and in so many directions, that it was to transform the entire economic, social, and political structure of Great Britain, and to remove agriculture from its former dominant position.

THE INDUSTRIAL REVOLUTION

The term industrial revolution, which is often applied to the sum of technical advances in the hundred years from the mid-18th to the mid-19th century, has today fallen out of fashion. Its critics justly draw attention in particular to the flourishing state of the woollen industry in earlier centuries. There can, however, be no dispute that between 1750 and 1850 the rate of industrial development was greater than anything previously known, and that in this period were laid many of the foundations of our present industrial economy. The geography of Great Britain was indeed revolutionised, and the term will therefore be retained.

Iron and Steam

Two great achievements of the industrial revolution were the discovery and development of processes for producing cheaply large quantities of iron, and the application of steam power to machines. In themselves, these achievements were no more than technical advances. Iron-smelting had already been practised for thousands of years before the 18th century; coal-mining had been carried on for hundreds of years, and a coasting trade in coal from the north-east was already well established; mechanical power had been employed for a very long time in the windmills, water-mills, and fulling-mills which were scattered up and down the country, and in the water-powered hammers in the more localised forges of iron-makers. Nor was an elaborate organisation of manufacture

90

unknown. Wool and flax were spun and woven mainly in the home, but the supply of raw wool, the distribution of yarn, and the marketing of finished cloth were largely in the hands of powerful clothiers and merchants. There were even a few factories in the present-day sense of the term. All the precedents for industry existed long before rapid growth took place. Two things only were lacking: an abundant supply of power, and adequate engineering materials.

These were provided by the steam-engine and by great improvements in smelting practice. The use of mechanical power and of cheap iron led to the concentration of manufacture in large factories, to the concentration of the factories on the coalfields, to the emergence of new towns, and to the astonishing rise of Great Britain as the first great industrial nation.

Production of iron during the Middle Ages fell short of demand. Armour and cannon, or ready-smelted iron for making them, were in part imported from abroad. In Tudor times the matter became very serious, for smelting-furnaces were fired by charcoal, and charcoal-making threatened to destroy much of the country's timber. There was an illustration of competition for the use of land —the small furnaces of the iron-makers competed with one another for supplies of timber, and iron-making as a whole competed with shipbuilding. Under Elizabeth I, the demand by the navy for slow-growing oak timber was so great that cutting was severely restricted by law. Iron-making, already much dispersed because the furnaces tended to follow the receding edges of the woodland, declined steeply. The Weald, which had been the chief region for the production of iron, was particularly hard hit. By the mid-18th century the domestic output of iron in the British Isles fell to the wholly inadequate total of 20,000 tons a year, and iron was regularly imported from Sweden, Russia, and the North American colonies.

Many experiments had been made in smelting with coal instead of with charcoal. All had failed. The main difficulty was due to the sulphur which is often present in coal, combined with iron as iron pyrites—the sulphur entered the iron during smelting and made it brittle. But if coal is baked in closed ovens, many of its impurities are driven off; it is converted to coke, which, being free of sulphur, can be used in smelting iron ore. The earliest authenticated use of coke in smelting is that by the two Darbys (father and son), one of whose first blast-furnaces can still be seen at Coalbrookdale in Shropshire. The Darbys produced coke-smelted iron early in the 18th century, freeing themselves from the need for charcoal and drawing on the accessible local reserves of coal. For a number of years they kept their process secret; but when in the latter part of the 18th century the knowledge escaped, many new ironworks were founded; they stood not in the forests but on the coalfields. The coke-fired furnaces could be larger than those which used charcoal, for the coke could support the weight of large quantities of iron ore. The total output of smelted iron increased rapidly, but smelting with charcoal declined; the last furnace in Sussex went out for the last time in 1827. Thus occurred both a rise in the output of the smelting industry and a change in its location. Only where smelting with charcoal had already been established on or near a coalfield, as in Staffordshire and South Wales, could the industry stay where it was and convert to the use of coke. The ores used in these two districts, as in most of the newly-developed smelting areas, came mainly from the Coal Measures themselves.

Iron run directly from the furnace and allowed to solidify is pig iron. If it is re-melted and run into moulds it becomes cast iron. Cast iron, containing from 2% to 5% of carbon, is brittle by comparison with wrought iron or with steel, but is reliable in quality and can be used for many purposes. For many years it was widely used; bridges, rails, and a great range of machine parts were made from it; cast-iron cooking-pots were still common until the 1920s. Wrought iron, on the other hand, can be hammered into shape; it is practically free from carbon and is not brittle. The manufacture of wrought iron in quantity was perfected by Cort, who by 1784 had discovered how to drive off the impurities from molten iron by puddling—that is, by stirring molten pig-iron—and had so improved earlier designs of rollers that he could produce rolled malleable sheets of chosen thickness. Although cast iron and wrought iron are both inferior to steel, they were far better than any engineering material which had previously been produced at a reasonable cost. By the later years of the 18th century, therefore, the rapid growth of civil and mechanical engineering became possible.

The application of steam power to manufacture and to engineering increased the pull exerted by the coalfields on the new industries of Britain. Steam-power was first used in pumping water. Savery invented a steam-pump shortly before 1700, and Newcomen's first patent was taken out soon after. In these early days the obvious use of steam-power was in the pumping of mines, for there was as yet no great engineering industry. Coal-mines at that time were mainly shallow workings on the outcrops of the seams, and the problem of drainage was seldom difficult, but in the deep Cornish tin-mines the inflow of water to deep workings caused endless trouble. It is not surprising that Newcomen engines were known chiefly in the south-west. They used much fuel to produce little power, and were by no means reliable; but they were the best steam-engines available until Smeaton and Watt made their great improvements on existing designs.

Like the development of coke smelting, the manufacture of the new steam engines was at first slow. Although Watt's engines were made by the firm of Boulton and Watt and also by other firms under licence, no more than 84 were in use in the British Isles by 1800. It was already clear, however, that they were good for other things than pumping; steam power was made to supply a forced blast in iron-smelting in 1790, and a hot blast was used in 1828. Thus the steam-engine, itself owing much to the improvements in the smelting of iron, contributed to further improvements. As soon as its use became at all general, its manufacture increased the demand for iron.

Textiles: The Background

The way in which the various developments of the industrial revolution reinforced one another is well seen in the changes taking place in textile manufacture. At first these changes were contemporary with, but independent of, the advances in the techniques of smelting and the improvements of the steam-engine. Nevertheless, the final result of changes in textile working was to concentrate much of the textile manufacture of the British Isles on coalfields, and to produce a whole new industry. As in other cases of industrial change, technical, social, and political factors are interwoven.

Textile manufacture in England had been officially encouraged for many years, e.g., by the prohibition in 1660 of the export of raw wool, and by the regulation of 1678 that corpses should be swathed in wool for burial. The Huguenot immigration from France after 1685 greatly stimulated the working of silk, and the linen industry of Scotland was given tariff protection. In the later Middle Ages there was a considerable export trade in woollen cloth, and by the 17th century the total output far exceeded home demand. Much of the spinning and weaving was commercial, and was additional to that needed to supply the needs of a family or even of a whole village. The country-wide manufacture of wool had, however, developed from spinning and weaving for family needs alone, and until the 18th century was widely dispersed in the homes of working people everywhere.

Machines of a kind had been known for centuries, but the traditional spinning-wheel and hand-loom were simple in construction and slow in working. Many experimenters realised that it was possible to make more elaborate devices, but not until the late 18th century did numbers of them succeed. Rather strangely, perhaps, the advances came first in the working of cotton, which suffered from the restrictions and prohibitions imposed by governments which aimed at protecting woollen manufacture. In a sense, however, it was these very limitations which eventually made possible the swift rise of a cotton textile industry. Despite adverse regulations, an export trade in printed cottons had been established with West Africa and the New World. By the late 18th century all restrictions on the use of cotton cloth in the British Isles were abolished, and at about the same time the Southern States of the U.S.A. became great suppliers of raw cotton. There was thus scope for great expansion in a manufacture which had hitherto been deliberately confined, and which, unlike the favoured manufacture of wool, had no extensive, well-organised, and nation-wide organisation already in being.

Mechanisation of Cotton-Manufacture

Inventions of cotton-working machinery came fast in the late 18th century. The first great difficulty of the newly-freed industry was a shortage of yarn—the supply of hand-spun cotton could not meet the demands of the weavers. It was a weaver, Hargreaves, who in the 1760s made the first successful spinning-machine, the jenny. Being hand-driven, it did not affect the location of weaving in the weaver's home. In the same decade Arkwright produced his water-frame, which was power-driven and unsuitable for home use. Like the mule developed by Crompton in the 1770s, the water-frame was a spinning-machine; the mule, at first small and hand-powered, was in time developed into a machine capable of turning hundreds of spindles and requiring a workshop to accommodate it. Here were the beginnings of cotton-making in large factories. By 1800 the cotton-spinning industry was fully mechanised, with much of the total output coming from new mills which depended on water-power.

Of the localising factors which influenced the rising cotton textile industry, two deserve special notice. One was the supply of power, the other the supply of raw material. Since the rise of the industry was closely associated with the development of powered machines, power supply was important in all but the earliest stages of expansion. Since the power first used was water-power, those areas most favoured were those where many streams, nourished by a rainy climate, descended the steep broken flanks of high ground. With the Southern States of the U.S.A. supplying most of the raw cotton, western ports functioned as inlets for raw material; and of these, Liverpool and Glasgow already had close trading connections with the New World. Thus it was that numbers of cotton-mills were established in their hinterlands, on the western slopes of the Pennines and in the Clyde Valley.[1] In both districts, similar in their general setting and in their external relations, the new industry flourished.

[1] It is true that in the early days of the new factories the humid atmosphere of these two districts was an advantage, for it helped to prevent the cotton threads from snapping; but there are many parts of the British Isles which are

Mechanisation of cotton-weaving was slower than that of spinning. In part this circumstance was due to technical obstacles, for the early power-looms were not very successful. The stimulus for invention was there, for output from the new spinning-machines outpaced the total capacity of hand-weavers to deal with the machine-made yarn, and the wages of weavers rose steeply. But when many returning soldiers took to weaving, after the peace of 1815, wages fell as fast as they had formerly risen. Hand-weaving of cotton lasted well into the 1800s. It was destroyed mainly by the application of steam-power to the manufacture of cotton textiles. The change from hand-weaving to the use of power-looms driven by steam, and the conversion from water-powered to steam-powered spindles, was quite slow, and was not sensibly completed until the middle of the 19th century. It eventually fixed the cotton textile industry firmly on or near a single coalfield—that of Lancashire—for, in the Clyde valley, shipbuilding competed successfully with cotton manufacture for the supply both of capital and of labour.

Mechanisation of Woollen-Manufacture

At first there seemed far less scope for mechanisation in the manufacture of wool than in that of cotton. The woollen industry was well organised, despite its wide dispersal; it was also well balanced. The supply of raw wool was roughly equal to the demand exerted by the markets and by the capacity of domestic spinners and weavers. Nevertheless, the hand-driven jenny was used in some places to spin wool before 1800, and the first half of the 19th century saw hand-working in rapid decline. Two fundamental changes occurred: the concentration of most woollen manufacture on a single coalfield, and a great increase in total output.

The rise in output resulted from the use of powered machinery, which was driven first by water and then by steam. It reflected the rise in the population of the British Isles, the increase of national wealth due to the growth of industry, and the expansion of overseas markets. As with cotton, industrial growth was aided by a rapid increase in the supply of raw material. Sheep-farmers in New Zealand and Australia, taking in enormous areas of land in the early 19th century, swiftly increased the numbers of their sheep and the size of their annual clip of wool. Wool produced by sheep-farmers in the British Isles was at first greatly supplemented by imported wool, and in the second half of the 19th century imports were so great that they competed strongly with the home product.

at least as humid, and in any case humidity in the cotton mills is now artificially controlled. The former and incidental advantage of a humid atmosphere has no significance today.

Although the manufacture of wool was in time converted from domestic craft to an industry carried on in factories, it has never become as highly concentrated as has the manufacture of cotton. In terms of output and of numbers employed, the textile-manufacturing districts of Lancashire acquired some 90% of the cotton industry; most of the remainder is located either in the hosiery-making towns of the Midlands (mainly Nottingham and Leicester) or in Paisley. The West Riding of Yorkshire acquired 75% of the woollen industry, rising thereby to undisputed dominance; but other manufacturing centres persisted in Norfolk, the Cotswolds, the Leicester-Nottingham area, the West Country and the Tweed valley. Factories in these areas succeeded because they specialised. Norwich retained its worsted-making while East Anglia generally lost its production of woollen cloth; some Cotswolds mills concentrated on blankets, others—like those of the West Country—on serge. Woollen manufacture in Nottingham and Leicester continued in association with the working of cotton, both kinds of textile being needed in the production of hosiery. The factories of the Tweed valley became noted for tweeds; in addition, the home craft persisted in the western highlands of Scotland and in Ireland, where it still survives.

The manner in which the West Riding came to dominate the woollen industry shows very clearly the combined influence of a whole group of circumstances. The area was noted for its woollens long before industry was revolutionised by the application of machine-power. Many monastic sheep-farms were to be found on the Pennines in the late Middle Ages, and after the dissolution of the monasteries in the 16th century graziers continued to produce wool which was used in the domestic craft. The villages set in the incised valleys of the Pennine flank benefited from the soft water flowing copiously off the Millstone Grit, for the treatment of wool demands a great deal of water and for some processes the water needs to be soft. Sheep-farms within reach, and water at hand, enabled the settlements of the West Riding to develop a manufacture of woollen cloth which had reached industrial proportions by 1700. The introduction of power-driven machines increased their advantages. Wool-workers in the West Riding were far better able to employ water-power than were, for example, those in Norfolk and the Cotswolds; in Norfolk all streams are slow because the relief is subdued, and in both areas streams are small because catchments are restricted and rainfall is not heavy. When in due course steam-power superseded water-power, some of the West Riding mills could obtain their coal almost on the spot. It was a mere accident of history that wool-working should have been firmly established on or near a coalfield before the days of machine-power; this one wool-working district was so favoured that it became pre-eminent in the industry, inevitably damaging others by its competition.

ROADS AND CANALS

The establishment of textile factories and of textile machinery, and the development of iron manufacture in which coke was used for smelting, were two of the three main achievements of British industry between 1750 and 1830. The third was the improvement of roads and the making of canals. The great railway boom did not take place until the mid-19th century, cheap steel was not produced in bulk until the later half of that century, and the remarkable increase in the output of coal from British fields was also achieved mainly after 1870. It is true that the greatest days of the woollen and cotton industries came as late as the early 20th century, but there is nevertheless a great contrast between Great Britain of 1750 and Great Britain of 1850, at the two ends of a century in which the foundations of her industrial greatness were laid. It was during these hundred years that manufacturing became dominant over agriculture in its output and in its demand for workers. The subsequent spread of railways, rise of the steel industry, and expansion of coal-mining continued trends already begun in the first phase of industrial development.

British roads in the Middle Ages were indescribably bad, and remained so until the 18th century. If any two reasons are to be cited, one must be technical and one political. Until the industrial era, the chief commodities moved about the country were wool and grain. Pack-trains sufficed to carry part of the wool; grain was moved by river wherever possible, and went overland by waggon in quantities which seem small by present-day standards. Until machines were used in overland transport, it was possible to make do with poor roads, especially since the country districts were roughly self-sufficient in foodstuffs and many small towns could be fed by their immediate surroundings. There was no irresistible reason to construct roads which would be serviceable in all weathers, and no sound technique of road-making was developed. Again, until the 18th century the maintenance of roads fell upon individuals or upon small groups. This state of affairs was a legacy of the former feudal structure of society; it made for much neglect, and was adverse to the spread of any satisfactory methods of construction which might have been invented.

Turnpike Roads

During the 18th century, however, private enterprise and the prevailing spirit of improvement led to the formation of many

Turnpike Trusts, each charging tolls which were supposed to pay for the maintenance of roads in addition to giving a profit. The first Turnpike Act was passed as early as 1663, but the turnpike system was not widely established until the later part of the 18th century. In spite of its many defects, it made possible the coaching services which connected important towns to one another. In the closing years of the 18th century and in the early 19th the technique of road-building was greatly changed. Macadam is the best-known of those who contributed to the new advances, but several other eminent engineers of the time were also concerned with road-building. The significance of improved roads lay in the improved facilities which they afforded to travellers rather than in their direct service to industry. It is impossible to estimate the effect of the increased and swifter travel upon the spread of ideas and the movement of people in this period of industrial and social ferment, but the new roads certainly helped to break down the barriers of remoteness which cut off many country districts from the towns, and thereby to unify the industrial society which was evolving.

The greatest single scheme of road-building was carried out not for civil but for military purposes, when roads were driven into the Scottish Highlands after the failure of the 1745 rebellion. Elsewhere, however, new construction was applied mainly to existing roads, so that the road network of today represents very largely the pattern of pre-industrial days.

Inland Navigation

When the rising industries demanded supplies of heavy goods in bulk, canals and rivers first met the growing need. Canals with locks were known before 1700—e.g., that which connects the Aire with the Calder—and various piecemeal improvements had been made to navigable rivers. But the great period of canal-making came in the late 18th and early 19th centuries. Canal boats were from the outset carriers of goods, and particularly of coal, which went by water as quickly as it could by road. Industrial sites alongside canals were eagerly sought. Now that some canals are derelict and many are little used, it is difficult to realise their former importance to industry; their decline has been due to several factors, chief of which was competition from railways. Canals in country districts were constructed in a spirit of optimism which has not been justified, while canal transport in industrial areas has suffered from the small dimensions of locks and barges and the variation of these dimensions between one canal and another. Like the Turnpike Acts, the Canal Acts were passed in favour of individuals or of small companies; each canal project was designed with little thought to other schemes, and no satisfactory network of canals arose. Those canals which still carry appreciable traffic serve mainly to link industrial areas with navigable natural water; such are the Bridgewater Canal between Manchester and Runcorn, the Aire and Calder Canal, the Gloucester and Berkeley Canal, and the Manchester Ship Canal which was not completed until 1893. There is today nothing that can be called a working system of canals.[1]

The absence of a general plan for canals must be regretted, but can scarcely be condemned. Planning and control by a central authority was not to be expected either in the 18th or in the 19th centuries. The railways of today suffer from the effects of a layout which evolved in a similar way to that of the canals. Obsolete though many canals may now be, they were highly effective in the first century of industrialisation.

RAILWAYS

Although the construction of railways does not belong to the first phase of industrial change, it may fittingly be discussed at this point. The impetus of canal-making had already run down when the great period of railway-building began; this period, lasting roughly from about 1830 to 1860, came after the industrialisation of the manufacture of iron and textiles, but preceded the further changes of the later 19th century, bridging the gap of transition between the first and second phases of industrial development.

Railways of a kind had been in use for more than a century before the first successful steam locomotive was made. The first ways were constructed of plates, which were in time superseded by rails, just as wood was superseded by iron as a structural material. Heavy goods such as coal and corn were carried in trucks hauled by men or horses. Locomotives began running on private mineral lines in the first years of the 19th century, and in 1825 Stephenson supplied a locomotive to the first *public* railway to use one. This was, as is generally known, the Stockton and Darlington line. The Liverpool and Manchester railway, opened in 1830, had immediate success with passenger trains drawn by steam locomotives. By 1840 there were nearly 2,000 miles of railways in the British Isles, and by 1860 over 10,000. Further expansion was to come, but a country-wide network already existed by 1860. Canals and roads could not compete with railways either in capacity or in speed; passenger travel soon became a leading interest of the railway companies, and the new railways influenced the location of industry and the spread of urban settlement as strongly as canals had formerly influenced the location of factories.

[1] See, however, Chap. 9.

INLAND TRANSPORT AND COMMUNICATION IN IRELAND

It may seem surprising that Ireland shared in the movements to improve roads and construct canals and railways, in view of the modest development of industry in the island as a whole. But many of the projects executed in Great Britain were promoted and financed by wealthy landowners, and members of this class were numerous in Ireland in the late 18th and early 19th centuries. So many short roads were made in Ireland during the late 1700s that the best-settled and least boggy districts came to be remarkably well served. In Ireland, as in southern England, it was hoped that canals would attract industry and stimulate trade, but few enjoyed any marked success. The Grand Canal, which connects Dublin with the Shannon and the Barrow and was completed in 1804, was the most effective, but even its traffic has now fallen below 100,000 tons of goods a year and is still declining. The most optimistic and the least successful scheme of all was that for a canal between Loughs Mask and Corrib, where the canal was made through Carboniferous Limestone and failed to hold water. The Newry Canal was busy at one time, but is little used now that the export trade of Northern Ireland goes mainly through Belfast. Total traffic on the canals of Northern Ireland does not now exceed 20,000 tons of cargo a year; building materials are prominent among the goods carried.

Railway-building in Ireland began with the linking of Dún Laoghaire (Kingstown) to Dublin in 1834—very shortly after the opening of the first passenger line in England. A complete network, with foci in Dublin and Belfast, was completed by 1863. Thus Ireland kept pace with Great Britain in the construction of railways, although it never developed such mazes of lines as are to be found in the industrial regions of England, Wales, and Scotland. The hope that the building of railways would be followed by the general rise of industry was false, for, like the canals before them, the railways could not compensate for the lack of industrial minerals.

GREAT BRITAIN IN 1850

Great Britain by 1850 had been transfigured by the growth of industry, and was being further changed by the rapid spread of railways. It dominated the world's export trade in industrial goods. Peace and prosperity at home were reflected in power abroad—for instance in the increase in the number and size of colonies, which provided raw materials and bought manufactures. Those larger and longer-established colonies which later became the first Dominions had increasing populations and carried on ever-growing trade with the homeland.

The distribution of industry and population as we now see them had been broadly sketched, and many of the details of the picture had already been filled in. Attention could be turned to political and social problems. Although such problems are outside the scope of this book, it ought to be observed that during the 19th century those changes were made, or at least begun, which have produced the present political and social structure of the U.K. and of the Irish Republic. The reformers of the 19th century could tackle their high tasks without—as it seemed—much fear of distraction from abroad.

CHAPTER 7

Coal and Industrial Power

IN the preceding discussion of the rapid expansion of industry in the British Isles, stress has been laid on the manufacture of iron, wool, and cotton, rather than on the use of coal for raising steam or in making industrial coke. It is true that, without the aid of coal, industrialisation could not have gone so far, or so fast, as it did go between the mid-18th and mid-19th centuries. It is also true that coal had been worked for many centuries before the 18th. The expansion of the coal-mining industry and of the coal export trade nevertheless occurred mainly in the second half of the 19th century and in the early part of the 20th. It was associated not so much with the establishment of the iron industry as with the rise of steel-making and with the growth of overseas trade.

RISE AND FALL OF THE COAL-EXPORT TRADE

All the coalfields of Great Britain, with the exception of the concealed Kentish field, were being exploited by the late 1500s. Annual output then ran at about 200,000 tons. The Northumberland and Durham field led the list of producers, supplying the 10,000 tons or more which were shipped to London each year as well as sending coal to nearby ports of Europe. A hundred years later— i.e., at about the end of the 17th century—the total output had reached the considerable figure of 3 million tons, of which 1¼ million were raised in Northumberland and Durham. A hundred years later still, in the middle of the industrial revolution, the total was more than 10 million tons. The northeastern field was still the greatest single producer, but mining in the Yorkshire, Derby and Notts. field, in the Black Country, and along the Welsh Border had already been stimulated by newly-founded industries. Demand and output had quintupled by 1850. Total production ran at about 50 million tons a year; by 1870 it exceeded 100 million (Fig. 44).

Up to this time, the demand for coal came mainly from consumers within the country. The rise in production and in sales is therefore a measure of the increase in population and of the expansion of home industry. In the 1870s another factor began to operate—a rapid

102

FIG. 44. Great Britain: output and disposal of coal,
from the mid-19th century onwards

increase in the demand for coal from abroad. In the earlier part of
the 19th century many European countries were politically unsettled
—Germany and Italy, for instance, had not yet emerged as nations—
and Great Britain had in any case gained a long lead in the development of heavy industry. When European politics became more
stable, and industrialisation on the mainland could go forward,
British coal found a ready market. An increase in coal exports began
suddenly in about 1875 and continued right up to 1913, raising the
tonnage annually exported from about 12 million tons to nearly 100.
At one time British coalfields supplied no less than 90% of the
world's seaborne coal, and over half the coal sent across all national
boundaries, whether by sea or by land. One-third of the country's
output went for export in 1913.

This spectacular rise in the coal export trade was associated with—
and assisted by—an equally impressive fall in the rates charged on
seaborne freight. During the period in question these were reduced
by two-thirds. The reduction was made possible in part by the use
of steel ships. Not only were these lighter than iron ships of comparable capacity, and therefore cheaper to operate, size for size,
but the general increase in the size of new ships also meant a fall in
operating costs per ton of cargo. Cheap shipment of coal over long
distances favoured, and was in turn favoured by, the replacement of
sail by steam, the substitution of iron by steel, and the expansion
of world trade as a whole.

In 1913 it was predicted that by 1951 the population of the
British Isles would have risen to 57 millions, and that the domestic

consumption of coal would be 265 million tons a year. The predicted population is remarkably near the census total of 54 millions. The actual consumption of coal, some 220 million tons a year, is less than that predicted, but the difference is easily explained by the increased use of oil in place of coal, by improvements in coal-burning equipment, and by industrial growth which has been slower than expected. But a third prediction, that by 1951 coal exports would be 270 million tons a year, has been grossly falsified by events. In fact, the coal export trade has almost vanished—at least for the time being. Output, too, is well below half the predicted total, being 220 million tons a year instead of nearly 500 million.

Political and economic events of World War I, of the inter-war period, of World War II, and of the post-war years have combined to produce a grave depression of the coal-export trade. Not only has this depression damaged the coal-mining industry—it has also had adverse effects on overseas trade generally. The low freight rates made possible by the coal trade were of the greatest help to British exporters, especially in the days when British shipping dominated seaborne commerce. Even during the later part of the inter-war period of 1919–1939, when coal exports were but 45 to 50 million tons a year, coal provided 10% of all exports by value and 80% by bulk. As in the prosperous years before 1914, the carriage of a bulky export kept a large volume of shipping at sea and maintained the freight-charges on imports at a low level. Since World War II, coal exports have amounted, at best, to 15 or 16 million tons a year. In some single years consumption has exceeded production, and the deficiency has had to be met partly by drawing on stocks and partly by importing. Exports today are no greater than they were a century ago, and annual production is 65 or 70 million tons a year less than the peak reached just before World War I. The present total of some 1,500 collieries is less than half the 1900 total of more than 3,000, and the number of men employed in coal-mining has sunk back to the 1900 level of some 700,000, after exceeding a million as late as 1925. The decline in the number of collieries is no bad thing, insofar as it reflects the closing of old and small pits; nor is the decline in the industry's labour force to be regretted, insofar as it reflects the increasing use of machines in place of muscles. But the fall in total output cannot be gainsaid; neither can the adverse effect of diminished coal export upon seaborne trade in general. In the present economic circumstances of Great Britain, with external trade more vital than at any other time in the nation's history, the influence of the loss of coal exports upon freight rates is exceptionally serious.

More than four-fifths of the coal exported from Great Britain in 1913 went to ports on the Atlantic coast of Europe, on the Baltic, or on the Mediterranean. There was in addition an appreciable traffic with South American countries, and a demand from coaling stations on the world's great shipping lanes. France, Italy, Germany, Russia, Sweden, the Argentine, Denmark, Egypt, Spain and Norway were the chief customers, in that order, in 1913, buying between them 57 million tons of British coal in the year. By 1931 their purchases had fallen to 27½ million tons in the year, and by 1955 to little more than 4 million. The loss of their custom accounts for much of the total loss of exports, which in turn is equivalent to the fall in production from 1913 to the present day.

World War I and the Inter-War Period

The first heavy blow to the coal export trade was dealt by World War I. Shipping during that war was needed for other purposes than those of normal trade, and exports had to run the submarine blockade. A new pattern of European economy emerged when the war ended. French mines which had been wrecked by the enemy were re-equipped with up-to-date machinery. In Italy industry grew apace, but with the aid of hydro-electric power developed in the Alps rather than that of imported coal. Exports to Germany were reduced by the competition of German lignite, which not only provided industrial power but also freed German bituminous coal for foreign markets; both in France and in Italy German coal competed successfully with the British product. In Sweden, Norway, Spain and Egypt, as in Italy, the development of H.E.P. reduced the demand for coal. The Argentine, too, came to rely more and more on hydro-electricity for industrial power; but in that country in particular there was another and still more formidable competitor—oil. During the inter-war period coal was coming into increasing competition throughout the whole world with water-power, oil, and natural gas. Coal no longer possessed its former near-monopoly in the supply of power to industry. Whereas for many years up to 1913 the world consumption of coal had increased by about 4% a year, in the inter-war period the rate was but 0.3%—less than a tenth as great. Great Britain, by far the principal coal-exporting country, was by far the worst hit. In addition to the adversities of falling demand, the British coal export trade with Europe had to bear the effects of the peace treaties. The reparations imposed by these treaties included the delivery of large amounts of coal, and the new boundaries of Poland included rich fields which enabled that country to become a large exporter.

The inter-war period was one of appalling fluctuations in the coal export trade and in the coal-mining industry in general. Nothing like the 1913 level of production and export had been regained before the slump of 1921. In the years immediately after 1921 exports did indeed rise in a remarkable fashion, but the rise was in the main due to the French occupation of the Ruhr coalfield from 1923 to 1925. In 1926, figures of production and of export plunged because of the general strike; the subsequent rise reflects, in part, the fulfilling of arrears of orders. The early 1930s, with their prolonged industrial depression throughout the western world, caused the annual output of coal in Great Britain to fall towards the level of 200 million tons. Neither output nor export were able to complete their slow recovery before World War II broke out in 1939, severely reducing output and almost stopping exports altogether.

World War II and the Post-war Period

Conditions in the post-war period differ in several important ways from those of earlier times. The expansion of industrial production for purposes of war pushed up the nation's consumption of coal during World War I. In the inter-war period, the general tendency was for home consumption to decline until the mid-1930s, as can readily be seen from Fig. 44. The rise in consumption which marks recovery from the Great Slump was sharply increased in the early part of World War II, but was followed by another decline as factories were damaged by bombing and as men were drafted into the armed forces. In the post-war period the rise in consumption has almost kept pace with the rise in total output—another reason for the depressed state of the export trade. Very little coal is now available for export; consumption has reached the 1913 level and is still rising.

CHANGES IN CONSUMPTION OF COAL

Over the years, there have been significant changes in the demands made by different classes of consumer. Up to 1913, industry was taking half the coal consumed within the U.K. The years since the Great Slump have witnessed a marked increase in the supply of gas and electricity—especially of the latter—until generating stations buy as much coal today as do industrial concerns. They take some 35% of all coal used in the country. In part the change merely reflects the replacement of steam-power in industry and coal fires in the home by power from the mains, but, even so, it indicates a significant alteration both in factory practice and in the habits of living. It is associated with the spread of light industry and the widening use of electrical equipment. The most rapid increase in the supply of electricity has been to homes and farms. In the years 1920–1956, their share in the total consumption of electricity rose from 8 to 32%; that of shops and offices rose slightly, from 11 to 13%; and that of industry fell from 69 to 51%. This does not mean that the actual consumption of power by industry declined—it increased more than fourteen times; but consumption by other users rose faster still. The installed capacity of generating plant increased by 8 times and the consumption per head of population by 15 times. Both of these increases were associated with the establishment of the national electricity grid and the extension of supply lines into rural areas.

Of the coal taken directly by industrial users, some 30 million tons a year—the largest single share—are taken by coke oven plants. Of the coke produced, some 13 million tons a year goes for use in blast furnaces, another 2½ million tons is taken by other metal and engineering works, and more than a million tons by the chemical industry. Since the metallurgical, engineering and chemical industries are planned to expand, it follows that their demand for coal and for thermal power is likely to increase. It is important, therefore, that the production of coal should rise, quite apart from any question of increasing exports.

RESERVES AND PROSPECTS

Ninety per cent. of the coal got in British coalfields is worked on the advancing longwall system, in which a long working face is driven into the seam. In all but a few pits the longwall is advancing: that is, the working face was first opened near the bottom of the shaft, and as the coal is taken out moves farther and farther from the pit-bottom. Hence the longer a seam is worked, the greater becomes the distance from the shaft to the face, the more time is lost, and the greater the costs of haulage underground—costs of working inevitably increase with the age of the pit. Rising costs can be held in check by mechanisation. The percentage of coal mechanically cut rose from 1.6 in 1900 to 61.5 in 1939 and 84.4 in 1954, and no less than 90% is now mechanically conveyed underground. But in the 1930s, despite a great deal of mechanisation already effected, the average profit on coal was only 7d. a ton, and the mine equipment was largely obsolete.

Reserves of coal in the U.K. are variously estimated at about 200,000 million tons. At the present rate of extraction this is enough for about a thousand years, but the estimated figure includes seams as deep as 4,000 feet and as thin as 1 foot. There is no reason to believe that coal will not in time be extracted from depths as great as 4,000 feet, or at least that it will not be used in the process of underground gasification which can be applied in thin seams as well as in

thick ones. Against the enormous reserves, however, has to be set
the fact that the seams first worked were the best and most accessible.
As time goes on, the proportion of coal coming from thick seams,
where working is easy and cheap, tends to decline. Nearly half the
coal raised at the present time is got from seams between 2 and 4
feet thick—i.e., less than the most convenient and most economical
thickness. It is not surprising that on all coalfields there are abandoned collieries. Some have been closed in the post-war period by
the National Coal Board because they were unprofitable, but the
process of abandonment goes back very many years—every depression
in the industry has left its records in forsaken pits. Many stand on or
near the outcrops of the seams, where working was easiest in the
early years but where reserves were least. The newest, largest and
most successful collieries are those which work hidden reserves. In
coal-mining, as in many other branches of industry, there has been
a tendency for production to be concentrated in a limited number
of undertakings of a large individual size (cf. Plate 14). Four-fifths of
the total output came from a quarter of the collieries as early as 1924,
and 60% of the output of today is got in mines with between 750 and
2,000 wage-earners on their books.

Trends in Single Coalfields

Individual coalfields have been variously affected. Fig. 45 makes a
comparison for each field of the outputs of 1870, 1913, 1927–8, and
1955—years which are fairly representative of the end of the industrial revolution, of the peak of success of the coal industry and its export trade, of the inter-war period, and of the present time. The main
exporting fields of Northumberland and Durham, South Wales, and
Scotland naturally suffered most from the decline in coal exports.
They and the Lancashire field show an absolute decline in output
from 1913 onwards: their peaks of production were in fact reached
in that year. Not all the decline can be referred to the fall in exports—
part is also due to increased difficulties and costs of working. By
contrast, the fields of Yorkshire, Derby and Notts., of Staffordshire
and the Midlands generally withstood reasonably well the afflictions
of the inter-war period, and are now producing more than they did
in 1913; in consequence, each accounts for an increased fraction of
the national output.

South Wales and the Northumberland and Durham fields were
the worst hit by the loss of exports. The former shipped 70% of its
production by ocean-going or coasting vessels in 1913, but less than
50% in the inter-war period. Shipments from the Northumberland
and Durham field were maintained at the 1913 level of two-thirds
of output, but only because a decline in exports abroad was

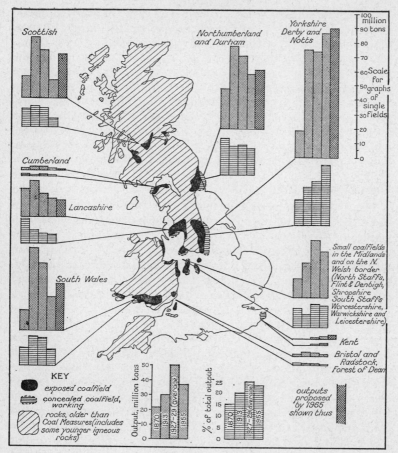

FIG. 45. Location and output of coalfields in Great Britain. The projected future outputs have been reduced for some fields

compensated by a rise in coastal traffic; in any case, the industry in that field suffered very severely in times of industrial depression. The Scottish fields, exporting either to Northern Ireland or to Europe, were also involved in the decline of exports. They were moreover affected, and continue to be affected, by the rise in costs of working which results from partial exhaustion of their best seams and from the increasing length of travel underground. The Yorkshire, Derby and Notts. field was able to maintain its output during the inter-war period and to increase it after 1945, chiefly because its seams dip gently away beneath younger rocks and extend at workable depths in the concealed coalfield for some distance east of the exposed field.

The conditions here contrast strongly with those in Scotland and in South Wales, where there are no hidden reserves, and also with those in Lancashire, where the hidden seams plunge sharply downwards and are much broken by faults. The Midland fields, which are grouped together in Fig. 45, display strong contrasts among themselves. As a group they produce more coal than in 1913, although less than in 1927–9, and have retained their full share in national production. Some individual fields within the group produce very little nowadays—the Black Country coal, for instance, is almost worked out—but output from the North Staffs., Cannock Chase, Leicestershire and Warwickshire fields tends to increase.

Plans for the Future

The coal-mining industry of the U.K. has been nationalised since 1947, the generation of electrical power since 1948, and the manufacture of gas since 1949. As the authorities concerned have announced their plans for the future, it is possible to give a summary of the developments expected in coal-mining and in power-production. The coal-fired generating stations, already the best customers of the coalfields, will increase their demands for coal as new stations come into service and as the consumption of electricity per head of population rises. In order to leave enough coal available to other users, it is necessary to supplement thermal electricity from coal-fired stations by power produced in nuclear reactors, oil-burning plant, and hydro-electric stations.

Planned output of coal from the various fields in the period 1961–1965 has been added to Fig. 45. Continued success is expected for the Yorks., Derby and Notts. field. Output from the Scottish fields is intended to increase sharply from its present low level by means of increased mining in the east, and a considerable revival is also projected for South Wales. Elsewhere the prospects are of modest increases or of continued decline. Of the Midland fields, those in Leicestershire, Warwickshire and North Staffs. are expected to benefit from plans for increased production.[1]

[1] Revised plans, which do not yet seem to be final, forecast a reduction of at least 10% in numbers employed in mining. The Northumberland and Durham field will lose 25,000 miners; Cumberland and Lancashire will also be affected, while closures in Scotland will include a pit sunk after the end of World War II. Investment will be concentrated in the most profitable fields—Yorks., Derby and Notts., and parts of South Wales. Competition of other fuels, already severe in respect of oil, has increased with the the import of natural methane gas in liquid form, from the Sahara; this gas may supply 10% of the demand for gas by 1965, and reduce the demand for coal by more than ¾ million tons. A methane pipeline links London with the industrial North (fig. 47).

ELECTRICITY

The increase in the generation and consumption of electricity during the inter-war period was greatly helped by the establishment of the national electricity grid. The linking of power stations into a single system made it possible to reduce working costs, for power could be transferred from one area to another according to variations in local demand. In addition, the large power stations built during this period were more efficient than the smaller, older stations which they replaced. The rapid extension of supply-lines not only widened the market for power, but also made possible a dispersion of light industry. The national grid, working at 132,000 volts, already promised to become inadequate before World War II. To it has been added the supergrid, transferring baseload current in bulk, at 275,000 volts, from stations on the Trent to southern England and South Lancs., and from the Aire and Calder stations into industrial Lancashire generally. A cross-channel cable, for exchange of electricity between England and France, was completed in 1961.

The cost of electricity has been kept remarkably low in the post-war period by means of continued improvements in the efficiency of generating plant. In comparison with working costs, the cost of coal has risen very high indeed, so that location with respect to sources of fuel is an important factor in the siting of power-stations. Water transport of fuel is cheaper than transport by rail over any considerable distance, but it is also cheaper to transmit power than to haul coal by rail at distances over 50 miles or so. The new power stations on the Trent, Aire and Calder lack the advantage of water routes, but obtain coal from nearby fields where the costs of mining are low.[1] In other parts of the country the main localising factor is access to tidewater, as for instance in the the case of the new station at Marchwood on Southampton Water which is equipped to burn oil as well as coal.

The huge new thermal stations, so prominent in the landscape, are most carefully sited. The *situation* of new plant—its location in a particular area—depends primarily on the demand for power, and is primarily determined by the relative costs of transmission and of haulage of fuel; but *sites* of individual stations are so chosen as to provide reasonably level ground which can withstand heavy loads, access by road and rail during construction, facilities for bulk delivery of fuel, and ample water—either for condensing, or, if cooling towers are used, for compensating for evaporation. Thus the factors governing situation are economic, while siting is a problem of civil engineering (cf. Plate 53).

[1] E. M. Rawstron: Changes in the Geography of Electricity Production in Great Britain. *Geography*, 90, 1955, p. 92.

Hydro-Electric Power

A striking increase in the generation of hydro-electricity has occurred in the Scottish Highlands during the post-war period (cf. Plate 37). Construction of new dams and generating stations is going on so quickly that it is impossible to give a general review of progress. A contrast can be drawn, however, with conditions in 1939. In that year, H.E.P. was developed only at Foyers, Kinlochleven, and Lochaber, where the plants are owned by aluminium smelters, and at Rannoch, Tummel, and Loch Luichart, where the stations belonged to electricity supply companies. The North of Scotland Hydro-Electricity Board today operates more than 30 H.E.P. stations. Some 10% of the potential has now been developed, and another 20% is under construction and survey for completion in the mid-1960s.

It is very doubtful if H.E.P. in the Scottish Highlands would have been so greatly developed if it had not been made a matter of national concern, for the market is very scattered. From the beginning, however, the policy has been to supply power to farms and crofts as well as to make it available to industry, and well over half the 20,000 farms and 20,000 crofts in the area are already connected to the mains. It is highly likely that the development of H.E.P. in the Highlands will bring about an increase in agricultural production, and possible that it will check the chronic loss of rural population (Chap. 14). New industries working with electrical power have been established, half of them however in Aberdeen, Dundee and Perth; they are concerned mainly with the production of electrical goods.

The great advantage of the Highlands in the development of H.E.P. is their heavy rainfall, which in some catchments averages well over 100 inches a year. Ribbon lakes are selected as reservoirs, having their levels raised by dams. Since the natural catchments are often small, tunnels and aqueducts are used to increase the drainage to the reservoirs (Fig. 46). In discussions of the location of H.E.P. stations, much is often made of the suitability of sites for building. To some extent this topic is irrelevant, for every site poses its own engineering problems. A head of water is usually secured in the Highlands by siting the stations at a lower altitude than the reservoirs, leading in the water if necessary by long pipelines or tunnels. The speed of the rivers themselves also has nothing to do with the siting of stations, since the water is drawn from reservoirs: in any case, the banks of the short swift rivers which are extremely numerous in the Highlands are eminently *unsuitable* as sites for H.E.P. stations, since short rivers are typically irregular in régime.[1] By contrast, the

[1] It is hard to account for the widespread impression that short swift rivers are advantageous in the developement of H.E.P. The reverse is true, as is well shown by the Kitimat scheme in British Columbia, where water is brought through a mountain range because the local short swift rivers are of no use.

FIG. 46. The Loch Sloy H.E.P. Scheme, Scottish Highlands

question of the supply of capital for construction is directly relevant. It alone is enough to account for the failure to develop all but a little of the potential H.E.P. of the Highlands until recent years.

Although much of the hydro-electricity generated in the Scottish Highlands is consumed in the Electricity's Board's area, this area includes a number of towns on the southeastern and southern flanks of the Highland region. Some electricity is transferred across the area boundary to the power lines serving the factories of Central Scotland. As more H.E.P. is developed such transfer is certain to increase, so that H.E.P. will join with nuclear power in moderating the increase in the demand for coal made by thermal-electric stations.

Nuclear Power

When sites are chosen for nuclear power stations, a different set of factors comes into play. The building-sites demand much the same qualities as those for thermal stations, but problems of the transport of bulky fuels do not arise. The policy has been adopted of locating nuclear power stations as far as possible from built-up areas (Fig. 47, Plate 15).

FIG. 47. Atomic power stations existing, under construction, or planned

Nine such stations had come into operation by 1964. Electricity from the Calder Hall station was switched into the national grid in 1956; Chapelcross, Dumfriesshire, followed in 1959. Commercial stations began full operation in 1962. The plant at Dounreay on the north coast of Scotland is a breeder reactor producing fuel. By 1968, a total output capacity of 5,000 megawatts is expected of nuclear stations, at a cost comparable with that of coal-fired plant, saving 18 million tons of coal a year, and generating at least as cheaply as the best coal-fired stations by the mid-1970s.[1]

Industrial Power in Ireland

Ireland as a whole is very differently placed from the U.K. with regard to supplies of industrial power. The geological map of Ireland shows extensive outcrops of Coal Measures, but the coal reserves are actually very small and the already almost-negligible

[1] See also bibliography, at P. R. Mounfield.

14. Kinneil Colliery, near Bo'ness, West Lothian. This modern, fully electrified colliery can produce 3,000 tons of coal a day, mainly from seams under the sea.

15. Berkeley Nuclear Power Station—an example of large-scale modern works of civil engineering.

16. Giant dragline excavator work in the Northamptonsh Ironstone Field. Draglines are us for stripping overburden and spreading soil when quarryi ceases. Spoil (stripped overburde here lies in ridges in the backgrou

17. Blast furnaces at Frodingham.

18. Charging an ingot of special steel into a Sheffield furnace, for heat-treatment.

output is still declining. The industries of Belfast and the neighbouring much smaller towns rely on thermal power raised by imported coal (mainly from the Ayrshire field). A nuclear power station in Northern Ireland is projected for the 1960s. The Irish Republic, with a dominantly agricultural population, makes little demand for power per head of population. Thermal power stations in the towns of the east and south coasts depend on imported coal. The chief hydro-electric station is that at Ardnacrusha, on the Shannon near Limerick, which illustrates very well what can be done on a river-reach where the average gradient is high, although there is no waterfall. The Ardnacrusha station still produces a quarter of the electricity generated in the Republic, but additional H.E.P. stations have come or are coming into operation, especially in the west of the country, and the consumption of electric power from all sources is now four times as great as in 1939. Use of peat in the generation of electric power is passing from the experimental to the commercial stage. The supply of power to rural areas and the policy of the government since the early 1930s have combined to result in a very wide scatter of industry. It seems inevitable that, if manufacturing in the Republic is successfully encouraged, the pattern of industrial distribution will come to resemble that of Southern Sweden rather than that of England.

CHAPTER 8

The Age of Steel

STEEL is an iron-carbon alloy containing not more than 1·7% of carbon. Mild steel, which is used in very large quantities at the present day, contains from 0·15% to 0·25% of carbon. The main problem of steel-making is one of controlling the carbon content of molten iron.

Various processes of steel-making were known in pre-industrial days. For instance, the material known as *wootz* was being produced in India two thousand years ago. Wootz was made by melting wrought iron in a crucible with carbonaceous matter, and by repeatedly forging the small ingot. The steel thus produced would take a fine cutting edge, and was used for making the famous swords of Damascus and Toledo. It was not until the early 17th century that European inventors developed processes almost identical with those of the Indian smelters, and not until the 18th century that the steel industry, as now understood, was founded.

The first advance was made by the Sheffield clockmaker Huntsman, who in 1740 produced a crucible which could withstand the very high temperature needed to melt steel. He was able, therefore, to produce homogeneous ingots which could be forged. Several factors, however, combined to prevent the immediate rise of a large steel-making industry. For some time the new technical knowledge was confined to a small group of men in Huntsman's factory. Even when it escaped, and when Cort's invention of the rolling-mill in 1783 enabled large ingots to be treated, steel remained far more expensive than iron. Steel was available to the engineers of the industrial revolution only in limited quantities and at a high price.

PROCESSES OF PRODUCTION IN BULK

It was not until a century after Huntsman that the change came. In 1856 Bessemer perfected his converter, in which carbon was removed from molten iron by the passage of a forced blast of air; the carbon combined with the oxygen of the air and was blown out in the waste gases. So successful was the converter that Bessemer produced steel at £12 a ton, compared with the £60 a ton charged

116

for crucible steel. Other notable discoveries followed in rapid succession. In 1862 Siemens invented the open-hearth process, in which a mixture of pre-heated gas and pre-heated air supplies heat for smelting. The open-hearth furnace takes longer to change iron to steel than does the Bessemer converter, but, on the other hand, permits easy control of the quality of the crude steel and the use of scrap as well as of pig-iron.

Both the Bessemer converter and the open-hearth furnace were originally designed to treat iron smelted from high-grade ores. The impurities to be removed included carbon, silicon and manganese. Furnace linings were chosen accordingly: they belonged to the acid type. Low-grade ores yield iron which contains the additional impurities of sulphur and phosphorus, which attack the linings of acid furnaces. Before iron from these ores could be used in steel-making, basic furnace-linings had to be perfected. The Gilchrist-Thomas process of smelting was developed by 1878; it is also known as the basic Bessemer process, since it involves the lining of the Bessemer converter with basic material. In Europe it was rapidly and widely adopted; but in Britain open-hearth furnaces were preferred, partly perhaps because of the many difficulties which Bessemer was known to have met in developing his converter. The change in this country, when it came, was from the acid open-hearth furnaces which used hematite iron to basic open-hearth furnaces capable of taking iron made from the low-grade Jurassic ores.

COMPETITION BETWEEN IRON AND STEEL

World output of steel was to rise from $\frac{1}{3}$ million tons in 1866 to 275 a year at the present time. The new steel industry, however, needed time to expand, and also had to overcome the established interests of ironmasters. For some time there was serious competition between steel and iron in the British Isles.

The early civil engineers achieved much with iron. Four of the best-known bridges in Britain are iron-built—Darby's structure at Ironbridge, which spanned the Severn in 1780, the Menai Suspension Bridge built by Telford in 1826, Stephenson's tubular bridge (also across the Menai Strait) finished in 1850, and the Newcastle high-level railway bridge, erected by Robert Stephenson in 1846–1850. The first great bridge of steel, the Forth Bridge, was not built until the latter years of the 19th century, being finished in 1890.

Railway engineers did much to encourage the iron-making industry from the 1830s onwards. When the Bessemer process of steel-making was invented, British iron-works were producing some $\frac{3}{4}$ million tons of iron rails a year—a figure which reflects not so much the extension of the railway network as the rapid wear of the rails themselves. On some lines the iron rails had to be replaced every four months. Tests begun at Crewe and Chalk Farm in 1861 showed that rails rolled from Bessemer steel lasted more than 20 times as long as iron rails, and steel was rapidly substituted for iron on railway track throughout the country.

At about the same time shipbuilders increased their demands for iron, for in shipbuilding the change from the traditional wood to the new industrial metals was gradual. After slow beginnings, the building of iron ships increased rapidly in the mid-19th century. There was still time for the shipbuilding industry to be transformed by the use of iron, not only because the Bessemer process had yet to be invented, but also because the first ships' plates made from steel were not consistent in quality. Cheap, ductile, reliable steel plates were not produced until 1870, the Admiralty did not begin using steel for warships until 1875, and the use of steel in building merchant ships did not become general until 1877. For twenty years, therefore, the use of iron predominated in the shipbuilding industry; but when the change to steel came, it came rapidly. Ten years served to prove that steel was reliable and that steel ships could be both lighter and stronger than those of iron. By 1890 nine out of every ten ships classed at Lloyd's were made of steel.

THE MODERN STEEL INDUSTRY: CHANGING STRUCTURE

During the period 1870–1890, iron-working was largely absorbed into the growing industry of steel manufacture. The production of iron was reduced mainly to a preliminary process. Four-fifths of the pig-iron produced in the British Isles today goes for conversion into steel, and the end-products of the combined iron and steel industry are mainly steel goods. The industry has continued to expand since the late years of the 19th century, undergoing profound internal changes. Not only has its output increased and its fundamental working technique improved—it has overcome, by the development of special processes, some of the competition offered by aluminium and aluminium alloys, in addition to providing a whole range of alloys of steel.

Basic furnaces were not providing much more than half the total output of crude steel as late as the 1920s; among the basic furnaces, open-hearth plants predominated greatly over basic Bessemer converters. Acid open-hearth furnaces and acid Bessemer converters, designed to deal with pig made from high-grade ores, were still producing nearly half the total of crude steel despite the ultimate dependence of many of them upon imported ore. By the year 1960, when the output of crude steel was more than double that of 1920, the basic open-hearth process had gained a long lead, with more than ⅘ of total production (Fig. 48). There had been some increase in the number and output of basic Bessemer converters, and a sharp increase in the use of electric furnaces (see below). The use of acid Bessemer converters and of acid open-hearth furnaces had markedly declined. The acid open-hearth process now produces less steel than either the Bessemer or the electric processes. This reorganisation of a whole industry has been associated partly with increased production of alloy steels, but mainly with the increased exploitation of domestic iron-ore of low grade.

FIG. 48. Great Britain: production of crude steel, by percentage and quality, 1920 and 1960

Alloy Steels

Alloy steels are produced in smaller quantities than mild steel and other carbon steels (see Appendix 2), but their share in the total output remains steady. They are of great importance in modern industry because of their distinctive properties—hardness, resistance to corrosion, and high tensile strength. Commercial production of alloy steel began in 1883, when Hadfield first produced manganese steel. The same inventor made silicon steel, which is used both in machine tools for cutting and in electrical engineering, for which its magnetic properties make it especially suitable. Stainless steel, a chrome-steel alloy, was developed by 1913, and in later years alloys of steel with nickel, chromium and vanadium came into widespread use. Research into the character and properties of alloy steels was to some extent forced on the steel industry by the growing use made of the light metal aluminium, but was also greatly encouraged by the needs of manufacturers of machine tools and of engines. Both steam-engines and internal combustion engines have been improved with the aid of alloy steels. In the early 1900s the standard steam boiler had to withstand pressures of 180 lbs./sq. inch at 500°F., whereas the modern boiler is designed for 900 lbs./sq. inch at 900°F. In jet engines and gas turbines even more rigorous demands are made, with complex steel alloys meeting stresses of 15 tons/sq. inch at temperatures higher than 1,000°F.

One result of the demand for alloy steels has been the increased use of electric furnaces, which permit fine control of the quality of the product. At the present day rather more than half the alloy steel made in Britain comes from electric furnaces, the remainder being made by the open-hearth process. Since the 1920s, electric smelting has doubled its relative importance in the steel industry.

Imported Ores

As the steel industry expanded, the failing supplies of high-grade domestic ore could no longer keep pace with the demands for pig-iron suitable for use in steel furnaces of the acid type. Home production was greatly supplemented, and later greatly surpassed, by imports. Domestic output of high-grade ore was 2½ million tons in 1913, against the imports of more than 7 million tons which came chiefly from Spain, Spanish North Africa, and French North Africa. Although imports were down to 6½ million tons in 1920, home output had fallen still more greatly—to 1½ million tons. It continued to decline during the inter-war period, whereas imports, recovering from the low levels reached in the Great Slump, ran at some 5 million tons a year just before World War II and have broken all previous records in the post-war period (Fig. 49).

Fig. 49. Great Britain: production and import of iron ore, from 1920

Sweden meanwhile, has emerged as the chief supplier (Fig. 50), followed in order by North Africa, Newfoundland and Canada, and South America. These suppliers account for nearly ⅘ of the total import, Sweden alone sending more than one-quarter. Ore is no longer imported from Northern Spain.

FIG. 50. Great Britain: sources of imported iron ore, by weight and percentage, 1938 and 1960

Imported ores are generally far richer than those produced domestically. Home ores average less than 30% iron content, while imported ores average nearly 60%[1]. Nearly half the iron content of the ore smelted is supplied by imported ores (Fig. 51). Imported ores need to be of high grade, for low-grade ores could not in present circumstances bear the cost of shipping. Overseas orefields which supply Britain all have easy access to tidewater, and the blast-furnaces in which imported ore is consumed are located on or near the coast.

FIG. 51. Great Britain: supplies of iron ore, 1963. The lower part of the graph shows the proportions supplied, in terms of iron content; the upper part, which allows for variations in richness, shows the actual tonnages supplied

Low-grade Domestic Ores

Some 30 million tons of ore are fed yearly into the blast-furnaces of Britain. More than half this total comes from domestic orefields,

[1] These figures are weighted averages, which take into account the quantities of the various ores as well as their iron content.

and more than $\frac{9}{10}$ of domestic production (by weight) is of low-grade ore. Over half comes from the Inferior Oolite formation of the Midlands (Figs. 52, 53), and nearly all of it is extracted from rocks of Jurassic age. In the early days of industrialisation, when the high-grade hematites of Cumberland, Lancashire, and Glamorgan, or the bedded ores which occurred in the Coal Measures, were used, there

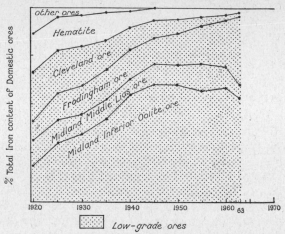

FIG. 52. Changing relative importance of domestic iron ores, in terms of iron content

was no need to exploit the low-grade Jurassic ores. When the steel industry first developed, the technical difficulties of treating phosphoric ores—in which group the Jurassic ores are included—encouraged the smelting of high-grade ores, the use of acid furnace-linings, and the production of acid steel. Thus by a series of historical accidents the iron and steel industry became located mainly on the coalfields, and came to depend largely on imported high-grade ore. The present minor significance of the high-grade domestic ores used by the early ironmasters is obvious from Fig. 53, and the decline in their production in recent years is brought out by Fig. 52. This diagram shows the rise to dominance of Jurassic ores, in the relative importance of which, however, changes have also occurred. In 1920 the Cleveland district was the main producer. Five years later it had already been outstripped by the orefields on the Inferior Oolite of the Midlands—mainly in Northamptonshire (Plate 16). While the Cleveland district was suffering from the rising costs due to partial exhaustion of reserves and to increasingly difficult working, the Midlands were profiting from their practical advantages. The essential difference between the two areas lies in the fact that the Cleveland ore passes deeply underground in the cuesta of the North

FIG. 53. Great Britain: use and movement of iron ore

York Moors, while that of the Northamptonshire ironfield is itself a scarp-former which lies either at the surface of the ground or beneath a thin overburden. The Middle Lias ore of the Midlands, much worked in the neighbourhood of Banbury and Melton Mowbray, is also a scarp-former, which over large areas has been cleanly denuded of its former cover of clay. The Frodingham ores similarly appear in small cuestas where they can easily be worked opencast.

Exploitation of low-grade domestic ore was severely checked by the slump of the 1930s, but was as greatly stimulated during the Second World War. Post-war production, now running at about the highest pre-war level, tends to increase.

Pig-Iron

By 1960, the annual production of pig-iron in Britain rose above 15 million tons. Broadly speaking, the inter-war period (1919–1939)

E2

was one of rapid changes in annual production, while the period subsequent to the Second World War saw a marked increase culminating in the record output of 1960. By 1963, however, output was no longer rising.

FIG. 54. Great Britain: output of pig iron from 1920

As the graph (Fig. 54) shows, 8 million tons of pig were made in 1920. This was a boom year, followed immediately by a short but severe slump; the subsequent recovery failed to raise production

FIG. 55. Location of blast furnaces in Great Britain, 1960

to the 1920 level, and output fell very low during the general strike
of 1926. The smelting industry was unable to regain the whole of its
lost strength before the Great Depression of the 1930s once more
seriously reduced activity, and the slow recovery which followed was
interrupted during the Second World War by a slight but steady
decline, which reflected the difficulty in importing foreign ores
(cf. Fig. 49). Not until the late 1940s did production of pig iron rise,
and remain, above the level reached in 1920.

Despite the marked rises and falls in output, the graph shows
clearly that during the inter-war period the steel industry was taking
an increasing fraction of the total output of pig. More than 90% of
that total now goes to steel works and steel foundries. Most blast
furnaces today are owned by steel companies; no less than 85% of the
iron is recorded as *used in own works*, and although this percentage
includes the material used in making iron goods, most of it is fed

FIG. 56. Location of steel furnaces in Great Britain, 1960

into steel furnaces. Furthermore, the greater part of the iron used in steel-making is taken from the blast furnace to the steel furnace in a molten state.

The integration of many blast-furnaces into steelworks means that the two distribution maps, Figs. 55 and 56, should be read together. They have been drawn separately in order to bring out the influence of locating factors on the smelting of iron. The first map, Fig. 55, shows that blast furnaces are located on or near the coalfields, on the orefields, or on tidewater at a distance both from coal and from ore. This last type of location is seen at Dagenham, where iron is smelted and steel is made for use in the motor industry. Location on orefields occurs on the Northamptonshire ironfield and in the Scunthorpe-Frodingham district, where the blast-furnaces are fed with low-grade Jurassic ore worked locally (Plate 17). The smelting industry at Barrow relied originally on local supplies of hematite, and had access to seaborne coal from the Cumberland coalfield. The most advantageous location of all is that of the Middlesbrough district, which produces about a quarter of all the iron smelted. Here coal is readily available from the northeastern coalfield; large quantities of ore were formerly to be had from the Cleveland fields, and seaborne ore can easily be brought in today.

The existing smelting industry is dominated by five groups of blast-furnaces: those of the Middlesbrough district, the two groups on the Jurassic orefields, one group on the southern part of the Yorks., Derby and Notts. coalfield, and one in South Wales (cf. Fig. 57). Smelting in the Black Country, on the western flank of the Pennines, on the north Welsh Border, on the north-eastern edge of the South Wales coalfield, and on the Central Scottish coalfield has declined sharply in relative importance since its early days. It has been hit by the rise in costs which accompanied exhaustion of the local ores on which the early industry relied. The Black Country, at one time begrimed—not to say devastated—by fumes of its blast-furnaces, has now lost all but two, and those on its extreme western fringe.

Output of Steel

The output of steel fluctuated wildly in the inter-war period, at the same times, in much the same ways, and for the same reasons as that of iron. But the graph (Fig. 58) reveals that the high level of steel production reached in 1920 was exceeded by 1935, and that output since that year has remained well above the 1920 figure. A high level of output was possible in the late 1930s because a great deal of scrap was available to the steel industry. Thus the recovery of the steel industry from the Great Depression failed to stimulate

FIG. 57. Output of pig iron and crude steel by districts, 1960

FIG. 58. Great Britain: output of crude steel from 1920

FIG. 59. Great Britain: use of pig iron and scrap in steel-making, from 1920 a corresponding demand for pig-iron—indeed, the present steel industry absorbs as much scrap as pig-iron (Fig. 59). This is why the total output of crude steel, 22½ million tons a year, is much greater than the output of pig-iron (cf. Fig. 54). Steel-making, like iron-smelting, declined slowly during the Second World War, but has expanded remarkably in the post-war period.

Present Distribution of Steel-Making

Thanks mainly to its new plant, South Wales was the leading steel-producing district in 1960, followed in order by the Northeast, Sheffield, Scotland, and Scunthorpe. Each concentration corresponds to well-defined characteristics of the steel industry. Heavy goods and fine steel products are typical of the Sheffield district (Plate 18), steel strip and tinplate of South Wales. Much of the steel produced in the Clyde valley is absorbed by shipbuilding and engineering, while the Middlesbrough district is noted for heavy steel. Production is rising at Corby, located like Scunthorpe on a Jurassic orefield. Steel furnaces in Lancs.-Cheshire, the Potteries, and the Black Country mainly serve the mechanical engineering industry. Other and more scattered groups of steel furnaces indicate that steel-working is more widespread than is the smelting of iron—a fact which implies the supply of pig-iron and ingot steel from furnaces in one locality to milling concerns elsewhere.

APPENDIX 1

GRADES OF CARBON STEELS

Grade	Percentage carbon content
Low carbon steels ..	(a) less than 0·07
	(b) 0·07–0·15
Mild steels ..	0·15–0·25
Medium carbon steels ..	0·20–0·50
High carbon steels ..	0·50–1·40

APPENDIX 2
CRUDE STEEL OF ALLOY QUALITIES

	Thousand tons, approx.				
	1956	1958	1960	1962	1963
Steel ingots of alloy qualities	1153	1040	1505	1225	1445
Steel of alloy qualities for castings	136	120	122	126	124
Total	1289	1160	1627	1351	1569
Total as % of all crude steel produced	6½	6	6¾	6½	7

Open hearth and electric furnaces take roughly equal shares in producing steel ingots of alloy qualities, but alloy steel for castings comes mainly from electric furnaces.

CHAPTER 9

Trade, Transport, and Communication

SOME fundamental contrasts between the respective external trades of the U.K. and of the Irish Republic were noted previously, when certain major differences between the two countries were established (Chap. 1). When trade statistics (Appendices 1, 2) are examined in somewhat greater detail, complex problems at once arise—problems of sources of imports, directions of export, change in progress, and the composition of the major classes of commodity. A complete analysis of external trade, item by item, would be as tedious as it would be unnecessary; the following sections are confined to broad implications, whether of trade in its present state or of the changes which have occurred since the years immediately before World War II.

EXTERNAL TRADE OF THE UNITED KINGDOM

Imports

As Fig. 60 shows, the import class of food, beverages, and tobacco cost more than any other class, in the three years illustrated by the diagram. But whereas in 1939 this class accounted for nearly half the total sum paid for imports, its share had fallen to two-fifths by 1950 and to one-third by 1962. The decreased share results in part from increased agricultural production at home, and from the decreased buying of meat, dairy produce, and eggs from abroad. In addition, changes in the consumption of meat, originating in wartime rationing and confirmed by the post-war state of the meat-trade, have exerted an influence of their own. Beef imports in the post-war period have run consistently below the pre-war mark; the Argentine Republic, once a great supplier, has increased its own consumption and failed to maintain its exports. The summary statistics from which Fig. 60 is drawn are affected by changes in the prices of single commodities. These prices in turn are affected not only by supply and demand, but also by changes in the rate of exchange between one currency and another, by currency shortages, and by the trade policies of individual nations.

130

FIG. 60. Classes of import into the United Kingdom, by percentage value

Although some commodities in the class of food, beverages, and tobacco are now imported in smaller quantity than in the immediately pre-war years, part of the relative decline in this class of imports is due to increases in imports of other classes. The import of crude oil in 1960 was 20 times as great as in 1938, and further increases can be expected. Reductions in the import of refined oil do very little to offset the rise in the imports of crude. The net increase is due to increased consumption, mainly by vehicles and by power plant, but the fall in the import of refined oil corresponds to increased refinery capacity in the United Kingdom.

The class of manufactured goods accounted in 1938 and 1950 for about a fifth of all imports by value, but rose to nearly one-third by 1962. Within the class, imports of cotton fabrics rose sharply, reflecting the continued difficulties of the cotton-textile industry which, far from continuing to export in quantity, was losing its hold on the domestic market. Increased imports of chemicals, on the other hand, correspond to a successful expansion of the chemical industry. The aircraft and automobile industries took increasing quantities of aluminium products, but the number of complete vehicles imported also rose from below the pre-war mark in 1950 to well above it in 1962.

Among the raw materials of the textile industries, decreased imports by quantity were recorded for raw wool, raw cotton, and jute. Imports of jute declined mainly because a jute-manufacturing industry was established in the Ganges delta; imports of raw cotton declined partly because of reduced consumption by the depressed home industry, and partly because the entrepôt trade in raw cotton was lost; imports of raw wool declined wholly on account of the loss of the entrepôt trade.

The post-war expansion of the steel and chemical industries was responsible for increased imports of iron ore, zinc ore, manganese ore, bauxite, and sulphur. Greatly increased imports of asbestos were needed by the electrical and structural industries. Rising imports of vegetable oils corresponded mainly to changes in eating-habits.

132 THE BRITISH ISLES

Increases in the volume of imports can mean either failure or success, according to the context of the consuming industry. In any event, trade tends to increase as a country's industries are progressively elaborated. The view that the trading nations are divided into two groups, one supplying raw materials and one providing manufactures, is far too simple: in actuality, the greatest exchanges usually occur between nations which are highly industrialised. Politicians and manufacturers alike hope to combine a large volume of trade with a favourable balance.

Exports

The relative reduction in the export trade in mineral fuels and lubricants between 1938 and 1950 corresponded to the wartime loss of most of the remaining portion of the trade in coal. The decline of the coal trade far more than offset the increase in exports of refined petroleum; indeed, in 1955 the value of coal imports was greater than that of exports, and would be higher than it is in the early 1960s without political pressure to encourage the coal industry and to keep imports down. Exports of textiles, once—like coal—a mainstay of trade, have much declined; the loss of the foreign market for manufactured cottons was mainly responsible, for the trade in woollens and worsteds has, generally speaking, been retained, and has actually increased in some divisions.

Metals and engineering products form large and complex classes of exports, in which some items have done better than others. The pre-war export trade in pig-iron has been regained and enlarged, as has that in crude and semi-finished steel; exports of finished steel were more than twice as great, by weight, in 1960 than in 1938. The most notable increases, however, were recorded for engineering products—powered machinery, vehicles, tractors, and aircraft:

Fig. 61. Classes of export from the United Kingdom, by percentage value

vehicles and aircraft brought in 15% of the money realised for exports in 1960. Manufactured chemicals also appear in force in the post-war data.

Textiles and coal, which were fundamentally significant to the export trade of the U.K. in 1913, and were still of great importance in 1938, have lost ground which seems to be irrecoverable. They seem likely to continue their decline, both in volume and in their proportionate share in the total export trade. The engineering industries, supplying $\frac{2}{5}$ of all exports by value, occupy a truly dominant position. But although these industries enable the total volume of export trade to be greater than it has ever been, the situation has its dangers. Foreign competition is especially severe in respect of some of the main engineering products—namely, vehicles, aircraft, and ships. At the present time the world's shipyards have more orders than they can well fulfil; it is impossible to say what is likely to happen when the arrears of work are cleared away, or if there should be a depression in world trade. All great manufacturing nations are engaged in severe competition in the manufacture and sale of aircraft and vehicles—especially cars. Because designs change so rapidly and the machines have a limited working life, the market as a whole is vast, but for the same reason it is possible for a competitor suddenly to lose ground.

Changed Trading Position of the United Kingdom

The volume of trade passing through the ports of the United Kingdom is far greater than in the immediately pre-war period—imports increased by more than half in volume, between 1938 and 1960, and exports by more than one-quarter. By comparison with the depressed economy and the stagnant trade of the early 1930s, the present picture is bright. On the other hand, the post-war years have brought extraordinary fluctuations in prices, and the great manufacturing nations are competing with one another for raw materials, some of which are not so plentiful as they once were; in the even more highly competitive export market, everything possible must be done to keep selling prices down.

Another weakness in the present trade of the U.K. is that re-exports are running at only about one-third of their pre-war volume. Re-exports of wool, and to a lesser extent those of cotton, have very seriously diminished. Several influences combine to depress the entrepôt trade: home industry tends to absorb more of the imported raw material than it did; because of the decline in coal exports, import freights are far higher than they were; newly-established industries in other countries tend to develop markets of their own and to trade direct; and—perhaps the most important of all—overseas trade in general was severely curtailed during World War II. The entrepôt trade of Great Britain was almost wholly brought to an end, and—once lost—has proved extremely difficult to recover. The

U.S.A., by far the leading industrial nation of the western world, enormously increased its merchant marine during the war and has maintained it subsequently.

Balance of Trade

Commodities imported and exported constitute visible trade. The end of World War II was followed by a period in which imports cost more than exports brought in, so that the balance of visible trade was adverse. But since services, as well as goods, can be sold abroad, and since money can be invested overseas to bring in profits at home, the total trade balance must allow for invisible trade—paper transactions—as well as for the movement of actual goods. With regard to invisible trade the U.K. is far worse off than in pre-war years, for, during World War II, overseas insurance business was lost, income from shipping almost vanished, and foreign investments were sold under compulsion. In the post-war period, therefore, the generally favourable balance of invisible trade has not compensated for the balance of visible trade, which was unfavourable in nearly every year in the period 1946–1963 inclusive.

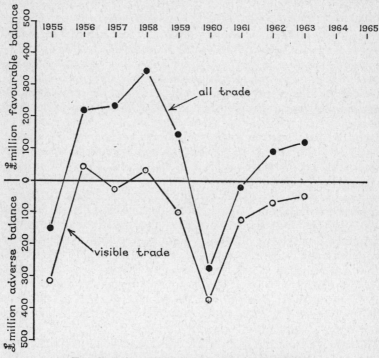

FIG. 62. Balance of trade of the United Kingdom

In 1960, rising hopes were destroyed by a very sharp decline in visible trade and by an accompanying loss of invisible trade (Fig. 62). Three direct effects of the difficult trading circumstances, which have been worsened by inflation of the currency, are the devaluation of the pound, the depletion of reserves, and increased official control of exporting and importing. The crisis renewed itself in 1964–1965.

Governmental Action

It would be quite wrong, however, to suppose that the tendencies expressed in these developments are new, or that they were the outcome of World War II alone. On the contrary—the conversion of the economy of the U.K. from an uncontrolled to a regulated condition occurred during World War I. Although the control was neither so rigorous nor so direct in the inter-war period as it is today, the change from the free economy of the period before 1914 was as revolutionary as it was abrupt. The various political influences exerted both on production and on trade have naturally been designed in many cases to counteract the effect of geographical and economic factors.

As G. D. H. Cole has written, 'Up to 1914 Great Britain furnished an almost perfect example of . . . the working of an economic system in accordance with the "natural laws" beloved of the classical economists. This freedom could not, of course, survive the experience of war [i.e., World War I] . . . production had to be directed to meeting war needs, and the Government . . . acquired an extensive power over industry and agriculture . . . Foreign trade necessarily ceased to be free . . . the export of capital ceased abruptly . . . Great Britain, from being the world's greatest lender, became a borrower of capital . . . overseas investments had to be sold.'

In all these ways the experience of World War II was anticipated by that of World War I. After 1918, very many controls were relaxed or abolished, only a few protective duties remaining; but neither the cotton trade nor the coal trade was fully re-established, and markets lost during wartime were generally difficult to regain, not only because of increasing competition from new factories overseas but also because the pound was overvalued in relation to the dollar. The great slump which started in 1929 reduced the prices of imports, so that the U.K., being the world's great free market, maintained for a time a high level of import trade, but exports declined severely, and a large adverse balance of payments was recorded by 1931.

Two political measures were adopted: the gold value of the pound was reduced, in order to bring down the selling price of British goods abroad, and protective tariffs were imposed to check the flow of imports. Free trade was abandoned. The Government was compelled to decide what quantities of imports would be allowed to enter from the main suppliers. Subsidies on the home production of sugar beet and wheat were already in force, and power was taken in 1933 to regulate the import of agricultural produce. Substantial tariff protection was given to the steel industry, and agreements on export shipments of coal were negotiated with customer countries. In Cole's words, 'Great Britain . . . departed a long distance from the almost entirely planless economy of the years before the slump, having . . . a managed currency, a largely managed foreign trade, a considerably managed system of agricultural production, and a managed system of industrial production extending to coal and steel. . . . All this adds up to a quite formidable total of State intervention in industry.'

Now that Government control of industry, agriculture and trade is far more extensive and far more direct than it was in the 1930s, it would be nonsensical to speak of the economic activity of the United Kingdom as if it were the outcome of geographical factors alone. Whatever may be the status in later years of industries which are now nationalised, it seems improbable that they will be left in the foreseeable future entirely to their own devices. Control over the volume and nature of trade can be exercised by means of the system of import and export licences, which also affects the direction of trade for political purposes. All the measures referred to are those taken by the home Government; further complications ensue from the political and economic policies of the governments of foreign countries.

Direction of Trade

Figure 63 illustrates the chief trading relations of the United Kingdom for the two years 1950 and 1960. The bars are drawn to represent percentages of total export and import trade, by value, and take no account of changed volume of trade. In a diagram of this kind, the impression given is affected by the grouping of countries which is adopted. The graph succeeds in representing more than $\frac{2}{3}$ of total external trade, and includes the leading customers and suppliers.

Between the late pre-war years and the mid-1950s, there was no very great change in the direction of trade, except for decreases in trade with the Argentine and Germany, and for increases in trade with Nigeria, East African countries, and oil-exporters in the Middle East. The comparison of 1950 with 1960, however, reveals that trade with Australia and New Zealand has contracted—relatively, at least —while that with the U.S.A. and West Germany has been enlarged. Shifts towards a less favourable balance occurred in trade with

FIG. 63. Direction of external trade of the United Kingdom, 1950 and 1960, by value

Scandinavia, the Low Countries, South Africa, the Irish Republic, and Canada and Newfoundland. Increased trade with West Germany illustrates the point made previously about the tendency of a high level of industrialisation to encourage the exchange of goods.

Commonwealth countries in 1960 took 42% of the exports of the United Kingdom, by value, and supplied 38% of the imports. The European Economic Community took $14\frac{1}{2}$% of exports and supplied $14\frac{1}{2}$% of imports. Grouping by geographical location shows that, in the same year, North America took 15% of exports and provided 21% of imports, while the export and import figures for Western Europe were both 29%.

Groups of countries have been combining in the post-war period. The customs union of Benelux was formed in 1948, the European

Coal and Steel Community (Belgium, France, West Germany, Italy, Luxembourg, Netherlands) in 1952. These six countries now form the European Common Market, proposing to remove all internal tariffs and to levy a common external tariff by about 1970. In 1961, the U.K. took the first steps towards joining the Common Market, but in January 1963 negotiations broke down, and the future relationship cannot yet be forecast.

EXTERNAL TRADE OF THE IRISH REPUBLIC

The external trade of the Irish Republic presents a far simpler picture than does that of the United Kingdom, in accordance with the general simplicity of the Republic's economy and its reliance on a single export market. Nearly $\frac{2}{3}$ of the imports meet industrial needs, and over $\frac{1}{2}$ of the exports consist of animal produce. Nearly one-third of export value is accounted for by live animals (Fig. 64), most of them cattle. Well over half the price realised for exported live animals comes from the sale of beef cattle, in which group store beasts exceed fatstock both in numbers and in value.

FIG. 64. External trade of the Irish Republic, by percentage value

The United Kingdom supplies $\frac{1}{2}$ by value of imports into the Irish Republic, and takes $\frac{3}{4}$ by value of that country's exports (Fig. 65). The sale of beef cattle in Great Britain constitutes more than 12% of the entire export trade—a trade highly dependent on a single item of export sold in a single market.

Foodstuffs of animal origin account for about a fifth—and in some years more than a quarter—of the total value of exports. Since this figure is additional to the 30% or more for live animals, the two classes are, in combination, outstandingly dominant in the export trade. The chief foodstuffs exported are beef, bacon, and mutton. Great Britain takes well over half such exports, despite the efforts made to develop markets on the European mainland, e.g., in

FIG. 65. Direction of external trade of the Irish Republic, by value

Germany. Changing trends are nevertheless perceptible in the external trade of the Republic, which will probably join the European Economic Community if Great Britain does.

Among other exports are confectionery, beer, raw wool, textiles and clothing, and paper and cardboard. The produce of Dublin breweries has been exported for many years, but certain other manufactures, fairly new additions to the list of items of trade, serve to indicate some of the industries which are at present developing in the Republic.

Manufactured goods and industrial raw materials cost nearly $\frac{3}{4}$ of the total price paid for imports. Machinery, vehicles, and electrical goods account for 20% of the total, textiles for some 9%, mineral oil for 8% and coal for $8\frac{1}{2}$%. These figures show the lack of industrial resources in the Republic, rather than a great industrial consumption.

LEADING PORTS

Of the goods exported and imported by the United Kingdom, more than half by value go through the two ports of London and Liverpool. London handles nearly a third, Liverpool nearly a quarter of the goods traffic with the outside world (Fig. 66). They are followed, in order of external trade, by Hull, Manchester, and Southampton (App. 3). Trade between Belfast and ports in Great Britain is not classed as external trade, but can be regarded as external to Northern Ireland; it has, in consequence, been taken into account in Fig. 66, which thus allows a comparison to be made between Belfast and Dublin. The volume of trade passing through Dublin is similar to that passing through Bristol, which has a greater total trade than either Swansea or the Tyne ports. Among other ports,

Goole, Grimsby and Immingham, Newport, Cardiff, Leith often rank in the first twenty by volume of total trade for single years.

The five leading ports of Great Britain account for nearly ¾ of all external trade, and the ten leading ports handle some ninety per

FIG. 66. Leading ports of the British Isles. Circles are proportional in area to the total volume of trade—oversea trade for ports in Great Britain and for Dublin, all trade for Belfast

cent. This concentration of trade on a few ports can be compared to the concentration of very many people in a few conurbations, or to the extinction of small fishing ports in favour of a few great landing-centres. It is an expression of that cumulation of strength in large towns which finds its industrial counterpart in the emergence of huge and dominant concerns.

Appendix 4 and Fig. 66 show that certain ports are mainly engaged either in importing or in exporting. Interest in the re-export (entrepôt) trade also varies considerably from one to another. London takes much the same share in importing as in exporting, and controls more than half the entrepôt trade of the whole nation. Liverpool, also with a large entrepôt trade, has a sizeable excess of exports over imports which reflects the industrial nature of its hinterland and its transatlantic connections. Belfast is to be compared with London rather than with Liverpool, for it is the one great port for a single hinterland, and functions in consequence as a general port, but differs from London in exporting primary products and importing manufactures instead of vice versa. Hull, apparently well placed to serve the industrialised West Riding of Yorkshire, encounters competition from Liverpool and Manchester, for the hinterlands of the three ports overlap. Hull, with a vigorous entrepôt trade, is better placed as an importer than as an exporter, but its export trade is stronger than that of Manchester, which takes twice as great a share in importing as it does in exporting.

Glasgow is the great port for Central Scotland, closely resembling Liverpool in its relation to its own hinterland and to the outside world. Its exports are nearly half as great again as its imports—a measure of the success of the industries which it serves, just as its large volume of general trade is an index of the dense population of the land behind it. Southampton is distinguished by an approximate balance between export and import trade, and by a share in entrepôt traffic which is third only to the shares of London and Liverpool. Thanks to the exports which it collects from a wide area of southern England, Southampton has greatly surpassed Bristol in total value of trade. Bristol, with its large volume of imports, produces goods which are sold within the U.K. rather than abroad, so that its export trade is relatively small. Swansea serves South Wales much as Glasgow serves Central Scotland, and the Tyne ports handle goods passing to or from the Tyneside conurbation. Dublin is the great general port for the Irish Republic, as Belfast is for Northern Ireland, and displays a great excess of import over export trade.

A well-known factor which has favoured the concentration of trade on a few large ports is the increase in the average size of ships, which began with the application of steam-power to shipping in the 19th century, continued with the use of steel in shipbuilding, and is continuing today. But this factor has never operated in isolation. While it encouraged the greatest ports to become still greater, it incidentally promoted the growth of coasting trade in goods additional to coal, so that numerous small ports retained a certain amount of seaborne traffic while losing their oversea connections. The growth of the great ports came to depend on the facilities which they could offer for docking. Southampton inevitably comes to mind in this connection, but in one way or another all the really great ports have had to solve their own problems of providing deep-water harbours. Problems of this sort arose because liner services depend on regular sailings.

The importance of uninterrupted arrival and departure is obvious in the case of passenger traffic, but a considerable volume of goods traffic is also carried by liners.[1] Ports which acquired docks were able to retain and extend their liner services, and, as they grew larger, were able also to secure an increasing share of the flexible services of tramps. The main cargoes carried by trampships are such bulky, low-cost goods as coal, grain, sugar, iron ore, fertilizers and timber. Although tramps can be sent to any port large enough to accommodate them, they are certain in practice to ply between the exporting countries and receiving ports which serve industrial hinterlands or are themselves the centres of such hinterlands.

The effect of increasing size of ships and of specialised port facilities is displayed best of all by tankers. The growth of tanker traffic, with petroleum and petroleum products as the essential cargo, is a 20th-century development. It seems unlikely that passenger ships will ever again be built as large as some of the giants which make the transatlantic run, but the average size of long-distance tankers is still rising. One interesting result is the development of Milford Haven as an oil-port capable of accommodating the huge tankers of today. Oil from one company's terminal is piped 60 miles to a refinery at Llandarcy.

TRANSPORT AND COMMUNICATION

Roads and Railways

The assembly and collection of goods for export, the distribution of imports, and the internal distribution of domestic products depend on internal transport and communications. The networks of

---

[1] The term *liners* is not restricted to passenger vessels, but applies to any ships which sail on regular schedules.

road and rail, supplemented in places by rivers and canals, must obviously meet present-day needs to some extent, for goods and people are in fact moved from place to place and the movement does not clog to a standstill. But, for a number of reasons, the services are defective; their defects appear mainly in the lack of flexibility and interconnections on railways, and in the congestion of certain roads at certain times. The shortcomings of the railways are due largely to the manner of their development; difficulties on the roads are caused mainly by the huge increase of traffic, which was made possible by the petrol engine and was effected on roads of medieval pattern or 18th-century design. It could scarcely have been expected that improvements of roads would keep pace with the growth of traffic; but additional difficulties arise from the daily movement of great numbers of people to and from the centres of large towns, from the tendency of some industrial concerns to establish scattered factories working on a single product, and from the concentration of external trade on a few ports. All these factors affect railways as well as roads, but traffic jams can scarcely occur on railways; part of the congestion of some roads is due precisely to the fact that road transport is flexible where rail transport is not— road vehicles run from door to door and carry individual people and small consignments of goods, whereas railways are at their best with long hauls and bulky loads.

In Great Britain there are some 9 million road vehicles and about 90,000 miles of classified roads. The number of vehicles has tripled since 1938; the number of goods vehicles has also tripled and now stands at about 1½ million. Goods vehicles record a total run of more than 10,000 million miles each year—that is, the average annual mileage per vehicle is about 10,000.[1] They shift 1,500 million tons of goods annually—over six times as much as the 225 million tons moved by rail. It was long claimed that road transport is cheaper than rail over short distances and rail transport cheaper for long hauls; and in fact, the proportion of freight carried on hauls greater than 50 miles is higher on the railways than on the roads. Against this, the total tonnage carried on such hauls by road is three times as great as that carried by rail; and many short road hauls concern traffic delivered to, or by, railways. Rail still retains its advantage in the long-distance haul of coal, which provides more than half of all rail freight, but the rail loading gauges determined last century and in use ever since prevent the carriage of the very large single loads which modern industry increasingly generates (Plate 19). Road competition in recent years has had profound effects.

[1] 1952 estimate.

Up to 1913 the railways of England, Scotland, and Wales were on the whole highly successful, despite the over-optimism of some early promoters. In the inter-war period began the struggle between road and rail transport—a struggle which became especially severe in the 1930s. The railways have been forced to close a number of unprofitable lines since 1945, conceding victories to road haulage. Railways in Great Britain, however, are far more strongly placed than those in Ireland, simply because of the great volume of industrial goods which they still carry. Whatever happens to them in the future, the fact remains that they served industry well for more than a century.

Planned modernisation of British Railways (i.e., the nationalised railways of Great Britain) includes the provision of new stock, including diesel locomotives, and improvements to track, stations, and marshalling yards; and electrification, including the electrification of lines connecting London and Birmingham, London and Manchester, and Manchester and Liverpool (cf. Plate 20). It also includes wholesale closure of uneconomic branch lines and stations.

Branch lines began to fail in Ireland earlier than in Great Britain. During the period 1860–1900, numbers of narrow-gauge railways with 3-ft. track were built in Ireland—mainly in the west—with much financial help from the government. Few of them still operate today, and their numbers are still declining. Their traffic has been taken over, or at least greatly reduced, by road transport. In the absence of other signs of industrialisation, the railways of Ireland could scarcely be expected to flourish. In this connection, as in others, Ireland lies on the very fringes of the industrial world.

The chief items carried on the railways of Northern Ireland are livestock, grain and flour, oilcake, and potatoes. Much of the railway goods traffic in the Irish Republic consists of sugar beet, grain and flour, groceries, coal, and beer.

Transport in some parts of Ireland depends on bicycles and asses rather than on railways and motor vehicles. The internal combustion engine has nevertheless produced its effects, among them a much-needed scheme to modernise main roads. The Republic has some 10,000 miles of these, large stretches of which are now being reconstructed; the £10 million being spent each year on the roads of the Republic compares quite creditably with the £175 million in Great Britain, where, however, the total is rising as new works make progress. Since the Republic has only some 275,000 road vehicles of its own, an important function of the reconstructed roads is to encourage tourist traffic.

Canals

Difficulties afflicting canals in Ireland have been described previously (Chap. 6). Canal transport in Great Britain is generally known to be in a depressed state. Those few exceptional canals which are busy and profitable contrast strongly with the long mileage of little-used, obsolescent, or abandoned waterway which is typical of the network in general. The Bridgewater Canal and the Manchester Ship Canal, which connect the industries of the Lancashire coalfield to the Mersey estuary, carry respectively ½ million tons and 18½ million tons of cargo a year. The remaining canals and river navigations, with a total length of some 1,550 miles, carry but 10½ million tons a year. Half of this total consists of coal and other fuel; the remainder is supplied by general merchandise and by liquids in bulk.

A Commission on reporting in 1958 recommended that £5½ million pounds be spent on the improvement, restoration, and maintenance of selected inland waterways, in order to provide an integrated and efficient system. Of the 1,300 miles of waterway recommended for improvement, only a quarter at present carries substantial traffic, little of which is through traffic. The canals still in use serve mainly for short hauls, of average length 17½ miles. Very little traffic, for example, crosses the summit of the Leeds and Liverpool Canal, where cargoes consist mainly of coal at the eastern end and of coal and general merchandise at the western end. The Aire and Calder Navigation, where 250-ton craft and trains of compartment boats can be used, is among the canals which make a profit. The Sheffield and South Yorkshire Navigation is also profitable, as— perhaps surprisingly—are the narrow Birmingham Canals, where coal and general merchandise again top the list of cargoes. Petrol is distributed by canal from ports on the Humber, and oil and timber is carried up the Gloucester and Sharpness Canal and the navigable Severn. Salt and chemicals supply cargoes on the Weaver; lighters from the Port of London enter the River Lea and the lower part of the Grand Union Canal. Very little canal-borne cargo is recorded in Scotland, but the Forth and Clyde Canal and the Caledonian Canal are used by fishing vessels and yachts.

Air Transport

Civil aircraft operating from bases in the United Kingdom made 91,400 flights in 1938, carrying some 220,000 fare-paying passengers and flying more than 13 million miles. The post-war period has seen an enormous increase in civil aviation. The boom was already well under way in 1948; over a quarter of a million flights were made in 1963, when over 100 million miles were flown and 7¾ million fare-paying passengers were carried. More than 4 million of these were departing to, or arriving from, places abroad. Air travel is a great time-saver over long distances, and although internal airlines are steadily increasing their traffic, it is the external lines which have undergone the most spectacular development. The average length of travel on oversea journeys is now more than 450 miles. Transatlantic airways carry four transatlantic passengers in five, and promise to increase their activity in the future at the further expense of transatlantic passenger shipping. London, Birmingham, Manchester, Liverpool, Belfast, Dublin, Glasgow, Edinburgh, Aberdeen, and the outer fringes of Scotland are linked by lines of the internal network. London, with main terminals at London Airport and Gatwick, is the chief centre for oversea flights, but direct connections with the Continent are made by flights from Manchester, Birmingham, and Dublin. London, Glasgow (Prestwick), and Shannon Airport are the transatlantic air terminals. Special services include those run by independent operators, and the air ferries to the continent which carry cars and motor-coaches.

APPENDIX 1

EXTERNAL TRADE, BY VALUE, £MILLION APPROX.

1. United Kingdom.

Imports	1954	1956	1958	1960	1962
Total	3,359	3,862	3,748	4,557	4,492
Food, beverages, tobacco	1,314	1,436	1,491	1,545	1,570
Raw materials	1,015	1,086	889	1,063	902
Manufactures	687	912	914	1,449	1,446

Exports of U.K. produce and manufacture	1954	1956	1958	1960	1962
Total	2,650	3,143	3,176	3,536	3,791
Manufactures	2,159	2,605	2,670	3,001	3,182
of which					
Metals and Engineering products ..	1,345	1,702	1,819	2,044	2,185
Textiles (excluding clothing)	324	294	254	261	247
Re-exports total ..	98	144	141	141	158

9. A cracking tower, 126 feet long, at Manchester, during a journey from Stockton-on-Tees to Birkenhead. Enormous loads of this kind cannot go by rail. The tower was eventually launched at Birkenhead, and drawn by tug to the new oil refinery at Whitegate, Co. Cork.

Diesel-drawn tank wagons on the Western Region. The wagons are fitted with vacuum brakes, to ensure control at express speeds.

21. Buildings, mainly 18th-century, in the main market-place at King's Lynn. The spacious square is used as a car-park, except on market-days, but lies mainly empty on Sundays (as here).

22. Transformation of a town street; late 19th-century terraced houses at Enfield, Middx., with shop-fronts.

2. *Irish Republic.*

Imports	1952	1956	1958	1962
Total	172	181	198	274
Food, beverages, tobacco	40	42[1]	33	41
Raw materials and manu- factures	124	119	144	205

Exports of domestic produce and manufacture	1952	1956	1958	1962
Total	99	107	138	169
Food, beverages, tobacco	51	32	46	63
Live animals	32	45	47	48

[1] 1955.

APPENDIX 2

DIRECTION OF EXTERNAL TRADE

1. *Value of imports into the U.K., by source, £million approx.*

	1956	1958	1960	1962
Total	3,862	3,748	4,557	4,492
U.S.A.	408	351	567	477
Commonwealth .. of which Aus- tralia and New Zealand ..	1,718 433	1,545 359	1,738 384	1,558 355
Canada and Newfoundland	348	309	375	349
India and Pakistan ..	164	288	329	165
European Economic Community ..	492	533	662	708
European Free Trade Association	385	366	464	551
Middle East oilfields[1] ..	146	149	180	184

[1] Bahrain, Qatar, Trucial Oman and Kuwait.

F

2. *Destination of exports of U.K. produce and manufacture.*

	£million approx.				
	1954	1956	1958	1960	1962
Total	2,650	3,143	3,176	3,536	3,791
Australia and New Zealand ..	403	365	363	380	336
U.S.A.	150	243	272	322	327
Canada and Newfoundland	132	177	188	213	188
India and Pakistan ..	160	200	189	190	160
West Germany ..	71	92	123	159	199

3. *Value of imports into the Irish Republic, by source,*
£million approx.

	1958	1959	1962
Total	200	213	274
Great Britain ..	103	101	125
Northern Ireland ..	8	9	11
U.S.A.	14	14	21
West Germany ..	8	10	19
Canada	6	6	6
Netherlands ..	6	6	8

4. *Destinations of exports (including re-exports) consigned*
from the Irish Republic.

	1958	1959	1962
Total	131	131	169
Great Britain ..	80	78	103
Northern Ireland ..	21	19	21
U.S.A.	7	10	14
West Germany ..	3	4	5
France	1	1·2	1·5
Canada	0·8	1·3	1·7
Netherlands ..	0·6	1·1	1·7

APPENDIX 3
VALUE OF TRADE AT LEADING PORTS, 1948-1958
£MILLION APPROX.
(EXPORTS AND IMPORTS COMBINED)

	1948	1950	1952	1954	1956	1958
London ..	1,180	1,600	2,140	2,067	2,410	2,418
Liverpool ..	1,092	1,312	1,692	1,452	1,518	1,584
Belfast ..	33[1]	—	57[1]	424[2]	—	—
Hull	197	317	438	361	375	381
Manchester[3]	209	265½	359	338	365	374
Southampton	113	146½	219	255½	302	318
Glasgow ..	162½	200	264	263	302	270
Dublin ..	—	—	—	174	—	—
Bristol ..	108	122	180	156	185	176
Swansea ..	32½	73½	109	112½	124	111
Harwich ..	—	—	—	67	73	105
Tyne ports ..	56	81	100	107	111	100
Dover ..	—	47	—	63	76	94
Middlesbrough	—	45	—	61	74	85

[1] Trade with countries outside the U.K.
[2] All trade.
[3] Includes Runcorn.

APPENDIX 4

EXPORT AND IMPORT TRADE AT
SOME LEADING PORTS
1953–1955

Port	1953		1954		1955	
	Imports	Exports & Re-exports	Imports	Exports & Re-exports	Imports	Exports & Re-exports
London ..	1,123	904	1,167	846	1,379	1,031
Liverpool ..	712	756	673	779	736	782
Belfast ..	204	178	222	202	—	—
Hull	251	128	223	138	227	148
Manchester[1]..	190	101	237	102	259	106
Glasgow ..	105	153	105	158	122	180
Southampton	133	120	132	123	152	150
Dublin ..	—	—	115	57	—	—
Bristol ..	139	14	141	15	168	17
Swansea ..	66	50	58	54	68	56
Newcastle[2] ..	53	50	54	53	66	46
Goole ..	25	30	26	32	32	32
Grimsby & Immingham	38	14	40	14	50	12
Newport ..	15	26	15	32	23	39
Cardiff ..	25	14	29	13	41	15

[1] Includes Runcorn.
[2] Includes North and South Shields.

CHAPTER 10

Population

IT can be urged that the density and distribution of people epitomise much of the geography of the British Isles. During the last hundred-and-fifty years the total population has increased enormously, mainly through increases in England—Scotland, Wales, and Ireland are in some ways special cases; trends in England have had much in common with those of Western Europe in general.

CHANGES IN RELATION OF BIRTH-RATE TO DEATH-RATE

Quite simply, the high present total of population in England is due to a great excess of births over deaths in the period from about 1750 to 1880. During this time the population-total trebled. Numbers have continued to increase since the late 1880s, and were increased by half between 1880 and 1930, but a change has occurred in the ratio of births to deaths which has caused the rate of increase to decline.[1]

Until about 1750 the total did not exceed some 8 millions. Numbers had risen slowly during the Middle Ages, but times of gradual increase were offset by the sharp declines caused by epidemic diseases. The Black Death of the 14th century was the greatest setback of all, but mortality from plague was frequently severe until (and including)

FIG. 67. Population-growth in the British Isles, by countries

[1] The immediately following paragraphs about population trends are based on *World Population and Resources*, a report by P.E.P. (1955).

151

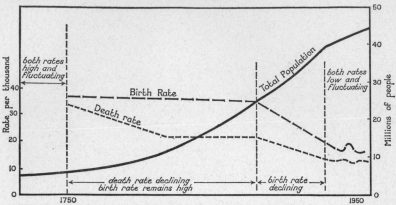

FIG. 68. Trends in birth-rate, death-rate, and population-total from 1750.
Simplified from the P.E.P. Report

the 17th century. Although the birth-rate was high, it was roughly
equalled by the death-rate, and no great rise in total numbers was
possible (Figs. 67, 68).

Improvements in Public Health

This first stage was brought to an end by what has been called
the medical and sanitary revolution. The medical discoveries of the
18th century eliminated many diseases and checked others, and the
rate of infant mortality was greatly reduced. Improvements in
agriculture prevented famine, technical achievements provided
means of transport and widened markets. It is quite impossible to
judge how strongly these several developments interacted on one
another, and to what extent they were all the outcome of the spirit
of the age, but numbers certainly grew. In the country as a whole,
people had about as good a chance of eating and working as in
former times; babies had a far better chance than before of living to
be adults, and adults had a better chance of reaching a reasonable
age. It was more than a century before a significant fall occurred
in the birth-rate, and by that time the population of England stood
at some 24 million.

Decline in the Birth-Rate

The second stage—the stage of rapid increase under the influence
of a high birth-rate and a low death-rate—came to an end about
1880. At this time the birth-rate began a steep decline, continuing to
fall until about 1930. The *rate of increase* was reduced, although
actual numbers increased and the total population of course remained high, standing in 1930 at about 37 million. Since 1930 the

birth-rate has been similar to the death-rate, but since the rate of births slightly exceeds the rate of deaths there is a tendency for numbers to increase slightly.

During the inter-war period, and especially during the 1930s, there was much speculation about the future population trends in Great Britain. It seemed to some observers that the birth-rate had fallen so low that numbers would scarcely maintain themselves. It seemed also that, in consequence, the proportion of old people to total population would rise, and that the death-rate must increase later in the century with a possible decline in total numbers. The rising proportion of old people has in fact become one of the urgent social problems of the day, although it has been partly offset by the lengthening expectation of life and by the sharp increase in the birth-rate at the end of World War II.

EMIGRATION AND INTERNAL MIGRATION

Scotland, Wales, and Northern Ireland have been affected by trends similar to those operating in England, but have also undergone losses of migrants to England, in addition to experiencing considerable migration within their own borders. The increase in population has been less spectacular than in England, Scotland and Wales having merely trebled their numbers of people in the last hundred-and-thirty years. Many people have deserted the upland districts since industrialisation began, moving into the manufacturing towns of Central Scotland, South Wales, and the English coalfields. The population of Belfast has been increased by the inward movement of people from the surrounding rural areas, and London has attracted many from all parts of the British Isles.

During the 19th century there was much emigration from the British Isles to countries abroad. At first the movement was directed mainly to the U.S.A. Canada took many British immigrants in the late 19th and early 20th centuries. At the present time emigration from the U.K. runs at about 150,000 a year, accounting for a loss of well over a million in an intercensal period. Australia, Canada, the U.S.A. and New Zealand are the chief receiving countries in that order.

The Irish Republic

Ireland is exceptional in Western Europe in having far fewer people today than a century ago. In 1840 the total was about 8 million, today it is but 4½ million. The astonishing reduction is due mainly to events in the south, i.e., in that part which now forms the Republic of Ireland. The population of Northern Ireland declined slightly from 1851 to 1891, but a slow recovery has again brought its numbers near the total of 1·7 million reached in the mid-19th century. Matters are very different in the Republic, where the total exceeded 6½ million in 1841 but was slightly below 3 million in 1961. The birth-rate and death-rate in the Republic are both low, but there is an excess of births over deaths which would result in a steady increase in numbers, were it not for emigration on an impressive scale. In some single decades more than half-a-million people have emigrated from Ireland. The movement is so pronounced and so continuous that emigration appears to be a national custom. The intercensal period 1946–51 was the first for more than a century in which a net increase of population was recorded—an increase of 5,500, and 1961-2 recorded an increase of 9,250.

The basic cause of emigration from Ireland is the poverty of much of the land. The small development of industry and the well-established attractions of the New World are complementary and contributing factors. But the first great wave of emigration was a response to a single event—the disastrous famine of 1845.

In the early years of the 19th century potatoes were the staple food of countryfolk in Ireland. In 1845 the crop was ruined by blight. Food grain was kept out by the Corn Laws; there were no reserves of food in the country itself, for much of the cultivated land was worked in small parcels which could provide subsistence only at the lowest level. It has been estimated that during the famine three-quarters of a million Irish people starved to death; among the survivors there was an understandable rush to emigrate.

After the initial disaster, another factor came into operation. The famine showed clearly that the minute subdivision of land had gone too far, and the custom was established of passing an entire holding to a single heir. While the new practice ensured that the chosen heir should receive a farm undiminished in size, the other sons and daughters of the dead farmer inherited no land at all. There were few towns where they could find work in Ireland, and emigration was in consequence further encouraged.

Prospective heirs of Irish farmers today tend to marry late. It is common for them to defer marriage until they inherit their fathers' land, and the Irish birth-rate is thus kept lower than it might otherwise be. With the total of population kept low by emigration and by late marriages, it has been possible for the average standard of living in the Republic to rise significantly during the last few decades, despite the fact that the country has never undergone an industrial revolution.

CONCENTRATION IN TOWNS

The increase in the total population of the British Isles during the last two centuries corresponds to an increase in the numbers and sizes of towns. The combined populations of towns have increased at a greater rate than has the total population, for numbers in many rural areas have been declining for many years. Several factors combine to attract people to towns—prospects of better pay, wider choice of employment, better conditions of living, and more varied social life than farms and villages can offer. Mechanisation of farm work has reduced the demand for rural labour, and the extension of country bus services in the inter-war period has tightened the grip of the towns on the country. Large towns became technically possible only when public sanitation overcame most epidemic disease, and when transport services were capable of bringing in enough food to supply large numbers who lived concentrated in small areas. Whatever the technical and social complexities involved in the growth of towns, the net result is simple—some 80% of the present inhabitants of the United Kingdom are town-dwellers.

A map of towns can thus be used to show some of the leading features in the distribution of people. Fig. 69, which represents towns with 50,000 or more inhabitants, locates 30 million people—57% of the inhabitants of the British Isles. In actuality it locates a higher fraction, for many towns have spread beyond the official boundaries to which population statistics are related.

Any town with 50,000 or more people can be taken as successful, in the sense that it is likely to have firmly-established manufacturing or service industries, and that it discharges the full range of urban functions. It can be assumed to provide its inhabitants with work, shops, markets, banks, schools, and places of entertainment, and to make similar provision for people from surrounding districts. The largest towns of all have a national or an international importance; but any successful town, simply because it is successful, is likely to increase in numbers of people, and to expand physically and in the complexity of its activities.

Although all fully-developed towns have certain functions in common, some are characterised by particular kinds of activity which have greatly aided their growth. At the same time, the functions of a town are typically so complex that they cannot adequately be indicated by a one-word label. It is very rare indeed for more than half the workers in a given town to be engaged in a single class of occupation, and any form of employment which takes one worker in every ten is likely to be the leading form.

F2

Location of Towns

Most of the towns mapped in Fig. 69 stand on the coast, on or near the coalfields, or in the English Midlands. These types of location are combined in a number of cases, as where the Tyneside Conurbation is both on the coast and on a coalfield, and where the West Midland Conurbation is (in part) on a coalfield and also in the Midlands. The relation between coal, industry and population is well expressed by the Conurbations of Clydeside, Tyneside, Southeast Lancashire and West Yorkshire, by the remaining manufacturing towns of Lancashire and the West Riding, by Nottingham and its neighbours, by Stoke and its neighbours, by the West Midland Conurbation and by the large towns of South Wales. On Clydeside and Tyneside, and in South Wales, some of the industrial towns are also ports, but the largest town of South Wales—Cardiff—does not

FIG. 69. Population-densities: location of towns with 50,000 or more people. Especially large symbols mark Dublin (nearly 600,000), Sheffield (nearly 500,000), Edinburgh (over 450,000), Belfast (over 425,000), and Bristol (over 425,000). Based on the 1961 census for the U.K., and the 1956 census for the Irish Republic

stand on the actual coalfield. It is thus similar to Middlesbrough and its neighbours, which are coastal (or nearly so) and have access to nearby coal. The greatest development of this kind has, however, taken place on the Mersey, where Liverpool and Birkenhead have effectively merged with adjacent settlements in the Merseyside Conurbation.

Hull, Bristol and Belfast are flourishing coastal towns, Hull with 300,000 people and the other two approaching the half-million mark. They are sufficiently far from large coalfields for emphasis to be laid mainly on their coastal location. Belfast illustrates better than any other town the triumph of locational advantage over lack of local resources for industry, but Dundee and Aberdeen also deserve mention.

The towns of the English Midlands include some where industry has enjoyed remarkable success. The expansion of Coventry has admittedly been associated with the industrial growth of the Black Country, but this town, like Leicester and Nottingham, was already

FIG. 70. Chief coastal resorts of England and Wales, showing proportion of all workers engaged in personal service

well-established before the industrial revolution. In recent times these three have profited by developments in the engineering industry, as to a lesser extent have Northampton, Oxford and Luton. Although some of the Midland towns plotted in Fig. 69 are famous for special-ised industry of one kind or another, engineering is the main single factor in their current expansion.

Significantly enough, the successful Midland towns lie between London and the industrial areas of the coalfields. There is a separa-tion of space and of function between these towns and the large settlements on the south coast, nearly all of which have grown large because they are resorts (Fig. 70).

Dublin, Edinburgh and London are all coastal. They stand on the eastern coasts of their respective countries, two facing con-tinental Europe and one facing Great Britain. Edinburgh has rather fewer than half a million people, and Dublin rather more. Both owe much of their present size to their status as capitals, just as Belfast benefits from being the chief town of Northern Ireland. Cardiff has become the official capital of Wales so recently that the effects of its new status have yet to appear.

Conurbations

The seven conurbations marked in Fig. 69 contain some 19 million people, about 1 in 3 of the population. They are composed of agglomerations of towns which are so close-knit that each forms an urbanised region. Building is far more continuous in some than in others—Greater London, containing 8 million people is very heavily built-up, whereas separate towns can still be distinguished in Southeast Lancashire—but each conurbation is marked by urban sprawl, by a tendency to spread, and by the progressive filling-in of its remaining vacant spaces.

The main development of most of the conurbations took place during the 19th century, although the spread of suburban housing continued up to 1939 and is again in progress today. Already by 1900 the rate of increase in population had fallen below the average for England and Wales in the Conurbations of Greater London, Southeast Lancashire, and West Yorkshire (Appendix 1); the rate of increase in the Tyneside Conurbation fell behind the national rate in the 1920s, and that of Merseyside in the 1930s. All these five now record very low rates of increase. The West Midland Conurbation provides an exception, for over the last 40 years its population has risen at a rate well above the national average. The difference between the trend here and that in the other conurbations is to be associated with the change in West Midland industry from heavy metallurgy to highly successful specialised engineering.

Rates of increase in the conurbations would be lower still if people did not move in from other towns and from the country. Four million people—one in four of their inhabitants—were born outside the limits of the six English conurbations; internal migration is still a powerful influence on the distribution of people in the British Isles. The conurbations also receive most of the immigrants from abroad. As a general rule immigration into the British Isles is limited, but in the post-war years many Irishmen and West Indians have come to find work in London and in the great industrial towns. Net immigration into the U.K. in 1958–1962 was 470,000.

Morphology of Towns

Large towns can usually be subdivided into parts which differ in function—shopping districts, residential districts, manufacturing districts and business districts. The discharge of particular functions in particular areas of a town is strictly comparable with the concentration of certain industries in certain industrial regions, and secures the same kinds of advantage. The study of functional subdivision in towns usually reveals that the various parts recognised differ in age. In very many towns, the shopping and business districts occupy the medieval site. They are typically surrounded, or partly surrounded, by 19th-century housing which is often terraced, and that in its turn is frequently enclosed by a broad belt of 20th-century dwellings in which the semi-detached house is the commonest feature. If industrial districts occur, they are likely to occupy extensive flat ground—if it is available—and in consequence to lie adjacent to a river. All kinds of variations occur in particular cases, and each town is unique, just as a geographical region is unique; but the concept of functional subdivision is a most useful one, aiding the study of an individual town and helping to reveal the changes which are going on.

If a town succeeds in its discharge of a particular function, it does more than merely grow in size. Buildings are converted from one use to another, often being altered, later entirely reconstructed, and eventually replaced. For example, when the number of shops increases in an old-established town, some houses are converted to shops merely by the construction of a counter in a room opening on to the street. The next step is the making of a shop-front which is built on to the house and provides a window for display (Plate 22). If business continues to be good, this alteration is likely to be followed by the reconstruction of the whole face of the lower floor, and that in turn by modernisation of the interior of the shop and by the conversion of the upper floor to offices or flats. The extreme case is entire rebuilding, during which the number of storeys is likely to be increased (cf. Plates 21–23).

Any of these stages may be omitted, and change may stop short of the last of them. In very many towns, however, examples of each stage are numerous, and it is easy to see how fast and in which directions the shopping districts are spreading.

The growth and reconstruction of a shopping district represents one kind of urban success, which can be compared to the establishment of climax vegetation (Chap. 3). Examples of urban failure, which are also numerous, have an equal value in showing change of function. In every large town there is at least one district which is degraded, having lost the esteem which it once held. London has many quarters where terraced streets of large 19th-century houses have become unfashionable and are no longer occupied by wealthy families; instead, the houses are let as single rooms or as flats, often without any reconstruction. In some such districts the houses are fast decaying, and decay of this kind is a cumulative process which, if unchecked, will inevitably produce slums. The change of status involves a change of inhabitants, so that urban failure as well as urban success means a shifting of people.

Both kinds of development are linked to the outward spread of all large towns (Plate 51). This spread is a result not only of increasing numbers, but also of the demands on the central districts made by commerce and business, and of the wish of many people to live near the country. The rapid spread of suburbs is a feature of our time, made possible by modern transport and in part enforced by competition for space. It is, however, merely one of the expressions of urban change; large towns are not static, but dynamic.

Except for towns dependent on unsuccessful industries, all the large towns of the British Isles must continue to grow. It seems likely that towns with populations between $\frac{1}{4}$ million and $\frac{1}{2}$ million will grow the fastest, so that the distribution of people roughed out by Fig. 69 will be modified in the future, but there is no reason to look for a reversal of the movement from country to town, or for any lessening in the strength and populations of towns in general.

APPENDIX

COMPARATIVE PERCENTAGE INCREASE IN POPULATION
SINCE 1871:
ENGLAND AND WALES, AND SIX CONURBATIONS

Period	England & Wales	Greater London	S.E. Lancashire	West Midlands	West Yorks.	Merseyside	Tyneside
1871–1881	14·4	22·6	21·6	17·1	19·2	19·4	23·1
1881–1891	11·7	18·2	12·3	11·8	11·1	10·2	29·4
1891–1901	12·2	16·8	11·8	16·9	8·1	13·4	23·1
1901–1911	10·9	10·2	10·0	10·2	4·3	12·3	12·3
1911–1921	5·0	3·2	1·4	8·5	1·5	9·2	7·1
1921–1931	5·5	9·7	2·8	9·0	2·6	6·6	1·4
1931–1951	9·5	1·6	0·2	15·7	2·3	2·7	1·0
1951–1961	0·51	– 0·21	0·02	0·46	0·06	0·00	0·20

PART TWO

CHAPTER 11

Introduction to Part Two

In the eyes of many geographers, regional geography is geography at its best. It is also geography at its most complex, requiring the synthesis instead of the analysis of information. It requires the setting of limits to the regions which are distinguished, the identification of regional unity, and the description of regional character.

The word *region* originally meant an area subject to a single governing authority. Its meaning, that is to say, was wholly political. In the course of the natural evolution of language the original meaning has been greatly modified—indeed, it has been almost lost, for *region* in everyday speech has no precise significance. A geographical region may be described as a part of the earth's surface with recognisable geographical qualities which distinguish it from adjacent regions; but this description, attractive though it may at first appear, makes no contribution to the problem of selecting, estimating, or measuring the qualities on which identification depends.

So long as the distinctive qualities of a region, whatever they may be, are recognisable in the central parts, the region can be given a regional name and accorded separate treatment. But those vaguely-apprehended properties which are held to amount, in combination, to regional character are extremely difficult to define. Personal impressions are as limited in value as they are subjective in nature. If relief, geology, soils, climate, weather, population, land use, livestock, agricultural and industrial production, and employment were analysed parish by parish, some kind of precision might be imparted both to regional character and to regional limits. The task of analysis would be enormous; even so, it would be insufficient, for regional boundaries cut across many parishes—particularly in those areas where strip-like parishes run across the grain of the country.

For all these reasons, the fixing of regional boundaries can amount at best but to an approximation. It is partly a matter of choice. No two textbooks on the British Isles agree completely on a scheme

163

of regions and of regional boundaries. In practice, varying criteria are used both in identifying a region and in fixing its limits.

Physical (or physiographic) regions, defined by reference to geological structure and surface form, differ from one to another because they have had contrasted histories of physical evolution. The simplest contrasts consist in the difference between high ground based on strong rocks and low ground based on weak rocks. The rise from low ground to high, coinciding with a geological boundary, is invariably accompanied by a change in climate, and usually by a change in soil. Physical boundaries in some parts of the British Isles coincide so closely with rapid spatial changes in land quality, land use, and the form and pattern of rural settlement that they fix the limits of geographical regions—as where the Scottish Highlands, ending at the Highland Boundary Fault, descend sharply to the well-populated farmland of Central Scotland. Elsewhere, however, physical boundaries and boundaries of other kinds are ill-marked, one region being separated from another by a fairly wide band of transition. The narrower the band, and the sharper the transition, the more satisfactory is the regional boundary which appears on a small-scale map as a solid line.

Except in the case of industrial regions, most regional boundaries are defined mainly with reference to physical and agricultural distributions; that is, the typical quality of the region as a whole, and its differences from adjacent regions, are determined largely by means of physique, climate, and agriculture. Industrial regions, however, are delimited by reference to economy and population. They transgress the boundaries which separate low ground from high, which distinguish contrasting climatic environments, and which mark changes in soils and agriculture. Deriving their unity neither from physique nor from land-use, industrial regions in the following text—as in reality—are superimposed on regions bounded by physical and agricultural limits (Fig. 83).

The term *industrial region* illustrates the way in which regional character may, on occasion, be indicated by a single word. Generally speaking, it is neither possible nor desirable to attach simple labels to regions, any more than to towns. Moreover, even the term *industrial region* tends to lose much of its apparent precision when it is closely examined. If an industrial region be defined as one dominated by industry, the problem at once arises of how to judge whether industry is dominant or not—by no means an easy problem to solve.

Even when they have been recognised and given boundaries of some kind, industrial regions raise further problems—those of accounting for the origin and growth of manufacture. Since heavy industry in the British Isles is based chiefly on or near coalfields, it is natural that the presence of workable coal should be recorded when any attempt is made to explain the distribution of heavy industry today. On the other hand, iron-working originally depended not on coal but on charcoal (Chap. 6). The well-known tendency for manufacturing industry to become concentrated on the coalfields was largely an expression of technical change—change in type of fuel and in source of power. While such a tendency is easy to understand, it is very difficult to describe in explanatory terms.

In one sense the matter is a philosophical one, for if the rise of industry is regarded as an effect it is proper to look for causes. As soon as the acts of men are admitted into the list of causes, the whole question at once becomes incredibly complex. It is so difficult to explain the activities of human beings in terms of causes that the classical economists invented the abstraction called *economic man*, to whom was imputed an intelligent self-interest which would ensure economic activity. The concept of economic man has lost favour, and the expression itself is no longer thought useful, but their one-time vogue illustrates an attempt to reduce the problem of explaining economic activity from a philosophical to a linguistic level—an attempt which succeeded merely in providing an additional way of stating that economic activity is carried on. In other words, description was achieved but explanation was not. In geography, as in economics, it is extremely difficult to arrive at satisfactory causal explanations.

Since people take the active part in establishing and developing industry, it is not permissible to speak of industry as *caused by* the presence of raw materials. The alternative statement, that the presence of raw materials led to the rise of industry, means something quite different—it embodies much more than a change of wording. It still, however, seems to imply too high a degree of inevitability and of direct causation. If it is said that the presence of raw materials made industrial growth possible, the statement becomes both reasonable and correct, but also so weak and obvious that it loses nearly all its force.

There is no reason to believe that any complete solution of the linguistic problem must exist. There may be no acceptable way of summarising the origins of industry in a brief phrase, especially since so much caution is required in implying causes. On the other hand, the concentrations of industry which we know today are the outcome of technical, economic and social developments which were typically localised in their effects and fairly rapid in their progress. The establishment of a single concern in a particular place is often to be ascribed to an individual, and it is far too much to expect that all industry will display geographical advantages of location; but in the case of an industrial region it is right to look for manifest physical advantages, and at the same time to appeal to history in order to show how industry developed along certain lines rather than along others. Industrial development in South Wales (Chap. 13) provides an excellent case in point.

In the following regional chapters, Ireland, Wales, and Scotland are taken first, in that order. Later chapters lead, in a general way, across England from north to south, ending with the London Basin and the metropolis. Some of the outstanding qualities of each region are named, and reasons are given for the choice of regional boundaries. The term *sub-region* is not used, because of its implication that there can be an orderly sequence of regional subdivision, and because it would involve cumbersome names; at the same time, quite strong internal contrasts are described for a number of whole regions. Statistical summaries for each region include area, data of land use and livestock, total population, and individual populations of leading towns. The town lists—some of them lengthy—are intended for purposes of reference, and to show where many of the people live and work.

Place-names have been kept to a minimum. Most of the places mentioned in the text are marked on the accompanying maps, but a large-scale atlas is an indispensable adjunct to reading, and the ¼-inch/mile and 10 miles/inch official maps are also strongly recommended. Selected maps of various scales, chosen as particularly relevant to the topics discussed, are specified in the bibliography for each chapter.

Wherever field-work can be carried out, it cannot fail to illuminate regional study. While a rapid traverse across a region cannot contribute to exact understanding, it is nevertheless capable of revealing that regional differences do occur. Detailed field-work can always be relied on to give significance to, and to amplify, the general statements of which regional accounts unavoidably consist.

23. Modern building—part of Crawley New Town, with flats above shops.

24. Border station at Newton Butler, on the border of Northern Ireland with the Irish Republic.

25. The centre of Armagh, a small Irish town.

26. Bullocks on permanent grassland, Irish Central Plain.

CHAPTER 12

The Regions of Ireland

THE small degree of industrial development in Ireland means that the regional geography of that island is simpler than that of Great Britain, and especially than the regional geography of England. Regional boundaries in Ireland, drawn mainly with reference to physical and agricultural distributions, offer the simplest examples of how such boundaries are defined. On the other hand, Ireland includes a political boundary—the sole instance of an international boundary (Plate 24) in the British Isles.[1]

The scheme of regional division adopted for Ireland is illustrated in Fig. 71. The regions fall into four groups. Group 1, consisting entirely of lowland, coincides with the Central Plain; Group 2 includes all the hill country and the wide but enclosed valleys between the Central Plain and the south coast, with the quite extensive lowlands flanking the Shannon estuary; Group 3 is formed by the mountainous northwestern fringe of Ireland from Galway to Donegal, while Group 4 is almost identical with the political unit of Northern Ireland. Groups 2, 3, and 4 include all the high ground of the island.

Limits of areas differing strongly in soil, climate, and agriculture correspond closely to the boundaries which separate the regional groups. Each group is subdivided in accordance with rapid spatial changes in physique, in the character and aim of farming, or in both. Agricultural distributions are highly significant in the regional geography of Ireland, not only because of the great importance of farming in the economy, but also because they display contrasts of the kind which might be expected in the climax communities of wild vegetation. Irish agriculture. like climax vegetation, displays complex adaptations which result from complex and long-operating causes, with few effects of political direction or influence. Thus, while some regions such as the Wicklow Mountains (2c) have well-defined physical limits, the single physical unit of the Central Plain is divided into two geographical regions (1a, 1b) in accordance with the use made of the land.

A number of general statements apply to most or all of the island. The differences between one region and another are superimposed

[1] The Channel Islands (Chap. 26), which have never formed part of a kingdom ruled from London, are conventionally excluded from the British Isles.

167

Fig. 71. Ireland: physique and regional division

on certain common characteristics—form of rural settlement, status of towns, and supply of labour for farm work.

In most districts rural settlement is typically dispersed (Fig. 74). It is by no means evenly spread, for the worst land has no inhabitants, while the peopled areas record densities of farm population which is high by English standards. Where houses occur, they are scattered singly or in tiny groups throughout the farmland. Dispersion of settlement in some areas is known to have occurred as late as the 19th century (cf. Fig. 32), when land tenure and the arrangement of holdings were reorganised and many nucleated settlements disintegrated. Late as it was, dispersion has been remarkably complete, and the main unit of rural settlement is the single farm. The architectural style of small country dwellings is far less varied than in England, and its variety is reduced to a minimum in the west of the country where single-storied, stone-built, thatched and whitewashed cottages are everywhere to be seen.

Most Irish country towns are small, depressing in appearance, and unlikely to expand (Plate 25). Few contain as many as 10,000 or even 5,000 people. To some extent Irish rural life is carried on as if towns did not exist. The sole function which every town is required to discharge is that of marketing; the tendency towards industrialisation is weak, except in the largest towns of all.

Farming in Ireland is typically a family affair, $\frac{4}{5}$ of the labour being supplied by farmers and their relatives. Paid labourers are scarcely known in the less prosperous areas, where the emphasis is on production for use on the farm rather than on production for sale. Of the total product of farms in the Republic, $\frac{1}{3}$ is consumed on the farms themselves. Thus farming involves the Irish country-dwellers directly, to a degree unknown in England for the last two centuries, and farming for subsistence is an important element in Irish agriculture, even though few farms sell no part of their produce.

The distinctive characteristics of Irish farming and of Irish rural life are most pronounced in the west, where remoteness weakens and retards influences from outside, where the Irish language is still used in daily speech, and where endemic rural poverty is still to be observed in places. Conversely, the eastern parts of the island contain the highest proportion of town-dwellers to total population, are the most deeply committed to farming for sale, and most readily employ paid labour on the land. They are also the best favoured agriculturally, as may readily be seen from Figs. 72 and 73.

1A. THE EASTERN CENTRAL PLAIN

Area: about 4,800 square miles.
Population: about 1,000,000.
Largest towns: Dublin (540,000; with suburbs, 585,000).
          Dún Laoghaire (48,000; with suburbs, 65,000).
          Dundalk (22,000).
          Drogheda (17,000).
Density of population: about 90 p.s.m. outside the towns named.
Nearly three-quarters of this region is in improved grassland.
Numbers of livestock: cattle, 950,000; sheep, 425,000; pigs, 175,000.

One out of every three people in the Irish Republic lives in the Eastern Central Plain, and one out of every five lives in Dublin. Dublin dominates the Republic even more strongly than London dominates England, for it is ten times as populous as the next

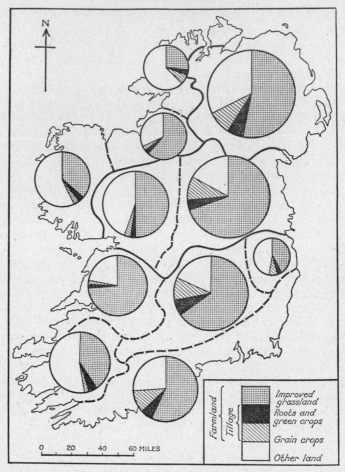

Farmland
Tillage

Improved grassland
Roots and green crops
Grain crops
Other land

0   20   40   60 MILES

FIG. 72. Land use of Ireland, by regions

largest towns of Cork and Dún Laoghaire, accounts for nearly half the industrial output of the whole country, and employs more than $\frac{2}{5}$ of the industrial labour force. As the capital of the Republic, the one large industrial town, and by far the greatest port, Dublin has a status far higher than that of the capital of its region; but the region under discussion is effectively that part of the Central Plain which sends a large part of its agricultural produce to the port of Dublin for export.

The Eastern Central Plain is a region of lowland, lying for the most part below 300 ft. and containing extensive bogs. Its foundation, chiefly of Carboniferous Limestone, is almost everywhere

FIG. 73. Farm livestock in Ireland, by regions

concealed by glacial drift or by peat. Bog is limited in extent within some 25 miles of Dublin, but becomes more common on the low divide which separates the Boyne and Liffey from the Shannon. The extent of bog increases still further on the far side of the watershed towards the Shannon river, which roughly marks the regional boundary. The region as a whole, and the boggy districts in particular, are diversified by eskers—long winding ridges of glacial outwash which stand above the peat and give access from east to west.

This is the least rainy part of Ireland, with between 200 and 225 rain-days a year and an annual precipitation averaging between 30 and 40 inches. The 40-inch isohyet runs approximately around the regional boundary (cf. Fig. 13). Climatically the region is comparable to the Lancs.-Cheshire Plain (Chap. 18), and like it, is intensively farmed.

Farming is dominated by the keeping of livestock, among which cattle are more than twice as numerous as sheep (Fig. 73). It is for the sake of cattle that so large a fraction of the farmland is kept in improved grass. The winter season is long for Ireland, but the frost-free period is no shorter than that experienced in the agricultural heart of Cheshire, and the generally humid atmosphere encourages a thick growth of grass to which the soils developed on limy glacial drift are well suited. In the immediate neighbourhood of Dublin, dairy-farming and market-gardening are carried on, supplying the large urban market on the coast, but throughout most of the region the production of beef cattle is the main interest (Plate 26). The live cattle sent for export from this region are noted in England for their good condition, but more store cattle than fatstock are exported. The Eastern Central Plain contributes largely to the live-cattle export which is so prominent in the external trade of the Republic (Fig. 64). Only in the southwest of the region does cattle-grazing lose its dominance, where a transition occurs through mixed farming towards the dairy-farming of Clare and Limerick. The racehorses for which Irish breeders are famous come from the eastern part of the region. Sheep-farming is scattered around its margins and on the acid peat of raised bogs. Tillage crops include oats, potatoes, and wheat, but—as throughout Ireland generally—the principal cut crop is hay.

The raised bogs began with the formation of mild fen peat in hollows of the lime-rich drift, but as the peat grew thicker, and rose above the level of its surroundings, its character changed. Proposals have been made to strip off the acid peat, in order to reveal the underlying fen peat which could be usefully cultivated if it were drained.

Settlement is widely scattered. In addition to the coastal towns listed above, there are small market centres inland, some loose-knit villages, hamlets, and many single houses. Dispersal is most marked in the north of the region, where holdings of land are small and rural dwellings closely-spaced (Fig. 74). The region here overlaps on to a belt of drumlins which extends broadly across the width of Ireland; dairying and mixed farming, with arable land intensively worked, become prominent in this part.

Dublin and Dún Laoghaire

The four largest towns stand on the coast. Dublin, as an old Gaelic name[1] shows, first developed as a small settlement associated

---

[1] Baile Atha Cliath, now the official name of Dublin.

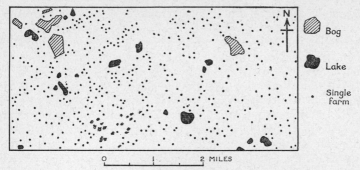

FIG. 74. Sample of dispersed settlement in Ireland: part of the main drumlin-belt
in County Monaghan

with a ford across the Liffey, becoming a fortified estuary-head town
under the Norsemen. The Norse stronghold stood on patches of
river-terrace and raised beach alongside the creek where the ships
lay. The Normans added a castle during the 13th century, when a
cathedral was also founded, and in later times Dublin became the
chief port of entry to Ireland and the centre of the fluctuating
English power. A great deal of rebuilding occurred during the late

FIG. 75. Dublin and its local setting

18th and early 19th centuries, its main legacy being the elegant Georgian architecture for which Dublin is justly famed (Plate 27). It was also in the 18th century that reclamation began in Dublin Bay, where the dock and industrial districts are located on reclaimed land (Fig. 75). The functional growth of Dublin has outpaced its rate of expansion in size, and some of the poorer residential districts are severely overcrowded.

The Liffey constitutes the long axis of an ellipse which, including the inner part of Dublin, is enclosed by the arcs formed by a ring-road and by the eastern ends of the Royal and Grand Canals. Growth of the town has been most vigorous towards the northeast and the southeast, where settlements in the coastal belt have been engulfed. The urban stimulus of Dublin is felt beyond the resort of Bray, twelve miles away to the south, and is responsible for part of the scatter of dwelling on the extreme northeast flank of the Wicklow Mountains.

The industries of Dublin include metal-working and engineering, the manufacture of wool, cotton, clothing and footwear, meat-canning and bacon-processing, brewing, distilling, and the making of biscuits, chocolate, jam, cigarettes, tobacco and fertilisers. Dublin absorbs much of the raw material imported into the Republic for industrial use, takes a large share in the processing of foodstuffs imported from abroad and produced at home, and commands the manufacturing industries which produce for export.

Dublin, with its ample bay sheltered on the north by Howth Head, is by far the best gateway into the Central Plain and into the whole of Ireland. Immediately to the south, the Wicklow Mountains rise almost directly from the coast, while north of Dublin the shore is low and sandy. It is natural that Dublin should have come to dominate the external trade of the Republic, but Dún Laoghaire is the main passenger port. Although the two towns are still admin-istratively separate, the former gap of five miles between them has now been closed by building. Dún Laoghaire stands where firm rock reaches the shore at the southern extremity of the sand-fringed bay, its two breakwaters enclosing the artificial harbour which shelters packets from Holyhead, $3\frac{1}{4}$ hours away by sea. Dublin has direct passenger services of its own to Liverpool and Glasgow.

Smaller Coastal Towns

Small coastal resorts have developed on the low shoreline north of Dublin. The two main breaks through the beaches occur at the mouths of the Boyne and Castletown rivers, on which stand Drogheda and Dundalk. These two towns resemble Dublin in being estuary-head settlements, each standing at the inner end of a drowned valley-mouth and being the lowest bridging-point of its river. With their small and shallow harbours, their more difficult access to the interior, and their inferior administrative status, they have grown but to modest size; they are, however, considerable towns for Ireland. Each has a small port trade, and manufactures tobacco, cotton, linen and beer. Fertilisers are made in Drogheda, cement and leather in Dundalk.

1B. THE WESTERN CENTRAL PLAIN

Area: about 3,000 square miles.
Population: about 300,000.
Largest town: Galway (21,500).
Density of population: about 70 p.s.m.
Half this region is improved grassland. There is little tillage, and non-agricultural land is extensive.
Numbers of livestock: cattle, 500,000; sheep, 900,000; pigs, 50,000.

The Central Plain is as low-lying to the west of the Shannon as it is to the east. It is much more boggy, for rainfall in this region rises above 40 inches a year and the number of rain-days increases correspondingly. A good deal of the unimproved land consists of bog, which is commoner here than in the adjacent region to the east, because the air is usually damp and because many enclosed hollows occur in the glacial drift. Among the lakes which occupy the largest hollows of all are Lough Ree, 17 miles long, and Lough Derg, 24 miles long. Their irregular shallow basins are probably due, in the main, to glacial scouring, but are thought to have been enlarged by solution of the underlying Carboniferous Limestone. The solid rock is rarely exposed, being masked by glacial deposits which in the north are moulded into drumlins. Eskers are numerous.

In this rainy and maritime region, sheep are as common as cattle are in the Eastern Central Plain. The contrast between the two regions in numbers of livestock is well brought out by the bar-graphs of Fig. 73, just as the general contrast in the use of land is shown by the wheels in Fig. 72. The region relies almost wholly on farming. There are very few towns of any size, and rural settlement is highly dispersed, being denser in the better-drained north than in the waterlogged and boggy south. The boundary of the belt of small farms marked in Fig. 71 coincides roughly with a transition from dominant sheep-farming in the south of the region to dominant mixed farming with production of store cattle in the north.

The regional capital, Galway, stands on the Atlantic coast where the Central Plain breaks through its rim of upland. Routes are focused on Galway by the deep bite of Galway Bay into the land,

and by the long stretch of Lough Corrib and its surrounding blanket-bogs, but the western districts are poor, and demands for urban services are limited throughout the area served. Galway is hampered as a port by a submerged dyke offshore, and nothing has come of the optimistic proposal that a terminal for transatlantic services should be established. The industries of the town include the milling of flour and timber, the making of furniture, and small-scale iron-founding, but Galway can scarcely be said to have taken a full share in the industrial development of the Irish Republic, limited though that development has been.

2A. THE SOUTH IRISH COASTLANDS

Area: about 3,200 square miles.
Population: about 500,000.
Largest towns: Cork (80,000; with suburbs, 114,500).
    Waterford (29,000).
    Wexford (12,000).
Density of population: about 80 p.s.m. outside the towns named.
    Nearly three-quarters of this region is improved farmland.
Numbers of livestock: cattle, 800,000; sheep, 425,000; pigs, 325,000.

The South Irish Coastlands stretch from the Wicklow Mountains to the head of Bantry Bay, including the lower valleys of the Slaney, Barrow, and Suir, and most of the basins of the Blackwater and Lee. The eastern part of the region is based chiefly on Cambrian and Ordovician sediments, metamorphosed in places and heavily in-truded by igneous rocks, while the west is underlain mainly by Old Red Sandstone. Structurally the region belongs to the belt of Altaid folding, and the east-west grain is well marked. It is reflected in the arrangement of numerous valleys excavated by subsequents along weak outcrops, but traces of an earlier drainage-pattern survive in reaches where streams break through the belts of strong rock towards the south. The terrain rises in a staircase of erosional platforms, which continues upwards beyond the inner limit of the region at about 600 ft. O.D. The rivers have cut deeply below the general level of the broad, subdued divides, but there is little ground at very low levels except near the estuaries. All of these have been drowned, and resemble the rias of Southwest England with which they are identical in origin. Wexford, Waterford, and Cork are located on the three largest rias, and the banks of some of the smaller inlets provide sites for lesser towns.

The region benefits climatically from its southerly position and maritime exposure. Although rainfall is quite heavy, ranging be-tween 40 and 50 inches a year, the frost-free period is from 7 months long at the inland boundary to more than 9 months on the coast in the west. The coastland around Waterford and Wexford is the sunniest part of Ireland.

There is some bog which can be used only for turf-cutting or as rough pasture for sheep, but most of the land is in improved farms. Farming is dominantly mixed, and it is this characteristic which separates the region from the adjacent inland region (2c) on the north, for in the latter dairying is the leading interest. The proportion of tillage in the South Coastland Region is high for Ireland. In addition to oats, tillage crops include potatoes, wheat, barley and sugar beet. These last three do best in the comparatively sunny eastern half of the region (Figs. 39, 40), barley being in demand by breweries and wheat and sugar beet being fostered by subsidy.

Cork, Waterford and Wexford

Cork (Fig. 76), the second largest town of the Republic, is the regional capital, although in practice Wexford and Waterford act as urban foci for their own surroundings. Cork has about 7% of the country's workers in manufacturing industry. Its engineering includes vehicle-building and the making of agricultural machinery; rubber, wool and leather are manufactured, and clothing and footwear produced for the wholesale trade. Steel-making was established near Cobh in 1938, alongside the deepwater harbour of the former naval base. Cork holds a leading position in the butter trade, and has jam factories, breweries, distilleries and flour mills.

FIG. 76. Cork and its local setting

When the whole of Ireland was politically united to the U.K., Cork's outport of Queenstown was a port of call on a number of transatlantic lines. The ria at the mouth of the Lee is the largest and most sheltered harbour on the south coast of Ireland, and has access to the interior of the country by gaps less than 500 feet high. The rail link with Dublin made possible the growth of a passenger traffic geographically comparable with that of Plymouth. Under its present name of Cobh, the terminal is busy enough to make it the second port in the Republic (i.e., second to Dublin) in tonnage of shipping. Dún Laoghaire takes third place, and Cork, dealing in freight rather than in passengers, fourth. Cork receives raw materials, including coal for its thermal-electric station, and exports agricultural produce and processed foodstuffs.

Waterford and Wexford resemble Cork as Dundalk and Drogheda resemble Dublin—that is, they are comparably sited, but are much smaller. Waterford commands the lowest bridge on the Suir, 8 miles from the head of Waterford Harbour and 15 miles from the open sea. Wexford possesses the lowest bridge over the Slaney ria, but Wexford Harbour is a lagoon cut off from the sea by long, arcuate spits. The entrance is shallow, and passenger services which require frequent and regular sailings are concentrated on Rosslare, 8 miles away to the southeast. The location of Rosslare resembles that of Dún Laoghaire, for the place stands on the open coast where firm ground appears at the side of South Bay. A breakwater protects the harbour from which packets sail to Fishguard.

Waterford and Wexford are shopping and market centres, with industries which are directly linked to farming. Both manufacture agricultural machinery—now under tariff protection—and Waterford has a bacon factory, breweries, and flour mills. Industries of a more general character might well have developed in each town if the official policy of industrial dispersal had not been adopted, but, as matters stand, neither of the two towns has acquired an industrial complexity equal to that of Cork.

2B. HILLS AND VALLEYS OF THE INLAND SOUTH

Area: about 3,800 square miles.
Population: about 300,000.
Largest towns: Kilkenny (12,500).
          Clonmel (11,000).
Density of population: about 85 p.s.m.
    Well over three-quarters of this region is improved farmland.
Numbers of livestock: cattle, 800,000; sheep, 300,000; pigs, 125,000.

The Inland South is roughly separated from the Southern Coastlands by the 600-ft. contour on the main divides, and by the change

27. Severe but elegant Georgian houses, Dublin.

28. Turf-cutting in Connemara. Bare rock protrudes through the peat, which contains roots of old forest.

29. Cottages in Donegal. One lies in ruins, but the other is newly lime-washed and thatched with flax straw. Reedy pasture occurs in the foreground, ice-scoured hills in the distance.

30. Lifting potatoes, County Antrim, in sight of Slemish Mt.

31. Horned blackface sheep in the Mourne Mountains. Small fields of low-grade pasture are enclosed by stone walls, while rough grazing covers part of the mountain slopes.

from dominantly mixed farming to dominant dairying. Any climatic significance which the boundary may possess lies in the moderation of maritime influences as the coast is left behind. The frost-free period in the Inland South falls below 7 months, the amount of sunshine decreases, and the annual and daily ranges of temperature rise a little. Precipitation increases to more than 50 inches a year on the outer flanks of the high ground, and, when it falls towards 40 inches inland side of the crests, the decrease is accompanied by cooler and longer winters. The contrast in actual temperatures between the coastlands and the interior is greater than that recorded in sea-level figures, for the ground rises generally from the coast inland, reaching more than 3,000 ft. in height in the Galtee Mountains. But the hills of the Inland South are interpenetrated by broad corridors of low ground, which blur the regional boundary drawn diagrammatically in Figs. 71–73; the Barrow is already less than 200 ft. above sea-level when it enters the region from the north, and the divide between the Suir and the Shannon lies little above 250 ft. at the highest, so that maritime influences are not blocked by a continuous barrier.

The really high ground is generally under rough pasture, with blanket bog on flat sites. The extensive lower slopes are developed on rocks mainly of Carboniferous age, with limestones prominent among them, although the Old Red Sandstone appears in the south. Glacial drift is patchy, and the soils into which it weathers tend to be limy or warm, like those formed on the solid rocks which constitute the parent materials of the drift. Although rainfall is more than adequate, the lower plateau steps are extensively farmed. The proportion of improved land to total area is high for Ireland, and the good land is well worked. Sugar beet is significantly important among tillage crops, although oats, potatoes and wheat cover larger acreages. The high ratio of cattle to sheep indicates a high agricultural status for the region. Dairying is dominant but not exclusive, for fat and store cattle are also produced.

Much of the milk produced on the dairy-farms goes to one or other of the scattered creameries. The size and shape of the area from which a creamery draws its supplies depends on accessibility. Butter is likely to be made on the farm if the nearest creamery lies at an inconvenient distance, while fresh milk can be sold if a town is nearby. Towns are characteristically small, however, and population is essentially agricultural, rural, and dispersed. The usual minor market centres occur at intervals. Kilkenny on the Nore and Clonmel on the Suir rank as major centres in this region, the one making clothing, footwear, and beer, and the other motor-bodies and cider.

G

More than any other region, the Inland South has profited from the subsidised growing of sugar beet. It possesses two of the nation's four sugar-beet factories, which have a total capacity roughly equal to the total demand for sugar in the Republic. Neither the processing of sugar-beet nor the making of creamery butter, however, encourages the growth of towns, and Kilkenny and Clonmel show little sign of expanding.

North of Kilkenny, between the Nore and the Barrow, occurs the only Irish coalfield with a noticeable output. In times other than those of war, annual production runs at about 200,000 tons. The seams are thin, but the coals are anthracitic—a fact which is a handicap rather than a help, since ordinary household coal of the bituminous kind would be more readily sold. Coal-mining has stimulated no industry to develop, and, except when imports are restricted by wartime conditions, this Irish coal cannot meet the competition of seaborne coal along the east and south-east coasts.

2c. THE WICKLOW MOUNTAINS
2d. THE PENINSULAR SOUTHWEST

These small regions differ from their neighbours by their generally high relief, their high proportion of non-agricultural land, and their low densities of population. The contrasts between them and the adjoining regions are apparent in Figs. 72 and 73, and in the following summaries:—

THE WICKLOW MOUNTAINS
Area: about 800 square miles.
Population: about 60,000.
Largest town: Bray (12,500).
Density of population : about 60 p.s.m. outside Bray.
  Little more than half this region is improved farmland.
Numbers of livestock: cattle, 75,000; sheep, 125,000; pigs, 20,000.

THE PENINSULAR SOUTHWEST
Area: about 2,600 square miles.
Population: about 130,000.
Largest town: Tralee (11,500)—on the regional boundary.
Density of population: about 45 p.s.m.
  Less than half this region is improved farmland.
Numbers of livestock: cattle, 275,000; sheep, 225,000; pigs, 75,000.

The Wicklow Mountains are based on a large granitic mass and on the cover of indurated sediments which surrounds the exposed granite. The Wicklows form the most compact block of high ground in Ireland, their broad spurs rising between glacially deepened valleys to heights of 2,500 feet and more; the highest summit exceeds 3,000 feet. This is a rainy region. with annual falls of 60 inches on the highest ground; the number of rain-days is little above that recorded in the nearby lowlands, but lifting of damp air over the mountains promotes instability, and individual falls are apt to be heavy. Dublin's problem of water supply has been solved, for the time being at least, by the raising of the level of Lake Poulaphouca, where H.E.P. is generated.

Cotton-grass moor occurs on the peat of the gently-sloping upland summits, with sedge moor in the shallow valley-heads. At lower levels come heather moor and gorse moor, while strips of woodland line the flanks of the trough-like valleys. Very few people live in the heart of the region, where the land is used as rough pasturage for sheep. Cultivation and cattle are confined to the deep valley-floors and to the low outer slopes. Stock-farming is practised on the western side, dairying for the Dublin market on the east, and the coastal strip between Bray and Wicklow is intensively farmed. Bray—previously noted as a resort for Dubliners—has doubled in numbers of people in the last 70 years, and is the chief centre for tourism in the Wicklows. The county town of Wicklow has fewer than 3,500 people and is not expanding.

The Peninsular Southwest is based on strongly folded sediments in which the Armorican trend is displayed with exceptional clarity. The east-west grain of structures is even better seen here than in the hinterland of Cork, for the upfolded outcrops of Old Red Sandstone form long spines of high ground, while the Carboniferous Limestone depressed in the intervening downfolds has been deeply eroded to form great longitudinal valleys. Between the drowned extremities of the valleys the highland projects in long promontories. In this western part of the region the land has undergone severe erosion, not only by rivers, but also by the ice which was nourished by snowy winds at glacial maximum. Corries bite savagely into the flanks of the mountains, but there are few cross-gaps, and travel across the trend of relief is difficult.

The whole region receives more than 60 inches of rain a year, and some central parts have more than 80. The high totals are explained partly by exposure to winds off the Atlantic, and partly by altitude—there is much land above 1,500 ft., and Macgillicuddy's Reeks surpass 3,400. A general decline in height towards the east is offset by a greater development of gentle slopes of high levels, which favours the growth of blanket bog.

Population is confined to low levels and to sloping ground. Losses by emigration have been very heavy and numbers are still declining, although farming is fairly successful. Cattle outnumber sheep, and milk is sent to creameries, but sheep are numerous enough to suggest that much of the land is of poor quality. A distinctive feature of the western coastlands is cottage farming,[1] a form of agriculture which represents an incomplete transition from crofting to commercial farming. The cottage farmer counts on selling some of his produce off the farm, thus differing from the crofter whose aim is self-sufficiency, but he is not sufficiently committed to producing for sale to be called a commercial farmer.

Like the Wicklow Mountains, this region is noteworthy for its tourist trade. The leading inland centre of tourism is Killarney, but the small towns at the heads of the western bays also take a share. Tralee, the largest town of the region, acts as an urban centre for the northern districts and also for part of the lowlands alongside the Shannon in Region 2e. The most notable industry of Tralee is the manufacture of enamelware, which has no particular geographical basis but enjoys a country-wide market.

2E. THE CLARE-LIMERICK LOWLAND

Area: about 2,600 square miles.
Population: about 225,000.
Largest town: Limerick (52,000); note also Tralee, on the regional boundary.
Density of population: about 50 p.s.m. outside Limerick.
About three-quarters of this region is in improved grass; there is little tillage.
Numbers of livestock: cattle, 525,000; sheep, 100,000; pigs, 75,000.

Most of the Clare-Limerick Lowland stands less than 250 feet above sea-level, where lowland extends broadly on either side of the upper estuary of the Shannon. Nevertheless, its affinities are with the hill country of the south of Ireland rather than with the central plain. It is partly enclosed by hills on the northeast, where Silurian, Devonian and Carboniferous strata rise to the surface and project in blocks of hills reaching 2,000 feet in places. Upland occurs also in the west of the region, where bare Carboniferous Limestone is exposed in wide, barren erosional platforms ranging up to 800 feet in height.

Rainfall varies from 40 inches on the low ground to more than 50 inches on the hills. Rain-days exceed 250 a year in some districts, and the mild winters do not compensate for the prevalent high humidity. Numerous patches of blanket bog variegate the clayey blanket of glacial deposits which borders the alluvial flats of the drowned inlets. Arable farming is very restricted, with oats and potatoes the chief crops, but improved grass used for cattle-pasture and hay is very common.

[1] The term is due to T. W. Freeman.

The southern part of the region—in effect, the hinterland of Limerick—is noted for its dairying. Rural creameries are numerous and well-established, but farm butter is a typical product of the less accessible north, where breeding and rearing of cattle for sale become common in addition to dairying. The limited number of sheep in this region corresponds to the rather limited extent of upland pasture, and to the very poor quality of the limestone plateaus in the west.

The terrain is more varied than altitude might suggest, for small hills break the profile of the plains, and soils of differing quality are very patchily distributed. The variety of detail emphasises rather than diminishes dispersion of rural settlement, and rural habitations are widely scattered. The figure given for mean density of population is, however, at least as misleading as comparable figures for other regions, for the best land in Clare-Limerick Lowland is about as well peopled as are the best parts of the Inland South. These two regions are linked by the broad strip of particularly productive land called the Golden Vein (or Golden Vale) which runs from Limerick past Tipperary into the valley of the Suir.

Limerick

Limerick (Fig. 77) is the undisputed regional capital. Founded as a coastal stronghold of the Norsemen, it was for a long time

Fig. 77. Limerick and its local setting

constricted by its medieval walls. With a population of some 50,000, it is today the fourth largest town of the Republic and the third most important industrial centre after Dublin and Cork. It shows a slight but persistent tendency to increase in population and to expand in area. Growth has been chiefly directed towards the southwest, along the left bank of the Shannon downstream of the medieval site, and suburbs have been stimulated into development on the far side of the river. But Limerick lags behind Cork in the speed of its growth and in its urban strength. It accounts for some 3% of the country's industrial production and 2% of the industrial labour force. The leading industries include flour-milling, tanning, clothing manufacture, the processing and canning of bacon and milk, and butter-making. Its port trade is not great, consisting of coastal traffic in imported grain and fuel and in exports of dairy produce. In terms of shipping movement, Limerick ranks well below the packet-station Rosslare and has traffic only half as heavy as that of Waterford. The nearby Shannon Airport, established in 1945, acts as a staging-point and as a point of entry for tourists, most of whom come from the U.S.A. The incoming tourists were at first those who had ancestral connections with Ireland, but nowadays the traffic has been broadened to include those who, with no sentimental ties, are merely touring Europe.

A useful contrast can be drawn between Limerick and Dublin. The latter, on the east coast where it faces Great Britain, is the vigorously-growing and industrialised national capital. Limerick faces only the Atlantic. Its old hopes of becoming a terminal for transatlantic traffic have little basis, even though the social and emotional ties of its region are with the U.S.A. rather than with Great Britain. The development of H.E.P. on the Shannon has not stimulated the industries of Limerick, for the spread of power lines is adverse to the concentration of industry, and industrial dispersal has been officially promoted.

Hydro-electric Power

In much of the Irish west, the people talk of 'having the Shannon Scheme'—the Shannon Scheme being popularly synonymous with electric power supply. The ambitious and successful Shannon project met with all the more approval because it was the first great public work in the Free State established in 1922. Work began on the installations in 1925 and was completed in 1929. A dam on the river three miles below Lough Derg raises the lake-level above 100 ft. O.D., and a wide canal 7½ miles long carries water to the power-station at Ardnacrusha. The remarkably high natural gradient of 13 ft./mile on the lower Shannon is perhaps due to incomplete rejuvenation controlled by a low sea-level in glacial times. The Shannon Scheme relies on the generally copious rainfall of its large catchment. Discharge falls off rapidly in time of drought—probably because water soaks into the highly permeable Carboniferous Limestone. Even with this limitation, the station at Ardnacrusha is still the greatest single producer of electricity in the Republic. Its success has undoubtedly encouraged the construction of plants on the Erne and in western Donegal.

3A. HILL COUNTRY OF MAYO AND GALWAY;
3B. HILL COUNTRY OF SLIGO AND LEITRIM;
3C. HILL COUNTRY OF DONEGAL

These three regions have much in common (Figs. 71 and 72). They contain much hill or mountain land, have extensive blanket-bogs, are on the average sparsely peopled, and are agriculturally poor. They suffer from an extreme development of maritime climate. Like peninsular Kerry, they have lost very many people by emigration and are typified by cottage farming in their remoter parts. Sligo alone among the towns has more than 10,000 inhabitants. Nevertheless, contrasts are strong enough to justify their separation from one another. The Hill Country of Sligo and Leitrim (3b) is much the most productive of the three, differing unmistakably from its neighbours on either side.

3A. HILL COUNTRY OF MAYO AND GALWAY
Area: about 2,200 square miles.
Population: about 100,000.
There are no towns of any size. The inland centre of Castlebar has about 5,250 people, and the railway-terminal town of Westport on the coast has 3,000. Density of population is about 65 p.s.m.
About a third of this region is improved grassland, and there is little tillage. Well over half the total area is unimproved.
Numbers of livestock: cattle, 150,000; sheep, 225,000; pigs, 25,000.

The two broad peninsulas in western Mayo and western Galway, lying between Galway Bay and Donegal Bay, are separated from one another by Clew Bay on which Westport stands. At the landward ends of the peninsulas occur huge lakes—Conn, Mask and Corrib. The centre of each peninsula consists of a knot of dissected mountain. The Mountains of Mayo are eroded in Carboniferous sediments and underlying metamorphic rocks, while metamorphic rocks alone predominate in the Connemara Mountains, which reach the west coast at some points. Both groups rise above 2,500 feet, and the mountain country is almost unpeopled. It has been heavily scoured by ice, its summits receive more than 50 inches of rain a year, and blanket bog is widely developed. Habitations are concentrated round the margins of both blocks of country, in districts where rural poverty on the small farms is a chronic problem, and would be still more severe without the money sent home by emigrants in America. The inhabited parts of the region combine a very low standard of living with a surprisingly high density of population.

3B. HILL COUNTRY OF SLIGO AND LEITRIM

Area: about 1,600 square miles.

Population: about 85,000.

Largest town: Sligo (13,500).

Density of population: about 65 p.s.m. outside Sligo town.

About two-thirds of this region is in improved farms. There is little tillage.

Numbers of livestock: cattle, 275,000; sheep 100,000; pigs, 50,000.

The Hill Country of Sligo and Leitrim is distinguished from the hillier regions on either side by its fairly extensive patches of lowland, which are underlain by Carboniferous rocks and covered by glacial drift. The Ox Mountains in the west of the region are developed on a strip of resistant metamorphic rocks, but the tabular hill-masses between Sligo Bay and the Erne are composed of gently-inclined Carboniferous sediments, in which limestone forms bold outfacing scarps. The subdued summits between 1,250 and 2,000 feet in height are in rough pasture, which also occurs at lower levels and amounts to a third of the total area, but many parts of the lowland are well farmed. The drift is lime-rich and drumlins are quite numerous—this region contains the westernmost extensions of the drumlin-belt mentioned above. Rainfall of below 50 inches a year is significantly less than that recorded in western Donegal, western Mayo and western Galway. The proportion of land improved is roughly twice as great in the Sligo-Leitrim country as in those regions, and cattle are more numerous than sheep. Dairying is dominant on the whole, with milk sent to creameries, but stock-rearing is also carried on.

H.E.P. is developed on the Erne at Ballyshannon,[1] where the output promises to exceed that of Ardnacrusha. Storage is provided by Lower and Upper Loughs Erne, where drumlins rise from the water and from the marginal bogs; drainage-works now in progress are likely to improve some of the land near the river.

Sligo town stands where the low coastal platform is constricted between steep-faced hills on the inland side and drowned sandy

[1] Ballyshannon is located in Co. Donegal, just over the county boundary.

inlets on the seaward. It is a shopping and market centre, with a bacon factory, flour mills, and a flourishing wholesale trade. Its population tends to increase slowly. As a port it has had little success, and is still declining. A recent development in the neighbourhood is the working of lead ore for export to Belgium.

3C. HILL COUNTRY OF DONEGAL

Area: about 1,600 square miles.
Population: about 100,000.
 There are no towns of any size in this region.
 Less than one-third of this region is improved farmland.
Numbers of livestock: cattle, 150,000; sheep, 225,000; pigs, 12,500.

A description generally similar to that given for the Hill Country of Mayo and Galway may be applied to the Hill Country of Donegal, where mountains rise to more than 2,000 feet in the midst of compact blocks of upland. The geological basis of this region comprises granitic masses and slowly-weathering metamorphic rocks, truncated by erosional platforms, ice-scoured and peat-covered. The Caledonian trend is highly developed, with some of the larger structures continuing those known in the Scottish Highlands. Rainfall varies from 50 to 60 inches a year, and at heights greater than 600 ft. the land is fit merely for rough grazing or peat-cutting. Population is again peripheral, cottage farming is dominant, and emigration has been

Enclosed and improved Farmland (internal field boundaries omitted)

Enclosed Bog, used for rough grazing or as a source of fuel

Open Bog

0   ¼   ½   ¾ Mile

FIG. 78. Farming settlement and farmland on two drumlins, Co. Donegal going on for at least a century (Plates 28, 29). Sheep, which are more numerous than cattle, are light in weight and not very suitable for meat-production. Their wool is the basis of a scattered manufacture of homespun cloth, with which knitwear and embroidery are associated, and of the industrialised making of the well-known Donegal tweed.

The lack of urban development in this region is well illustrated by the condition of Donegal town, which exemplifies the effects of the checks on urban growth typical of Ireland. Donegal town has fewer than 1,500 people, despite its status of county town, its position as the focus of a well-farmed drumlin-swarm at the head of Donegal Bay (cf. Fig. 78), its location on tidewater, and its narrow-gauge railway. In spite of all these apparent advantages, it has failed to grow. The demands for urban services in its hinterland are slight, and can be met by visits to the town on market-days and the distribution of groceries by vans light enough to run on mountain roads. Donegal town has spread very little beyond the edges of the open space at its centre. Such a space is very common in Ireland, where it is usually called the diamond, even where (as at Donegal) it is triangular.

H.E.P. is being developed in the west of the region, where glacial lake-basins provide the main storage but water is also being collected from several small rivers (Fig. 79). The aqueduct runs across the ice-scoured granite of The Rosses, an erosional platform laid bare by the cutting of peat, to a power-station near the shore where there is a sharp drop of more than 100 ft.

FIG. 79. The Clady power scheme, Donegal

Killybegs, on the south coast, is a fishing port, with a fish-meal factory and a tweed mill.

The Gaelic Language in the West of Ireland

Gaelic (Irish) has long been displaced from the east and is on the decline in all parts, despite its encouragement in schools. In some western districts, however, it survives as the language used in everyday speech, illustrating the way in which social influences spreading slowly westwards across the country become greatly weakened in the far west. In the counties of Donegal, Mayo, Galway, Clare and Kerry the percentage of people able to speak Irish varies from 15 to nearly 40, and in the westernmost coastlands exceeds 50.

FIG. 80. Concentration of the Irish language, and of private turf-cutting, in the west of Ireland

The Irish-speaking districts coincide roughly with areas of cottage farming and of rural poverty. They also rely on turf for domestic fuel, but the use of turf is much commoner than is the speaking of Irish. In Fig. 80 are plotted those counties with a higher-than-average production of farmers' turf per unit area; they are of course the western counties where rainfall is heavy and the air very humid at most times, but where also there is little money to spend on coal and coal cannot easily be obtained.

NORTHEAST IRELAND

Area: 5,800 square miles.
Population: about 1,400,000.
Largest towns: Belfast (436,250).
Londonderry (51,500).
Bangor (22,650).
Portadown (19,250).
Lurgan (18,000).
Lisburn (17,000).
Ballymena (14,750).
Larne (14,250).
Newry (12,750).
Newtownards (12,750).
Carrickfergus (10,250).
Coleraine (10,250).
Density of population: about 135 p.s.m. outside the towns named.
About three-quarters of this region is improved farmland.
Numbers of livestock: cattle, 975,000; sheep, 975,000; pigs, 800,000.

Much of what will be said under this head applies to the political unit of Northern Ireland, although, for purposes of regional description, most of County Fermanagh has been detached from the Northeast, and County Monaghan and some of eastern County Donegal have been added from the Republic. A careful comparison of the regional boundary marked on Fig. 71 with a map of Irish counties will show the difference between political and geographical divisions. Where the two kinds of boundary do not coincide, the regional division adopted here can be justified by reference to land quality, as well as by the fact that the areas served by certain market towns transgress the political boundary.

Some 45% of the inhabitants of Northeast Ireland live in one or other of the towns listed. A higher proportion of town-dwellers than this is recorded in the Eastern Central Plain, but the Northeast, area for area, has a higher proportion of sizeable towns than any other part of Ireland. The density of rural population is also higher than usual. The physique and quality of the land, the nature of the climate, and the political status of Northern Ireland combine to favour this region. Although the Northeast includes four blocks of upland, it also possesses lowland which can be intensively farmed, and enjoys the climatic advantages of the eastern side of Ireland. Its farm products find a market in Great Britain, and its principal towns are engaged in a successful textile industry. Belfast has overcome the lack of local coal and iron-ore in becoming a major centre of shipbuilding and heavy engineering.

Subdivision of the Region

Statistics for the regional groups distinguished in the Irish Republic can be derived, with fair accuracy, from data for whole counties. Figures quoted for single units (e.g., 3a, 3b, 3c) have been obtained from county figures by a process of somewhat arbitrary adjustment, but the tables and the diagrams (Figs. 72, 73) alike show that real differences distinguish one unit from another. No adjustment of county figures is possible within Northeast Ireland, for no grouping of counties can be made to correspond to the division into upland and lowland shown in Fig. 71. Consequently, the contrasts between lowland and highland and the internal variation of both cannot be defined statistically, but must be described in general terms.

The Lowland Districts

Fig. 71, representing in diagrammatic fashion the distribution and geological basis of relief, shows that the heart of the region consists of the Bann valley, in which Lough Neagh is centrally placed. Tongues of lowland radiate from the plain around Lough Neagh. One tongue extends down the valley of the lower Bann; one passes along the Lagan valley to Belfast; a narrow corridor forms the gap commanded by Newry, and a broad strip of low ground passes southwestwards towards the valley of the upper Erne; the Erne valley is linked by a broad low saddle with the valley of the Foyle.

All the lowlands in Northeast Ireland show signs of glaciation, in the form of outwash deposits and boulder clay. Drumlins are characteristic from the coastlands southeast of Belfast to the middle Erne, and lesser swarms occur in the Bann valley north of Lough Neagh. Although the quality of the soils developed on the drumlins varies with the parent material of the glacial drift, their slopes are everywhere free of bog. Some of the intervening hollows are quite well-drained in the natural state, and artificial drainage of others has extended the total area of improved farmland. It is no accident that plantations carried out under the Tudors and Stuarts spread along the wide belt of drumlins far into the northern Central Plain.

There are variations in farming within each lowland subdivision. Dairying predominates on the middle Erne, where much of the milk produced is taken by creameries, but grades into mixed farming in the lower Foyle basin where many fields are under the plough. Mixed farming is also typical of about half the branching lowland of the Bann Valley and its extensions. It is displaced by dairying around Ballymena and in the Lagan Valley, where the demands of Belfast are strongly felt, while the Bann Valley upstream of Lough

Neagh and the drumlin country southeast of Belfast are characterised by the raising and fattening of beefstock. Market-gardens occur patchily from Bangor to beyond Portadown, with a concentration of fruit-growing around the southern end of Lough Neagh.

The character of lowland farming accounts for the fact that, in Northeast Ireland, cattle outnumber sheep. Sheep, typical of the uplands rather than of the lowlands, outnumber pigs, but pigs are proportionately more numerous here than in any other region of Ireland. Pigs take a shorter time to become ready for market than do fat beef cattle, and they pay better than fat sheep. In consequence, they head the list of farm produce, in order of gross product by value. Next come milk and dairy produce, eggs, and cattle.

Agricultural exports from the northeast include beefstock, dairy cows, eggs, and pigmeat. The success of pig-farming in this region is due partly to the deliberate processing of bacon to suit the southern English market. Numbers of livestock in the region tend to increase, and the total extent of tillage crops to decline. Oats and potatoes are far and away the most extensive tillage crops (Plate 30); the area under flax has been diminishing for a long time, and although planting was stimulated by World War II, the total acreage under flax is now below 1,000. Flax takes very little cropland in Northeast Ireland, and the domestic crop makes an insignificant contribution to the supply of the linen industry.

The Upland Districts

The four upland blocks of the northeast are varied in origin and in landform, but the highest ground is everywhere open, windswept, and peaty. Most of it is given over to rough grazing for sheep. Whereas the lowland receives about 40 inches of rain a year, totals in the upland districts generally rise above 50 inches and surpass 60 inches in the central Mournes.

The Antrim Plateau is based on basalt sheets of Tertiary age, rising to more than 1,200 ft. over wide areas and presenting scarped edges to the east and north. Despite its compactness and its tabular, moor-covered top, the Plateau is less of a barrier than might be expected, for a raised beach at about 25 ft. O.D. allows an easy coast road to run far northwards from Belfast and to give access to the farmland of the glens which gash the coastal edge. The basalts are downwarped beneath Lough Neagh and the Bann Valley, reappearing on the western side, where they form scarps facing westwards on the flanks of the Sperrin Uplands in the second upland block. The Sperrin Mountains proper are formed of ancient metamorphic rocks, with rounded summits rising to more than 2,000 feet between wide valleys. The road from Belfast to Londonderry climbs to 1,000 feet in Glenshane Pass, descending on the western side between open hillsides and coniferous plantations. The uplands fall away towards the south, where farmland laps on to the drift-plastered slopes eroded in Old Red Sandstone and Carboniferous rocks.

The rainy Mourne Mountains, the third hill-mass, have a granitic core like that of the Wicklow Mountains, and, also like the Wicklows, make step-like descents between deeply-cut valleys. There is rough grazing on the heather moors of the higher slopes (Plate 31), some coniferous plantation at lower levels, and farmland in the valleys. Just as the Wicklows supply water to Dublin, so do the Mournes supply Belfast from the Silent Valley reservoir.

The fourth upland subdivision of the Northeast lies in Armagh and Monaghan, athwart the boundary between Northern Ireland and the Republic. At few points does it exceed 1,000 feet in height, but it effectively divides the hinterland of Dundalk Bay from the lowland corridor between the Bann and Erne valleys. The bedrock in this subdivision consists of fine-grained Cambrian and Silurian sediments, so that the glacial drift is generally clayey, but a rainfall less than 40 inches a year makes cultivation possible on the numerous drumlins. Rough grazing occurs at heights greater than some 800 ft. O.D., and there are patches of bog in some of the enclosed hollows.

Industrial Structure

Figures in brackets show the percentage contribution to total net output made by the principal groups of industries in Northeast Ireland: engineering and metal industry (29); textile manufacture (21); manufacture and processing of food, drink and tobacco (18). More than half the workers in manufacture are in Belfast, and only 1 in 20 in the second greatest town, Londonderry. The industrial dominance of Belfast is much greater in engineering and metal-working than in the other two groups, which are considerably dispersed through the region. Textile-working was established before Belfast grew large, partly in the form of a domestic craft, while the processing of foodstuffs is apt to be located in the producing areas; engineering works on the other hand were located in Belfast at the outset, depending (as they still do) on the port for their raw materials.

Textiles and Clothing

Linen manufacture had early beginnings as a domestic craft, which developed rapidly during the 18th century and was slowly superseded by factory-working during the 19th. Local flax was undoubtedly the basis of the industry, but it is seldom realised that the home supply was insufficient as early as the late 1700s, when imports had already become necessary. Like the wool-manufacturing of England, the linen-working of Northeast Ireland was well and widely established and resisted centralising tendencies. Of the towns indicated in Fig. 71, Londonderry, Coleraine, Lurgan and Portadown in addition to Belfast have large linen mills. The industry as a whole employs some 45,000 people.

The clothing industry is centred in Londonderry, which has about half the region's total of clothing workers. Shirts are the chief product. Since workers in clothing factories are mainly women, Londonderry suffers a chronic surplus of employable males, whereas Belfast provides employment for men in engineering. An important fraction of the output of linen and clothing, of the cordage produced in Belfast, and of the recently-added products of hosiery and synthetic textiles, goes for export.

Shipbuilding and Marine Engineering

Work on the port of Belfast began in 1840, and the shipyard was founded in 1853. With 20,000 workers and a huge output of ships, this is one of the greatest single yards in the whole world. It is particularly noted for large vessels—aircraft-carriers, passenger liners, and modern oil-tankers. Gross tonnage launched runs at about 120,000 a year (p. 265). Associated with shipbuilding is marine engineering; other engineering activities include the construction of aircraft, textile machinery, electrical goods, and agricultural machinery.

Towns

Londonderry (Fig. 81) possesses the lowest bridge across the navigable Foyle. It owes something (including the first element of its name) to its mercantile connection with London—a connection dating from the 17th century, when London Companies were given land and rights here. Although it is somewhat hampered today by lying close to the political border, it is still the chief urban focus of well-cultivated land of the lower Foyle valley, profiting by the harbour works carried out during World War II and by the overland distance of Belfast. Freight routes connect it with Glasgow and Liverpool. Its clothing and linen industries have been referred to above; there are also flour-milling, distilling, tanning and bacon-curing. The numbers of population tend to rise slowly, as Londonderry tightens its economic grip on the surrounding farmland.

Coleraine also lies at the head of an estuary and commands the lowest bridge. This former Norman stronghold and present centre of linen-manufacture has a small port trade on the routes which serve Londonderry. It is the principal town of the lower Bann valley.

Fig. 81. Londonderry and its local setting

Ballymena also shares in the manufacture of linen, but is chiefly noteworthy as the market centre of a dairying district. Portadown, Lurgan and Lisburn are the largest of a group of towns southwest of Belfast, in a lowland district where the industrial power of the capital makes itself felt. Portadown is the largest, with jam-making and fruit-canning related to the market-gardening of its surroundings, and carpet-making, bacon-processing, and linen-working. Lurgan and Lisburn, smaller than Portadown, are still dependent principally on linen-manufacture, but are likely to attract subsidiary manufactures from Belfast—e.g., of light engineering products.

Newry commands an ice-deepened corridor which penetrates the upland rim of Ireland and reaches the sea, to which the town is connected by a ship canal. Its port trade was once flourishing but is now very small, Newry having been superseded as a port by Belfast, and the town is no longer growing in population. It too manufactures linen, and is the market of an agricultural countryside. In the intensively-farmed hinterland of Newtownards, early potatoes are a well-known crop; the town itself is fast becoming an industrial outpost of Belfast. Bangor, at the mouth of Belfast Lough and with a frequent train service to the capital, is a residential town and seaside resort. Larne exercises a number of functions. It is at the same time a local centre for marketing and shopping, a seaside resort, a port, and an industrial town with manufactures which include aluminium products for the industries of Belfast. A cargo link to Preston has been added to the packet service to Stranraer, enabling Larne to supersede Londonderry as the second port of Northern Ireland.

FIG. 82. Belfast and its local setting

Belfast stands at the head of its wide Lough where the Lagan reaches the shore (Fig. 82). Its physical advantages in shipbuilding are confined to the depth of water in the Lough, which in the early days was generous, and to the sheltered anchorage. These alone cannot account for the development of shipbuilding and of the dependent or ancillary engineering industries, and any attempt to explain the industrial success of Belfast in physical terms is bound to fail. Heavy industries can obtain coal from Ayrshire and Cumberland, and steel can be shipped in from Clydeside. Nevertheless, the persistence and growth of shipbuilding and engineering in such a location are the result of far more complex factors than access to seaborne raw materials.

The fundamental factor in location was the original decision to found the industry at Belfast. Once that decision had been taken, the local reserve of labour was a distinct advantage, for wages remained for a long time below those paid for comparable work in Great Britain. The low level of wages enabled shipbuilders in Belfast to offset the cost of importing coal and metal. Once the industry was well established, industrial inertia enabled it to withstand the serious fluctuations to which shipbuilding was subject from time to time. The original advantage of low labour-cost no longer obtains, for wages in the shipbuilding and engineering industries are uniform throughout the U.K. It is partly for this reason that the purchase of industrial coal is subsidised in Northern Ireland at the present day.

Official support is also given to industrial expansion and to new industrial development. This support, responsible for a certain dispersal of light industry in Northern Ireland in the post-war period, is to be compared with the similar but longer-standing measures taken in the Republic, but it seems unlikely that any serious challenge can come to the prime industrial position of Belfast. Whereas distilling and the manufacture of farm products are quite widely dispersed, Belfast is pre-eminent in the manufacture of food, drink, and tobacco. It is the main focus of the linen industry, possesses the usual flour-milling and furniture-making of large towns, and has a wide range of miscellaneous industry. Wholesale and retail trade are naturally considerable.

External Trade

Through the port of Belfast goes three-quarters of the external trade of Northern Ireland, trade which is dominantly with Great Britain. Manufactures amount to nearly 60% of imports, the chief imported items being cotton and woollen goods and yarns, machinery and vehicles, petroleum, paper, iron and steel plates and sheets, coal, flax, timber and wool. Leading exports are textiles, ships, aircraft, tobacco, eggs and pigmeat. The nature of trade is clearly related to the agricultural and industrial status of Northern Ireland. In volume, trade is half as great again as that of the Republic, and nearly $3\frac{1}{2}$ times as great per head of population.

CHAPTER 13

Wales and the Welsh Borderland

THE combined extent of Wales and the Welsh Borderland is about 10,250 square miles, and their total population is about 3,100,000. The significance of total figures is, however, more than usually weakened by geographical variation, which requires a subdivision of the area into three regions—the Welsh Massif, Industrial South Wales, and the Welsh Borderland (Figs. 83, 84).

FIG. 83. Regional division of England and Wales: compare Fig. 6

The Welsh Massif is mainly plateau country, high, bleak, rainy, and open, with much land in moor and with settlement and improved farmland concentrated in the valleys and along the coast. A fundamental contrast divides the broad upland from the limited and scattered lowland. Industrial South Wales, based upon the coalfield and its coastal fringe, is superimposed on the division between central moor and peripheral farms. The Welsh Borderland is hilly and irregular in relief, but most of it stands much lower than the interior plateaus. It benefits from rain-shadow and is well farmed, but differs strongly from the highly urbanised West Midlands in being poor in towns.

Boundaries of geographical regions coincide neither with geological boundaries nor with the political limit of Wales. A well-defined

FIG. 84. Wales: physique and main settlements

geological boundary, at the western limit of Permo-Trias, separates
the Welsh area from the marl-filled Midland basins and their extensions towards the estuaries of the Dee and the Severn. In places—
but only in places—this boundary coincides with the break of slope
where the plains end and the hills of the Borderland begin. Elsewhere, the geological junction is obscured by glacial deposits. Elsewhere again, the ancient rocks of the Welsh block have been much
denuded—as in the neighbourhood of Shrewsbury, where a structurally complex prong running towards the northeast is reflected
merely in isolated hills which rise from English plainlands. In
addition, small coalfields occur on the very margins of the plains,
modifying or blurring the regional boundary.

The regional boundary between the Borderland and the Massif
is fixed where the irregular terrain of the former passes into the
largely intact plateaus of the latter. The change does not agree with
geological divisions, but is defined by a marked change of relief
and landscape-texture and by the associated change in climate—
the change from the rain-shadow of the Borderland to the severe
climate of the interior uplands. In places—but again only in places—
the political limit of Wales runs along the margin of the interior
plateaus, having been driven right across the Borderland by successive
conquests and encroachments.

THE WELSH MASSIF

Area: about 7,500 square miles.

Population: about 2,775,000; some 1,650,000 of these live in Industrial
South Wales, leaving 1,125,000 for the rest of the area.

Largest towns (apart from those of the Industrial South) :—

>   Colwyn Bay (23,000).
>   Rhyl (20,000).
>   Llandudno (18,000).
>   Bangor (14,000).
>   Carmarthen (13,250).
>   Pembroke (12,750).
>   Conway (11,500).
>   Aberystwyth (10,500).

About half the extent of the massif is in improved farmland,
grassland being roughly four times as extensive as tillage. More than
a third of the whole area is in rough grazing.

Numbers of livestock: cattle, 950,000; sheep, 4,150,000; pigs, 215,000.

One impressive fact about Wales is that the Welsh language has
maintained itself as successfully as any other native language
of the west. Cornish has vanished entirely, Scots Gaelic has almost
gone, Manx survives only in ceremonial use, and the Norman-
French patois of the Channel Islands are steadily fading out. Both

Welsh and Irish have long been on the decline, and the former
is rapidly falling into disuse at the present time; but even so, some
700,000 can still speak Welsh—a slightly higher proportion of the
population than is represented by 600,000 who can speak Irish.
Irish has admittedly suffered from deliberate attempts to destroy
it. No comparable attacks were made on Welsh; nevertheless, it
still seems remarkable that Welsh should have resisted, for so many
centuries, the effects of an accepted political union. The inherent
strength of Welsh is associated with a strong consciousness of cultural
heritage and tradition.

If there is a geographical basis for the survival of Welsh language
and Welsh culture, it lies in the great physical differences between
the terrain of Wales and the terrain of the English Plain. That
difference has its foundation in geology, and its superstructure in
erosional history and in climate. On the other hand, the facts of
physical geography obstructed the unification of an independent
Wales, and assisted penetration of its margins. It was in the valleys
that the independent Welsh of the Middle Ages lived, and in the
valleys that their food was produced. The valleys radiate outwards,
offering no natural focus to the plateau country—all physical guidance is centrifugal. Wales became politically united only under
recurrent attacks from Romans, English, Danes, Scandinavians,
and Normans. Significantly enough, the English counties of the
Borderland were established and extended precisely where wide
valleys and well-drained ridges struck far to the west, but the routes
of much of the Borderland led merely to the high plateaus of the
interior. Lines of fortresses were extended along the northern and
southern coastlands, in a kind of pincer movement; as the jaws of
the pincer closed, the still-independent Welsh were driven into the
Welsh heartland of Gwynedd in the northwest. It is here that the
Welsh language and the distinctive qualities of Welsh life are most
prominent today, having endured the subjugation and political
union of the 13th century, and having been least affected by industrialisation.

The Plateaus

The rigid crustal block which constitutes the Welsh Massif is
based mainly upon fine-grained sediments of Ordovician and
Silurian age. The pronounced SW–NE structural trends of the stumps
of the Caledonides are well displayed by these rocks in the centre
and north, but the ancient folds have been broadly truncated by
erosion, and plateaus are very extensive (Plate 6). Under the influence
of a falling base-level, very subdued land-surfaces developed between
1,700 and 2,000 feet, between 1,200 and 1,600 feet, and between

800 and 1,000 feet. At lower altitudes, old wave-cut benches run along the coastlands. Up-domed Cambrian rocks appear in the Harlech Dome, forming concentric infacing scarps. Sandstones and conglomerates of the Old Red Sandstone lap on to the flanks of the older rocks from the southeast, rising above 2,500 feet in the Black Mountains and closely approaching 3,000 feet in the corrie-scalloped Brecon Beacons. For the most part, however, heights in the region of 3,000 feet are confined to volcanic rocks, which rise dramatically from the monotonous platforms in the Snowdon District, in the Arenigs, and in Cader Idris. Craggy landforms and the features of highland glaciation—peaks, corries, tarns, ribbon lakes, and fretted ridges—are well developed on the volcanic rocks (Plate 32), as on some of the coarser sediments, but in much of the region the main effect of glaciation has been to deepen the larger valleys into grooves, to scour rock-waste from the high ground, and to line the valley-floors and lower hillsides with boulder clay.

Actual mean temperatures on the highest ground are in the neighbourhood of 35°F. in January and 56°F. in July. Precipitation is frequent, coming on two days out of three. Although actual temperatures increase, and precipitation decreases, with decrease of height, the climate remains cloudy, cool, and rainy at least as far down as the 800-foot contour, with annual totals of precipitation exceeding 50 inches. Peat tends to accumulate on all gently-sloping summits; blanket-bog is less typical in Wales than in the soaking air of western Ireland, but the plateau soils all have a high content of raw humus.

FIG. 85. Sample of land use and dispersed rural settlement, central Wales

Whatever the effects of felling and of centuries of sheep-grazing, the windy high plateaus can scarcely be regarded as natural woodland. The area at present in rough grazing—approximately enclosed by the 60-inch isohyet—includes varieties of molinia moor, with a continuous fringe of mountain fescue round its lower edge. Patches of heather moor occur in the east, where precipitation decreases, while heather fell is found on the rainy flanks of the Snowdon group (Fig. 20).

The moorland of the central plateaus has little use except as rough pasture for sheep, which are very numerous indeed on the uplands (Fig. 41, Plate 33). Sheep can survive severe weather better than cattle can. They do not require the daily attention which is given to dairy animals; they graze closer than do cattle, and are adapted to living on poor or coarse pasture.[1] For all these reasons they have been largely displaced from the improved farmland to the districts of rough grazing (cf. Chap. 5). Sheep-grazing on moorlands employs few men in comparison with the size of the area grazed, and in any case many of the shepherds live in the valleys. The high plateaus of Wales are very scantily peopled; the average of less than 50 per square mile for the rough-grazing districts, which is in any case low, includes the populations of the higher valleys.

Settlements in the interior of Wales are typically small (Fig. 85). There are scattered single farmsteads as well as small groups of grey stone cottages. The small irregular fields characteristic of early and piecemeal enclosure contain the farmland in a net of stone walls. Woodland is sparse, the merest remnants of hardwood forest having survived the axes of charcoal-burners and the teeth of sheep. One ubiquitous feature is the stone-built set of pens, where sheep are brought to be washed in the waters of a mountain stream.

The Valleys and the Coastlands

The valleys are an altogether different proposition from the divides. They possess soils other than the peaty soils of the uplands, they are largely in improved farmland, and many parts of them are sheltered from the raw winds which sweep across the plateaus (cf. Fig. 86, Plate 3).

[1] In some inexplicable fashion, the legend has arisen that sheep cannot be kept in rainy areas because of footrot. This erroneous belief is completely refuted by the actual distribution of sheep in the British Isles, as mapped in Fig. 41, which shows clearly that sheep today are numerous in the very rainy uplands but scarcely anywhere else. Footrot is due not directly to dampness underfoot but to a micro-organism, which is favoured by dirt as well as by wetness. Thus the danger of footrot is absent from dry pastures, but present in overstocked folds on arable land. Stagnant conditions are far more likely to encourage the disease than are the moorland pastures, where water runs freely down the steep slopes or soaks into the peaty soil. Moreover, the hooves of hill sheep are continually abraded by the bare rocks underfoot.

M | Meadow (permanent grass)   h | Heath (all rough grazing)

F | Forest (all woodland)   ▨ Arable   g | Gardens

0   ¼   ½ MILE

FIG. 86. Land use in the Aber valley, North Wales. The low coastal platform (raised beach) is in improved farmland; rough grazing appears at 200 or 300 feet; and woodland occurs on the valley-sides

The present valley-system has evolved from one initiated by uplift in the west. The original consequent rivers ran northeast, east, and southeast from a watershed some 20 miles inland of Cardigan Bay. Capture has modified the original pattern, especially in the upper basins of the Dee, Severn, Wye, Towy, and Teifi, where subsequent streams have extended themselves along northeast-southwest or southwest-northeast lines of weakness, but the radial tendency is still apparent. The short rivers draining directly into Cardigan Bay show very clearly the effects of repeated rejuvenation. Glacial grooving has converted many of the larger valleys into steep-sided troughs, and ice was responsible for diverting a number of streams in the Welsh Borderland.

As the head-valleys are left behind, and the middle and lower reaches approached, settlement becomes progressively denser, individual settlements larger, and farmland richer and more extensive. Sheep-farming is still the main interest at the higher levels, but in the lower valleys, and on the broad coastal benches of Anglesey and the south, the emphasis changes from sheep to cattle. Soils generally have undergone heavy leaching and are poor in lime—in the natural state, they tend to be podsolised. Climate, however, improves greatly with decreasing height and with increasing nearness to the sea; the frost-free season lengthens to 7, 8, or even 9 months, the yearly total of precipitation falls towards 40 inches, cloudiness decreases, mean temperatures rise. The annual range of temperature decreases very rapidly—a sign of greatly improved winter weather. Thus it becomes possible and profitable for farmers to take advantage of the long growing-season and to concentrate on cattle.

Tillage is subordinate to grassland, not only in extent but also in the character of its crops. About a quarter of all tillage is under oats, a crop intended for animal feed as opposed to food for human beings; mixed corn and fodder crops are also widely grown. Dairying is more common than the rearing and fattening of beef-stock, as it is in Southwest England; and, again as in Southwest England, the rise of dairying has been a response to the growth of industrial towns and to the spread of railways. The difficult gradients of much of Wales limited the possible choice of routes for railways; the only two through-routes run along the coastlands in the north and south to the packet-stations of Holyhead and Fishguard, providing rapid services for the dairying districts of Anglesey and Pembrokeshire. These lines follow the early routes of armed conquest, which were also guided by the terrain. They tap country where the climatic advantages of a western location and of fairly low ground are particularly great in dairy-farming.

The Welsh Black breed of beef cattle, well known for being extremely hardy, is most common today in northwest Wales. Welsh Black cattle from the massif, and Herefords from the Border country, used to be driven in herds along the drove roads which in the 18th and early 19th centuries led from Wales to London. Welsh Roads are still so called in the Midlands, but the droving trade has been superseded by rail transport. Store cattle are still sent for fattening to the Midlands, where some Welsh graziers have followed them to take over Midland farms.

The markets for Welsh dairy produce are not all in England. Anglesey and the narrow coastal plain of North Wales—with its extensions up the rifted valleys of the Conway and the Clwyd— naturally contribute mainly to the supply of the Lancs.-Cheshire region, but the farms of Pembrokeshire, south Carmarthenshire, and south Glamorganshire can depend on a heavy demand from Industrial South Wales. Agriculture in the Plain of Gwent has been particularly stimulated by the nearby industrial towns, and includes considerable market-gardening. It is favoured by the equable climate which results from location near the coast, and also by soils which, developed on Permo-Triassic and Jurassic sediments, are deeper and warmer than the soils of almost every other part of Wales. Geologically speaking, the Plain of Gwent belongs to Lowland Britain.

Intensive dairy-farming in Europe is often associated with small farms, so that a district dominated by dairying is liable to have a quite high density of rural population. There are however at least two ways in which these conditions may arise. In Denmark and Holland they have been deliberately brought about. In more broken terrain they can result from the conversion to dairying of existing farms, which were already small because the limited good land available had been repeatedly subdivided. Such is the case in parts of southern Sweden and of Ireland, and also in the dairying districts of Wales; in Anglesey, for instance, more than a quarter of the farms are between 5 and 15 acres in size, and farms in the same group are also numerous in Pembrokeshire.

The early subdivision of farmland in Wales was accompanied by a dispersion of the rural settlement which, in some districts at least, had been originally nucleated. All the valley lands were affected by the process of redistribution, and their settlements are mostly small today. As in Ireland, there is little demand for urban services, especially since sheep-markets are far less frequent than cattle-markets. As the tentacles of the very large towns outside rural Wales reached into the interior, they drew countryfolk away instead of touching off town growth. Rural Wales, like the rural parts of

Ireland and Scotland, has lost many of its people by emigration, which did more than keep numbers down. Industrial South Wales, the great and growing towns of England, and the New World all received their groups of Welsh migrants. Local industries of the plateau and its margins could support few people.

Town Population and Industry

Montgomery, although a county town and a centre of woollen manufacture, with a site on the upper Severn, has few more than 900 people. The neighbouring town of Welshpool, lower down the river, has about 6,500. Both are roughly static in population. The largest towns of North Wales are the most successful resorts, but none exceeds a modest size, and the tourist trade is widely dispersed. Colwyn Bay, Bangor, Llandudno and Conway are strung along the coast, while very small but well-known settlements in the mountains cater for visitors to the Snowdon group. Aberystwyth is the leading resort on Cardigan Bay, located at the centre of a crescentic low-lying platform. Carmarthen and Pembroke are collecting and distributing centres for the farmlands of the southwest.

No large settlements have grown at the ends of the passenger routes to Ireland, for the rail and shipping services are designed to move travellers through Holyhead and Fishguard as rapidly as possible. The water-supply undertakings which serve Liverpool and Birmingham and which include the Vyrnwy and Elan Valley schemes, employ small numbers on maintenance, and cannot be expected to affect local towns. H.E.P. is as yet developed only on a minor scale. Manufacturing industry is limited in scope and extent throughout the central and northern massif, and the slate-quarrying of the north has seen its best days. The great quarries on the flanks of the Snowdon group, where the shales have been metamorphosed into slate, are working at about a third of their capacity. The demand for slate is much less than it was in the 19th century, when other roofing materials were less common and less cheap than they now are, and when the rapid growth of English towns produced terraced rows of brick-built and slated houses. Anglesey is acquiring new light industries, but its mines in Parys Mountain are derelict today. They once led the world in the production of copper ore, but the reserves now available are complex lead-zinc ores which could not be treated by the smelting techniques of former days. The most recent and most promising industrial development is the construction of a terminal port for oil-tankers in the huge ria of Milford Haven. The settlement of Milford Haven was once a naval base and is now the chief fishing port of Wales. It has become a centre for

the importing of oil, the ria having been selected as a harbour because
of its capacity to accommodate the huge modern tankers which bring
in ever-increasing quantities of crude petroleum.

INDUSTRIAL SOUTH WALES

Population: about 1,650,000.
Largest towns: Cardiff (256,250).
                 Swansea (166,750).
                 Newport (108,000).
                 Rhondda (100,250).
                 Merthyr Tydfil (59,000).
                 Port Talbot (50,250).
                 Barry (42,000).
                 Pontypool (40,000).
                 Aberdare (39,000).
                 Caerphilly (36,000).
                 Pontypridd (35,500).
                 Gelligaer (34,500).
                 Neath (31,000).
                 Llanelly (30,000).
                 Mountain Ash (29,500).

This region is usually called South Wales for short. Its area is of
the order of a thousand square miles, so that something approaching
two-thirds of the people of Wales inhabit one-eighth of the total
area. The people are most unevenly distributed, for densely-settled
industrial valleys are divided from one another by unpeopled belts
of moorland, and stretches of open country intervene between the
large coastal towns. Interpenetration of urban and rural landscapes
is more pronounced than anywhere else in the British Isles, except
perhaps along the fringes of the industrial region of the West
Riding (Fig. 87, Plate 34).

FIG. 87. Land-use sample for the Tawe valley, upstream of Swansea

The close-packed inhabitants of the towns are supported either directly or indirectly by industry—industry dominated by the manufacturing of ferrous metals, and drawing on local coal for its power. The coal seams are contained in a basin produced by Altaid folding; the outcrop of the Coal Measures narrows westwards, and in the same direction the rank of coal rises, until anthracite occurs in the western part of the field. Although coal-mining is so prominent in the industrial geography of South Wales today that the region is often called the South Wales Coalfield, industrialisation began before coal-mining. Metal-working in this region has developed along highly distinctive lines, and the whole industrial life of South Wales has undergone violent fluctuations in output in addition to marked shifts of location. The region provides outstanding examples of changes in geographical values.

Rise and Fall of the Iron Industry

The first establishment of an iron-smelting industry in South Wales constituted a response to the national demand for iron goods, at a time when the Wealden forests had long been inadequate and the timber of Staffordshire was already seriously depleted. Iron-manufacture in the early 18th century was located with reference to supplies of timber and of iron-ore; South Wales was well supplied with both.

The ores used in smelting with charcoal included those occurring in the Coal Measures. In South Wales, as on certain English coalfields, the rather limited local reserves of ironstone were ample in the early days. They were exploited mainly along the northeastern rim of the coalfield, where the Carboniferous strata dip quite gently and where the land is dissected by a series of deep young valleys. On both these counts the ores were accessible. Accessibility was important at a time when mining technique was crude and the thin beds of ore were taken from shallow pits or short drifts. The change from charcoal to coke fixed the iron-works firmly upon the outcrop of the coal-bearing rocks, and a vigorous iron-smelting industry developed. Most of the blast-furnaces and foundries were built in the district where charcoal-smelting was already established—i.e., in the northeast of the coalfield—where the gently-dipping rocks and deep valleys constituted great practical advantages in coal-working. In this development can be seen the joint effects of physical environment and of inertia. There was no reason why the smelting industry should be displaced from its home district when the new fuel, coal, could be locally worked in drifts along the northern outcrop or in adits in the valleys.

The ironworks which depended on coke were accordingly concentrated in and near Abergavenny, Brynmawr, Ebbw Vale, Tredegar·

32. Snowdon (3561 feet) from the northeast, showing features of highland glaciation. Contrast Plate 6.

33. Dipping sheep in the interior of Wales, near Cader Idris.

34. A Welsh mining valley, at Ferndale, Glamorganshire.

35. Half-timbered buildings at Weobley, Herefordshire, in the Welsh Borderland. Medieval timber frames indicate a former abundance of deciduous woodland.

Rhymney, Merthyr Tydfil, and Aberdare (Figs. 84, 88). These towns lie in, or at gateways to, a long depression excavated in the gently-dipping Lower Coal Measures, stretching in a line from the Usk to the Taff. On the north, the Carboniferous Limestone rises in a north-facing cuesta to 2,000 feet. To the south, the productive Lower Coal Measures disappear beneath the barren Pennant Sandstone, which forms flat-topped hills rising in many places to more than 1,500 feet. The early coke-using ironworks arose in the strike vale and in the heads of valleys leading southeastwards from it.

The gentle dips of the northeastern rim of the coalfield belong to the northern flank of the coalfield syncline. The thick, coarse, well-cemented Pennant Sandstone separates the northeastern outcrop of productive Coal Measures from the downbent, coal-bearing Upper Coal Measures of the axial part of the field, and from the reappearing Lower Coal Measures of the southern flank. The 20 miles' journey between the iron-making towns and the coast was eventually to prove a grave handicap. The first severe blows came in the latter half of the 19th century, when steel was replacing iron as an industrial material, and when the Coal-Measure ores were running out. Steel-working was established on or near the coast. The towns in the northeast failed to secure many steelworks, and their metallurgical industry fell on hard times.

Rise of the Coal Export Trade

Meanwhile, the coal-export trade was flourishing. Coal had been worked in South Wales at least as early as the 13th century, and a small export trade came into being long before industrialisation began. Cardiff, however, was still *importing* coal at the beginning of the 18th century, and did not share the export trade until the 19th. In the vast increase in British coal exports during the second half of the 19th century and in the early years of the 20th, however, the eastern part of the South Wales Coalfield, and particularly the northeastern part, became heavily involved.

In addition to the change of rank from bituminous coal in the east to anthracite in the west, changes occur within the bituminous series. There are large deposits of coal highly suitable for coking, for firing large boilers, and for household use. The demand for coking coal rose with the growth of smelting; the demand for household coal kept pace with increase in population and with rising living-standards; sales of steam coal were promoted by the vigorous expansion of world trade and of steam-powered merchant navies. Bunker coal from South Wales was distributed along the sea-lanes of the world.

H

Cardiff, Newport, and somewhat later Swansea, became very great exporters of coal. Each lies at the focus of valley-routes. The western part of the dissected coalfield plateaus is drained by the southwestward-flowing Loughor, Tawe, and Neath, which are partly adjusted to lines of faulting and shattering. In the east, the Taff, Rhymney, Ebbw and Usk form, with their tributaries, a group of sub-parallel consequents, superimposed on the structures of the coalfield and draining towards the southeast. Roads, railways, and canals in the incised valleys connected the mines to the ports, bringing coal from the northern outcrop, from the Upper Coal Measures in the centre of the field, and from the flexured and more steeply-dipping seams of the Lower Coal Measures in the south. Mines were able to absorb some of the men no longer wanted by the ironworks. Some of the ironworks were abandoned, others continued to produce, partly because they had plant in running order. But the facts of location were as adverse to the iron industry as rising demand was favourable to mining. The emphasis of industry changed, accordingly, from manufacture to primary production. In the circumstances this retrograde step was only to be expected, but the mining industry and the coal trade were to prove at least as vulnerable to changing demand as iron-manufacturing had already been. While the export trade continued to flourish, the port facilities were extended and the port towns grew. Mining centres in the narrow valleys expanded into elongated towns, their brick-built terraces of 19th-century houses crowded on the lower slopes.

Rise of the Steel and Tinplate Industries

The steel-working which developed on and near the coast of South Wales derived great benefits from its location. High-grade ore could be brought in by sea, coal came by short hauls down the valleys, and metal manufacture of various kinds was already in being. Here also, however, industry became concentrated on a limited range of activities which were from time to time much hampered by changes outside the region.

One notable early development was the refining and smelting of the ores of non-ferrous metals. The bases of this industry were coal from South Wales itself, and ores of copper and tin from Southwest England. The furnaces and mills were established mainly in the valleys of the Loughor, Tawe and Neath. Competition tended in time to concentrate them near the coast, for works inland had to pay for the haulage of ores and concentrates without saving much on the transport of coal. There is still a copper industry, but it has been little concerned with initial processes since the U.S.A. became dominant in the production and control of copper ores. By contrast, the processing of tin has been retained and successfully developed. The U.S.A. has no domestic supplies of tin ore, while South Wales was able to draw on Malayan supplies when the mines of Southwest England began to fail. Of the three great producers of tin ore— Malaya, Nigeria, and Bolivia—two were under British control at a critical period, and tin-manufacture in South Wales was able to persist and to expand, even though it lost its nearby reserves of raw material.

Tin was required, as it still is, for use in plating. The plating industry uses zinc as well as tin in the production of a wide range of materials, which consist of sheet steel with a thin protective covering of some base metal. The ultimate uses of the products are manifold, but two main types are of particular importance. Tin-plate is widely employed in the making of rust-resistant metal containers, especially containers for foodstuffs. Output of this kind of product increased with the development of canning, particularly the canning of the fruit shipped in increasing quantities from the tropics and the southern hemisphere to Northwest Europe. Demand for tinplate is still expanding, for sales of canned and standardised fruit and vegetables continue to rise, and the manufacture of containers absorbs four-fifths of the output of tinplate. Canning has the great practical advantages that canned goods can enter distant markets and seasonal gluts of perishable foodstuffs can be held over. One factor contributing to the demand for canned goods is the post-war labour shortage in the British Isles, which has encouraged women to work in factories and has reduced the time available for home cooking.

The second leading type of product is galvanised sheeting, either flat or corrugated. When parts of the tropical lands were developed economically during the later 19th century, the materials known rather loosely as corrugated or galvanised iron proved of great value. In countries where local timber was either too soft or too hard to be usable, and where imported softwood was liable to be devoured by termites, rustproofed steel was imported as building material. It also found a wide market in Great Britain, first in industry and later in agriculture. Plated steel sheet is used in great quantities today in the manufacture of car-bodies.

The steel industry of South Wales, then, developed largely as one of the processes in the manufacture of tinplate. This manufacture absorbed a great deal of the steel made in South Wales. Although tinplating and galvanising spread to all parts of the coalfield, it remained typical chiefly of the western part, and especially of Swansea, Llanelly, and their smaller neighbours. Few of the towns concerned with plating grew to a large size, and the industry is still quite well dispersed. Some of the older works, however, are poorly designed and inefficient by modern standards, and a number have already been closed down in the course of industrial reorganisation.

Industrial Vulnerability and Recent Change

While the eastern part of the coalfield relied very heavily first on iron-working, and then on coal export, the western part, having lost much of its copper manufacture, depended on coal export, and on tinplating and galvanising with their associated production of steel sheet and strip. Because of their lack of variety, the industries of South Wales were dangerously exposed to change. Destructive change came in the inter-war period, in the forms of falling demand for coal and of industrial slump.

The origin and character of the difficulties which beset the coal trade (Chap. 7) included the alternation of boom and slump in the inter-war period, the disturbance of European coal traffic, and the progressive replacement of coal by oil as a fuel for ships. Difficulties reinforced one another, for, with the whole mining industry severely depressed, it was impossible to modernise pits or to repair dilapidations. Mining in some districts became more and more expensive and risky because of the sporadic and unrecorded working of the early industrial days. Unemployment reached appalling levels in the early 1930s; nearly 90% of the men in Rhondda then depended on coal for employment, and more than half of them lost their jobs. At Brynmawr 75% were unemployed; in the region as a whole there was no work for one man in three, and in the steel industry none for two in every three. Nearly half a million left for London and the industrial Midlands.

The worst-hit towns were those depending most directly on mining. Cardiff, Newport, and Barry increased in population between the censuses of 1931 and 1951, and have continued to increase subsequently. Swansea and Neath, losing numbers during the slump, have not yet fully recovered, while Llanelly, its population reduced by 10% in the period 1931–1951, has not reversed the falling trend. Far higher losses, however, were recorded in the mining towns, rising to more than 20% in Ebbw Vale and Rhondda. At very few places on the coalfield is population tending to increase at the present time.

Nevertheless, the industrial scene has changed profoundly. The threat of large-scale unemployment seems far more remote than at any time in the inter-war period. Industrial recovery and industrial change, greatly stimulated by the demands of World War II and by deliberate encouragement in the post-war years, were actually under way before 1939. Government aid was given to a mixed range of light industry, producing such goods as clothing and foodstuffs. The war gave new life to old industries, produced new industrial premises, and introduced a new variety into manufacturing. Whereas coal-mining, steel-making, and plating employ 175,000 people, other industries now take nearly 200,000.

With 400 new factories established by Government action alone, it is impossible to specify all the kinds of development. The Treforest Estate outside Cardiff exemplifies the success of official schemes. Independent firms have established, at Pontypool, manufactures of plate glass and of nylon; the production of nylon yarn in the Pontypool works is largely responsible for Britain's rank as the second greatest producer of this commodity in the world.

The new town of Cwmbran, 5 miles from Newport on the Abergavenny road, with a planned population of 35,000, is being built to solve problems of travel to work rather than those of unvaried industry.

The coal-mining, steel-making, and plating industries are being reorganised and expanded. The coal output planned for South Wales is 32 million tons a year; this is well below the record output of 57 million tons in 1913, but represents a healthier state for the mines than that of 1939. Because of the obsolete condition or limited reserves of some pits, 60 collieries have been or will be closed. Others are being modernised and increasingly mechanised; the power-loading which is already widely practised has enabled output per man-shift to rise greatly. Prospects are best in the anthracite field of the west, and on the southern rim of the main part of the field where much coking coal is still available. It is hoped to raise the level of exports to between 10 and 15 million tons a year; in the meantime about half the coal raised in South Wales goes for local use, and a quarter to power stations in Wales, on the Channel coast of England, and on the Thames.

Present Status of the Iron and Steel Industry

Little iron is now smelted on the northeastern rim of the coalfield. The combined output of blast-furnaces here, at Cardiff, and in the Port Talbot-Briton Ferry area amounts to some 20% of the total for Great Britain. The hematite worked near the southern margin of the coalfield in Glamorganshire is far too limited to meet the local demand for ore, which is imported from Sweden, Spain, French Africa, Newfoundland, and France. Similarly, the blast-furnaces of South Wales produce too little pig-iron for the local steel-making industry, and pig-iron is brought in, mainly from the Northamptonshire ironstone field, but local output is steadily expanding. Imported scrap metal is used in great quantities.

Steel furnaces occur on the northeast margin of the coalfield, but the main concentration is in the coastal belt, where Newport, Cardiff, Briton Ferry, Port Talbot, Neath, Swansea and Llanelly are all great steel-producers. South Wales produces about a quarter of Britain's total output of crude steel, almost the whole of the tinplate, and nearly two-thirds of the hot mill make of steel sheets. Great changes have occurred in the steel and plating industries since the depressed years of the early 1930s, for industrial recovery has been accompanied and much assisted by modernisation. Many of the older plants were ill-organised, poorly sited, and working with outworn machinery. In 1936 a new integrated iron and steel works, built on a coastal site at Cardiff, was opened. In 1938 an integrated works was completed at Ebbw Vale, including coke ovens, rebuilt blast furnaces, a basic Bessemer converter, a continuous strip mill, and plating works. An electrolytic tinning plant has been added here since the end of World War II. Four great companies combined to form the Steel Company of Wales, which is responsible for the Margam complex of new factories. The Abbey works at Margam itself, built on an area of marshland and sandhills adjoining Port Talbot, begin with blast-furnaces and end with the continuous strip mill and rolling mills, where the strip can be rolled into light and medium steel plates. Plant for the cold reduction of Margam strip into tinplate has been built at Trostre, near Llanelly, and at Velindre, near Swansea. A new hot strip mill at Llanevern, near Newport, has a planned eventual capacity of 12 million tons of ingot steel a year. Gas from the new coke ovens at Margam and Cardiff is fed into the system of pipelines which now serves South Wales. A new railway marshalling yard was opened at Margam in 1960.

Towns and Industrial Employment[1]

The towns of Industrial South Wales fall into two groups, one located on or very near the coalfield, the other along the coast. Although the coast and the southern edge of the coalfield converge towards the west, there is in practice no significant overlap between the two groups of towns, for the coastal towns offer little employment to miners (Fig. 88).

The group of coalfield towns can, in turn, be subdivided. Along the northeastern rim of the field stand Aberdare, Merthyr Tydfil, Tredegar, Ebbw Vale, and Abergavenny. In the first three of these, collieries employ between one-fifth and one-quarter of all workers, taking twice as many as do metal-work and engineering. The two occupational classes account for one in three of all workers in

[1] For recent trends, see bibliography at H. W. E. Davies and D. F. Hagger.

Fig. 88. Employment (all occupations) in Industrial South Wales

Aberdare, Merthyr, and Tredegar, and also at Ebbw Vale, where, however, the workers concerned are equally divided between mining and the metal trades. In Abergavenny, commercial and financial work needs more people than do mining and the metal trades together, as the town is a centre of distribution.

The second set of coalfield towns, scattered across the centre of the field or located near its southern edge, includes Pontypool, Caerphilly, Pontypridd, Gelligaer, Mountain Ash, and Rhondda. In these, mining and the metal trades are again dominant, taking some one-third of all workers (Fig. 88). Rhondda, Caerphilly, Mountain Ash and Gelligaer resemble Aberdare and Merthyr Tydfil in having a high proportion of miners.

The highest percentages of mining employment in the coastal towns are found at Port Talbot (3½%) and Neath (3%). All coastal towns are heavily committed to the metal industries, which take at least 10% of their workers, but some have very strong interests in other activities. Llanelly, Neath, and Port Talbot employ between one-fifth and one-quarter of all their workers in metal-manufacture and engineering, which are as dominant here as mining is on the northeast of the coalfield. The metal trades take one-sixth of the workers in Swansea and Newport, where they head the list of occupational classes, but transport employs more people than the metal industries in Barry, while commercial and financial occupations lead in Penarth and Bridgend. In Cardiff, one in three is employed in commerce, finance, or clerical work. The town had already developed the characteristics of a regional — if not of a national—capital, before it gained official status as capital of Wales.

All the towns in the coastal group have access to some part of the coalfield. All but Neath and Bridgend are on the coast itself, and all but Barry are on the main coast road. Both Neath and Bridgend are served by main-line railway; the former is connected by the Neath valley with the northeastern coalfield, and the latter is without a nearby rival of equal size. But Cardiff, Newport, and Swansea are outstandingly large among the towns of Industrial South Wales. They include about a third of all the people in the region. Except for Newport, which is surpassed in numbers by Rhondda, they are more populous than any of the remaining towns.

Their success has, no doubt, been promoted in part by their focal positions, although it is hard to say exactly how location has produced its effects. Like Llanelly, Briton Ferry, Port Talbot, and Barry—all of them industrial ports—Cardiff, Newport and Swansea are set at the junction of firm rising ground with flat, low-lying coastal and riverine alluvium. Much of this part of the shore is fringed with marine mud, and the lower ends of the valleys are filled with river-laid sediments. Dock-making began in the mid-19th century, in response to the increasing demands of the coal-export trade and of metal-works. At all seven ports, the docks were dug in the weak sediments fringing the coast.

At the beginning of the 19th century, Swansea already had 6,000 inhabitants. With an interest in copper-smelting dating back nearly a

FIG. 89. Swansea and its local setting

hundred years, it was significantly larger than Cardiff (less than 2,000 people) and Newport (just over 1,000). Although copper-smelting has been lost, Swansea retains the making of copper goods. Zinc concentrates are smelted, yielding zinc for galvanising and sulphuric acid for use in making tinplate. Swansea is a great centre of steel-making, most of the steel going to tinplate mills. The export trade in anthracite is only half what it was in the 1930s, but oil refining flourishes.

Swansea's growth occurred mainly during the 19th century. Its present population is just over the figure for 1931, and the steel-works and plating-mills built in the vicinity since 1945 are expected to encourage new expansion. The town has spread in two main directions—along the coast on both sides of the Tawe, and up the

FIG. 90. Cardiff and its local setting

valley alongside the canal, railway and main road. Suburbs have
appeared on the hilly ground west of the river-mouth (Fig. 89).
Cardiff (Fig. 90) experienced phenomenal expansion during the
19th century. In the first fifty years its numbers increased 15-fold, and
a further 7-fold increase converted a population of some 30,000 at
mid-century to one of 200,000 in 1900. In later years the rate of
growth declined, for no more than 50,000 inhabitants were added in
the first half of the 20th century.

Among the measures taken in response to industrial growth were
the construction of the Taff Vale Railway in 1840–41, and the making
of the first dock, in 1839. Given docks, and a railway link with its
mining hinterland, Cardiff was very well placed to develop a most
vigorous export trade in coal, at a time when the demand for bunker
coal was rising fast. Its metal industries date from the latter part

FIG. 91. Newport and its local setting

of the 19th century, although it served as the outlet for the Merthyr Tydfil works from the time of their foundation in 1759. Engineering in Cardiff includes ship-repairing and the making of railway wagons, oil engines, vehicles, and electrical gear. As would be expected from a regional capital, there is a great range of light industry.

The heart of the town is located on a patch of river-terrace, between the valleys of the Taff and the Rhymney, above the level of the coastal alluvium where the docks and many of the factories are found. The immediate surroundings are much less industrialised than are those of Swansea.

Newport, on the tidal Usk (Fig. 91), commands routes along the valleys of the Usk itself, of the Ebbw, and of the Lywd. Two miles upstream lies the Roman stronghold Isca Silurum (Caerleon), where, as at Newport, firm ground closely approaches the river on both sides. In many respects the industrial history of Newport resembles that of Cardiff, and, like Cardiff, Newport owes its present size mainly to 19th-century growth. But Newport, unlike its larger neighbour, has not developed that complex range of employment which typifies a highly successful town. It has ship-repairing facilities and a modest shipbuilding industry.

Cardiff, Newport and Swansea have much in common in their port trade. Leading imports include crude petroleum, pig-iron, steel bars, ores and concentrates of non-ferrous metals, grain, and timber. Among the chief exports are refined oil, iron and steel manufactures, tinplate, coal, coke, and patent fuel. Large amounts of general merchandise are handled. Judged by value of trade, Swansea far surpasses the other two as a port. The total port trade of the three is not much inferior to that of Southampton, and is considerably greater than that of Bristol.

THE WELSH BORDER

Area: about 2,800 square miles.
Population: about 500,000.
Largest towns: Shrewsbury (49,750).
            Hereford (40,500).
            Wrexham (35,500).
            Malvern (24,500).
            Oswestry (11,250).
            Ludlow (6,750).
            Leominster (6,500).
            Monmouth (5,500).

Three-quarters of this region is in improved farmland, with tillage rather less than half as extensive as grassland.

Numbers of livestock: cattle, 520,000; sheep, 1,000,000; pigs, 180,000.

Physique

The structure, pattern of geological outcrops, and relief-pattern of this region are, in detail, very complicated indeed. Rocks exposed at the surface vary greatly in their resistance to erosion. Quite severe dissection has left the stronger rocks rising abruptly above the deep valleys cut in weak outcrops. Carboniferous rocks dip off the Welsh block in the north, the Carboniferous Limestone forming impressive west-facing scarps, and the Coal Measures constituting the Flint and Denbigh coalfields. Hills project northeastwards in south Shropshire, where a fine belt of scarpland is developed on Primary sediments in the Wenlock country. The pattern is confused by the appearance of pre-Cambrian rocks, including the metamorphics of The Wrekin and The Lawley, and also by considerable faulting; Carboniferous sediments, including Coal Measures, occur patchily and disappear beneath the Permo-Trias of the adjacent plains. The immediate environs of Shrewsbury belong to the Midland Triangle, but there is no powerful objection to linking the town itself to the Welsh Borderland.

North of the defile cut by the Severn at Ironbridge through the prong of Primary rocks, drainage of the Border country is collected either by the Dee or by the upper Severn. Below the defile, the Severn receives the Teme and Lead as principal left-bank tributaries, with the Wye and Usk entering its estuary. These rivers drain various parts of the highly-dissected Old Red Sandstone country which is somewhat loosely known as the Herefordshire Plain. A better although more cumbersome term would be the Plains of Herefordshire and Monmouthshire, for maps on a scale of about 1 : 2,000,000 show quite clearly that part of the basin of the lower Usk is quite as deeply dissected and as widely opened as is the middle basin of the Wye. In these two areas the country is by no means flat; the lower ground is based generally upon marls, while strong sandstones and conglomerates interbedded with the marls stand up as hills. Folding, faulting, and lateral variations of rock strength combine with dissection to produce alternating broken hills and stretches of wide valley. This irregular terrain is partly enclosed on the east by elongated compact blocks of resistant rock which separate it from the Midland Triangle, but, even when no such blocks intervene, there is an immediate change in the texture of relief as one passes from the subdued Permo-Trias country to the hill districts of the Old Red Sandstone. The two principal barriers are formed by the Malverns and the Forest of Dean. The Malverns are composed of an upthrust slice of highly metamorphosed pre-Cambrian rocks, which rises as a long ridge to summits exceeding 1,000 feet in height. The Forest of Dean is synclinal in structure, with

Coal Measures preserved in the centre and with the top planed off by erosion at about 800–900 ft. As is well known, the Wye has been superimposed obliquely across it and exposes the Carboniferous Limestone in sheer cliffs in its valley meanders.

Climate and Soils

There is a very rapid climatic transition across the Welsh Border-land from the Welsh Massif to the Midland Triangle. In the Border-land itself the effect of rain-shadow is strongly felt, and annual totals of precipitation fall sharply from about 50 inches along the edges of the plateaus to some 35 inches along the eastern boundary. The number of rain-days falls below 200 a year, the number of mornings with snow lying falls to about 10, and the average length of the frost-free season rises above 5 months (Figs. 11–13). In all these ways the Borderland is far better favoured than is the heart of Wales, but ranges of temperature increase with distance from the sea, mainly because of increasing winter cold. The most valuable improvement of all is one not usually recorded in atlas maps, namely, a rise in actual temperatures during the warmer months. This rise is due partly to the release of latent heat to the air over the Welsh plateau, and partly to the decrease in altitude in the Border country.

Parts of the Border are well favoured in their soils. In the natural state, many of the soils of this region belonged to the group of Brown Forest Soils formed under deciduous woodland. As agri-cultural material they are mainly warm, having developed on glacial drift derived from the Permo-Trias in the north, and on Old Red Sandstone or drift derived from it in the south. In many places they are of the sandy loam grade, stiff enough to support plants but coarse enough to respond rapidly to rising air-temperature. With such soils, and in the climate of a rain-shadow area, the Welsh Borderland has become a notable farming region. The generally prosperous look of its fields owes something to the high standards maintained on the best farms, and something also to the vigorous growth of hardwood timber in hedgerows and small woods (cf. Plate 35). Trees are especially numerous because parts of this region underwent enclosure at an early date (cf. Chap. 4), with the result that fields tend to be on the small side and hedges a prominent feature of the scene. The southern part of the region is perhaps best seen in spring, when the soil of newly-ploughed fields shows reddish-pink and combines in a patchwork with the solid green of pasture and the delicate tints of sprouting crops.

Land Use

On the general maps of agricultural distributions (Figs. 37–41) the Welsh Borderland shows up reasonably well, partly because of the contrast with the Welsh Massif, and partly because it is very roughly comparable to the three counties of Shropshire, Herefordshire, and Monmouthshire. It differs from the Midland Triangle not so much in its proportion of land in farms as in the aims of its farming. Its improved grassland is used chiefly for cattle-grazing. Dairy cattle far outnumber beefstock in the northern part of the region, where many of the industrial towns of the Midlands, Lancashire, and Cheshire lie within a radius of 50 miles. In all parts, dairy cattle have increased in numbers and fodder crops have increased in extent since the beginning of World War II. Dairy cattle outnumber beefstock by two to one in the Herefordshire Plain, but the rearing and fattening of the native Herefordshire breed still flourishes.

The most extensive single crops are grains—wheat, barley, oats, and mixed corn. Roots and green crops for stockfeeding are widely grown, as also are potatoes and sugar beet. The northern part of the region has particularly large numbers of poultry, which produce eggs for the great urban markets. The large numbers of sheep recorded for the region represent an extension into the bordering hills of the sheep-farming typical of the Welsh interior, and to some extent correspond to the presence of rather poor pasture in some hilly areas.

One highly distinctive feature of the farming of this region is the fruit-production of Herefordshire. The dairying and poultry-farming of the north is to be compared with the town-controlled economy of the farms of the Lancs.-Cheshire Plain, and the fruit-growing in the south should be likened to that of the Avon valley about Evesham. Orchard fruit is more typical than small fruit, and the chief product is cider apples. The Herefordshire Plain is rather too liable to late frosts to become an outstanding producer of soft fruit, and it is in any case traditionally committed to the cider industry which absorbs a large part of its apple crop. Some of the firms which produce cider for the national market have their own orchards in Herefordshire. The great physical advantages of orchard cultivation include warm soils, shelter supplied by hills, and cold-air drainage across sloping ground (cf. Fig. 92). Hop-growing, also extensively practised, benefits in the same ways.

Towns and Industries

Wrexham stands on the Flint and Denbigh Coalfield, where coal-mining was known as early as the 14th century. During the early 17th century coal was shipped out via the Dee; the field played a part in the industrialisation of the 18th century, but the exposed part of the field is now largely worked out, and future prospects

▨ Arable	rg *Rotation grass*	M *Meadow (permanent grass)*	h *Heath (all rough grazing)*
F *Forest (all woodland)*	g *Gardens*	o *Orchards*	*Waste (non-agricultural land)*

0 ¼ ½ MILES

FIG. 92. Land-use sample for the Herefordshire Plain

are doubtful. The best that can be hoped for is some 2 million tons a year, partly from the one colliery in Flintshire which works coal under the Dee estuary. Some coal is sent to the industrial towns of Lancashire and Cheshire, but most is used locally. Iron ore is smelted at Mostyn, smelting and steel-making are carried on at Brymbo, and Shotton has a fully-integrated works, where the processes begin with smelting and end with the production of continuous steel strip. Wrexham's main industries are metal-manufacture and mining; industrial chemicals are also produced.

The site of Shrewsbury on a meander-core of the incised Severn has been described on p. 66. For centuries its defensive properties were of much importance. The original British settlement was taken by Offa during the Dark Ages, when he pushed the boundary of Mercia westward across the region. The Norman Earl Roger of Montgomery made Shrewsbury his principal stronghold, and it was involved in the Border disputes of the Middle Ages. Prosperity under the Tudors and in the 18th century is recorded by Tudor and 18th-century architecture in the central parts. Later expansion has, perforce, occurred outside the loop of the encircling river, residential suburbs and new factories arising on the north bank. Shrewsbury today is the urban focus of a large area, with flourishing cattle- and produce-markets. Its manufactures include safes, vehicles, and machine tools, modern industry being strongly influenced by the spread of engineering in large towns generally.

Hereford is approached by ridge-routes and valley-routes from all parts of the surrounding Plain. This cathedral centre is, like

Shrewsbury, notable for its markets. Its most distinctive industries, depending on local agriculture, include brewing, cider-manufacture, the canning of fruit and vegetables and the milling of flour.

Oswestry is less centrally placed than is Shrewsbury, and Leominster and Ludlow compare similarly with Hereford. There was no call for more than one large town in either part of the region, and none has developed. Monmouth during the Middle Ages was a heavily-fortified Border stronghold, but has remained small in subsequent times. Its defensive site at the junction of the Wye and Monnow has lost its value, as has the site of Chepstow, whose castle guarded a more southerly crossing of the Wye.

Malvern includes part of a group of resorts, originally dependent on the fame of the local springs but now expanding steadily under their own impetus. These settlements, finely placed along the lower flanks of the hills and overlooking rural countryside, differ in every possible way from the settlements of the Forest of Dean coalfield. The Forest itself is well-managed, although patches of young conifers are inevitably supplanting some of the older hardwood forest; against the background of trees the mining settlements look incongruous, for small pieces of early 19th-century town seem to have been scattered at random through the countryside. There are signs of former iron-working in abandoned tips and foundries, and of former coal-working in abandoned drifts. The drift-working by the free miners and in the three working pits produces little more than half-a-million tons a year, and future prospects are poor.

CHAPTER 14

The Scottish Highlands

Area: about 20,000 square miles.
Population: about 850,000.
Largest towns: Aberdeen (187,000).
  Inverness (28,600).
  Peterhead (12,900).
  Elgin (11,700).
  Fraserburgh (10,400).
  Wick (7,900).
  Oban (6,000).
  Lerwick (Shetlands) (5,600).
  Stornoway (Hebrides) (5,300).
  Kirkwall (Orkneys) (4,200).

Outside these towns the average density of population is about 30 p.s.m.; large areas are uninhabited.

Less than 15% of the region is in improved farmland, most being in rough grazing (including deer forests). Grassland is rather more extensive than tillage in the farmland as a whole.

Numbers of livestock: cattle, 720,000; sheep, 3,645,000; pigs, 215,000.

In several ways the Scottish Highlands resemble the upland block of Wales. Each of the two forms a massif, each has been denuded under the control of a falling base-level, and both have been glaciated. In both, the northeast-southwest Caledonian trends of geological structure are reflected in the grain of the relief. In the Scottish Highlands, as in Wales, the resistant rocks of the higher plateaus sink eastwards under a cover of Old Red Sandstone on which is based a distinctive eastern border (Fig. 6). But of these two massifs the Scottish Highlands possess the more resistant rocks, rise the higher, and have been much the more heavily glaciated. Correspondingly, the Scottish Highlands are scenically more attractive than Wales, but far more severe climatically and far poorer agriculturally (cf. also Figs. 36, 43).

Physique

Most of the region is based on ancient metamorphosed rocks which have been invaded in places by large bodies of granite. Parts of two distinct structural belts are present (Chap. 2). The Hebrides

227

and the extreme northwestern coastland, a rigid crustal block composed of Torridonian Sandstone and Lewisian gneiss, represent the foreland of the Caledonides. The main mass of the Highlands is based on the highly altered and much deformed rocks of the Moine and Dalradian Series, which were incorporated in the northwest flank of the Caledonian mountain system. The block is transected by Glen More, a hundred-mile-long trench which, eroded along the line of a fault, separates the Northern Highlands from the Grampians. These latter are notable for the huge outcrops of granite which deep denudation has revealed. On their southeastern side the Grampians overlook the lower ground of Central Scotland on the line of the Highland Boundary Fault.

One result of the intense glaciation of the Scottish Highlands is the presence of deep fiords all along the west coast. These flooded ends of glacier troughs cut deep into the land, leading towards the great fault-guided glens in many of which occur ribbon lakes—the freshwater lochs. The rugged and irregular west coast is still further diversified by the impressive ruins of Tertiary volcanoes in Skye, Mull, and Arran; typical features of highland glaciation are particularly well developed in the Cuillin Hills of Skye.

Severe and general glaciation of the interior included the scouring of plateau-surfaces, the cutting of corries in peaks rising above the ice-cap, the deepening of main valleys—including Glen More—and the excavation of numerous lake-basins. North of Glen More the land has been greatly impoverished by the general removal of weathered rock. Here, in the Northern Highlands, passes were cut through the main watershed by tongues of ice streaming westward. South of the Great Glen, compact blocks of high ground in the Cairngorms and in the Ben Nevis District, rising above 4,000 ft., were scalloped and fretted by ice and frost. Great lake-basins are typical of the southwestern part of the Grampians, while the deep but wide valleys of the Spey, Don and Dee lead down to the sea in the east (Fig. 93).

The east coast is less lofty and more regular than the west coast. Around Moray Firth the metamorphic rocks disappear beneath the sediments of the Old Red Sandstone, just as the massif of Southwest England vanishes eastward beneath the Permo-Trias. Even on the Aberdeenshire coast, where crystalline rocks reach the shore, there is no deep inlet of the fiord type.

Climate

In Scotland, as in Wales, climate deteriorates rapidly from the west coast inland. and the high ground of the interior divides the climate of the western coastlands from the contrasted climate of the lowland on the eastern fringes. The frost-free period in the west is about a month longer than that in the east (7 months against 6), and the west has the slightly smaller mean annual range of temperature. The west, however, is fully exposed to strong winds from the Atlantic, and is cloudy and rainy, with more than 50 inches of precipitation a year. The extreme east is remarkably dry, with as little as 25 inches on the coast itself.

FIG. 93. The Scottish Highlands: Physique (much generalised) and main settlements. Compare Figs. 6, 20

In the interior is developed the worst climate in the whole of the British Isles. Latitude and height combine to bring the annual total of precipitation to well above 100 inches in the wettest districts, which include Ben Nevis and the summits immediately beyond the Great Glen. Farther eastwards, although the highest ground still lies high, precipitation diminishes. It has been lost on the western flanks of the highlands, where the ascending air of the westerlies becomes unstable and releases most of its moisture. The wettest areas of all, therefore, lie somewhat to the west of the main axis of high ground; they are the areas of most frequent cloud, with the sun obscured for three-quarters of the time, and of the most frequent precipitation, with rain or snow on two days out of three.

Very many places in the interior record lying snow on at least 20 mornings in the year, and in about half the region the number rises above 40 (Fig. 12). Even if the snow-cover were concentrated in a single, unbroken spell, it would last for six weeks in many places. Frost is very frequent, the frost-free period diminishing to 90 days in the high eastern parts of the Grampians (Fig. 11). Ben Nevis just fails to rise high enough to have a permanent snow-cap, and snow lies throughout the summer, in some years, in high sheltered gullies which face north. Throughout this whole region, deeply grooved as it is by glacier troughs or by large stream-valleys, local variations in climate, altitude, slope and soil count for much.

THE WEST

In the west, where high ground rises abruptly from the sea, the only possible sites for cultivation are raised beaches and valley-flats; the latter result from the redistribution of rock-waste in glacier troughs, the former from the intermittent recovery of the crust from its heavy load of ice. Settlement in the west is concentrated near the shore. A typical location for a loose group of dwellings is at the inner edge of a patch of raised beach, with little tilled fields on the seaward side and rough grazing on the hills behind (Fig. 94). The main tillage crops are oats and potatoes, which may be combined with hay in some kind of rotation; most of the hay crop, however, is taken from permanent grass. Cattle are confined to low levels, while sheep graze on the hillsides.

Part-time and spare-time farms account for more than three-quarters of all holdings. Family labour is widely employed, being most common in the northwest of the Highland region.

Crofting

The present farming practices in the western coastlands owe much to crofting, which developed not only a system of land-management

Rough grazing   Hay (Skullomie only)   Oats or potatoes (Skullomie only)

0   ¼   ½ MILE

FIG. 94. Crofting settlements on raised beach, Northern Highlands of Scotland

but also a style of domestic architecture. Crofting in its pure form is a kind of subsistence farming. It is well suited to unproductive land remote from large towns, being designed for self-sufficiency and not relying on cash transactions. The arable land of a croft can produce a vegetable crop comparable to that taken from an English allotment, although less varied. The oat and hay crops provide oatmeal and winter feed. Cattle supply milk, with meat from time to time, and the sheep yield meat in addition to the wool used for hand-made clothing. Dwelling-house and cowshed were traditionally combined in the stone-built *black house*, which externally was quite similar to the typical country cottage of Ireland. Despite the name, the black house was often whitewashed on the outside. It was the inside which was blackened by the smoke from peat fires. The dividing wall between the two parts—one occupied by humans and one by animals—rose but to the level of the eaves. Today, many black houses are used only to shelter cattle, and cottages of a more modern type have been built by the crofters for their own use.

To people living in English towns, the idea of self-sufficient agriculture often seems romantic and attractive, but a visit to the poorer rural areas of Ireland or of the Scottish Highlands would soon make it clear that the actual inhabitants have no illusions. Many are bound to their birthplaces by ties of affection or of habit, but many others leave. Crofting represents a close adaptation to a highly characterised environment, and in consequence is greatly interesting to the geographer, but to the people of the crofts it offers very little. The poor land and the harsh climate lay a heavy burden of work on crofters, who cannot hope to share the material wealth of better-favoured regions.

Improvements in communications have been followed by emigration. Roads and railways have not brought wealth in—they have led many of the people away. The number of crofters in the region today is less than 6,500, while the number of crofters' sons and daughters at work on the crofts is but 500. Scottish crofts are fast losing both their labour-supply and their potential inheritors.

The crofting system has been modified considerably during the last two centuries. Some holdings have been converted to commercial farming, where produce can be sold off the farm in a nearby town, but the scope for commercial farming is limited, since there are few towns on the west coast. The rise of Oban and Mallaig as commercial fishing ports has tended to reduce the number of fishermen-crofters, for fishing has become a full-time occupation—whether in inshore fishing, in deep-sea fishing, or in Antarctic whaling. The number of fishermen-crofters in the whole Highland region is less than 250. Fish caught for home consumption remain, however, an important item of diet in the coastal settlements. Spinning and weaving for domestic use is dying out, but hand-made goods are produced for the luxury markets of the great British towns (Plate 36).

In these various ways, the principle of self-sufficiency has been losing force. Hill sheep, largely kept on common grazing, are the main interest of the Highland croft today. Even where it is best represented—in the Hebrides, the Orkneys, and the Shetlands—crofting is something of a survival from a past age; and even in the islands, it is disappearing under the influence of commercial fishing, tourism, and hydro-electricity. The Hebrides and the west coast of the Scottish mainland are freely accessible in summer to pleasure cruisers, which ply from Glasgow and Fort William. Skye and the Ben Nevis group are much favoured by climbers. The roads of the mainland are frequented by tourists, whether in private cars or in coaches. Coach touring in the Highlands has boomed in the post-war period, and many hotels are wholly given over to feeding and lodging coach-parties. The tourist trade, however, is strictly seasonal, and commercial fishing is concentrated in a few ports. Agriculture in some form or other is still the greatest employer.

Hydro-Electric Power

Factory industry has been slow and limited in its development on the west coast. It is represented mainly by the aluminium works at Kinlochleven and Fort William. The use of hydro-electric power in the processing of aluminium at these two places suggests a comparison with Norway, which the west Scottish coast generally resembles. The factories, H.E.P. stations, dams and aqueducts, constructed in the inter-war period, rely on the heavy precipitation on the high ground behind the coast, and on water-storage in ribbon lakes. The lake-levels are raised and controlled by dams, water being led to the Fort William plant by a tunnel round the flank of Ben Nevis. Aluminium ore (bauxite) comes by sea to the factory piers. The two sets of works are excellent examples of industrial location, for the long inlets on which they stand penetrate the land deeply and reach to the very feet of the rainy mountains. These were the only successful developments of H.E.P. in the Highlands before the current Governmental projects were begun, but, for all their success, they have not resulted in the growth of large settlements.

THE INTERIOR

If the west coastlands are unrewarding, the interior of the Scottish Highlands is still more so. Considerable parts have no inhabitants at all. The Northern Highlands have been heavily dissected, and glaciers have cut deep trenches through the axis of high ground which runs from the head of Loch Linnhe in the south towards Loch Erribol in the north. Widely-spaced main roads run through some of these passes, linking the east coastal route with the tortuous west-coast road. Without the ice-deepened gaps, the west coast of the Northern Highlands would be remote indeed. As it is, the district is accessible to tourists. Its agricultural resources are low. Several of its corrie-bitten peaks rise above 3,000 ft. O.D. and carry arctic-alpine vegetation, while at medium levels, where the rocks have been heavily scoured by ice, fescue-agrostis grassland is common; at lower levels, molinia and sedge moorland come in (Fig. 20). There is little low ground in the interior of the Northern Highlands, and no cultivable flat ground except on the floors of the glacier troughs. The severe climate all but forbids tillage (cf. Plate 1).

The Grampians are higher and more compact than the Northern Highlands. Extensive remnants of old plateaus between the incised valleys record the erosional history of the Grampians; there is a wide distribution of bleak, exposed upland surfaces at about 3,000 ft. O.D., overlooked by the even bleaker and more exposed hill-masses of the Ben Nevis group and the Cairngorms which surpass 4,000 ft. Here, as in the Northern Highlands, peat soils are widely developed, and nearly all the land is classed as rough grazing. Fescue-agrostis and mountain fescue are typical of the west, while a decrease of rainfall towards the east brings in heather moor. Very little remains of the native forests of Scots pine. The stools of trees are often to be seen where peat has been cut or eroded away, showing how a centuries-old increase in rainfall diminished the extent of woodland; the trees which survived this change in the natural environment have been nearly all destroyed by felling or grazing in historical times. Coniferous forests have been planted on some hillsides, and oakwoods occur in some of the valleys in the east; Strathspey is quite well wooded, but a very great deal of the whole Highland region is bare of trees.

Where farmlands exist, half the farms are run as part-time or spare-time undertakings. Family labour is slightly less usual than in the west, but is still common.

Deer Forests

There are far fewer sheep than might be expected from the huge extent of rough grazing, even though the combined total of the various flocks is large. Between one-quarter and one-fifth of the entire Highlands are in deer forests, which cover 3 million acres of ground. The term *forest* used in this context does not indicate the presence of trees, but merely means *hunting preserve*. About 1¼ million acres of the 3 million could be used for grazing livestock, and a small fraction of the total area is so used; but sheep kept on land classed as deer forest number less than 150,000, and cattle less than 1,500. Very large expanses of the Highland region remain unproductive, used only for sporting purposes. The Spey, Don and Dee are noted for their salmon.

Loss of Population

As has been explained in Chap. 7, the post-war period has been marked by rapid progress in the development of H.E.P. in the Scottish Highlands (Plate 37). It is hoped that the spread of power lines and the distribution of current will help to check the movement of people from the region. With very few localised exceptions, the Highlands in general have been losing people by persistent emigration for well over a century. It remains to be seen whether the development of H.E.P. can reverse or even arrest the decline in numbers, for the factors which encourage emigration are as complex as they are powerful. Far more is involved than a shift from Highland country to Lowland town; the movement had its origins in the deliberate abolition of the structure of Highland society. This socially and economically disastrous abolition was the culminating act of centuries of hostility between Scotland and England. In a sense, therefore, it had its origins in the emergence of independent and hostile kingdoms. Little is known of events in Scotland during the Dark Ages, but the Picts and Scots united in about 850 in the Kingdom of Alban. In the course of complex medieval changes this became the Kingdom of Scotland, which was extended westwards when the Hebrides were ceded by Norway in the 13th century. On the south there was repeated war with the English until 1603, when the two kingdoms were joined under a single king. But peace had not yet come—risings

36. Domestic weaving—a crofter working a loom in the Hebrides.

7. View from the southwest across Quoich Dam, part of the Garry H.E.P. cheme. Glaciated mountains rise above cloudbase, with boulder clay swathing their lower slopes.

38. The fishing fleet in Aberdeen harbour.

took place in 1689, 1715 and 1745. After 1715 forts were built in the Highlands—e.g., at Fort William, Fort Augustus and Inverness—and military roads began to open up the region. After 1745 punitive measures of the harshest kind were enforced. Some chiefs had been killed at Culloden, others were banished and their lands confiscated; laws were passed to forbid the carrying of arms and the wearing of the tartan, and to abolish the powers of clan chiefs. It was perhaps inevitable that the clan system should be modified as the Highlands were brought into contact with the Scottish Lowlands and with England, but there can be no doubt that the aftermath of rebellion was a great increase in the rate of social change. The arrival of new landowners and the conversion of much land to sheep-pasture may well have been less influential than the suppression of the clan system. The Highlands illustrate the familiar process of a breakdown of economy associated with a breakdown of social order. One of the obvious responses was emigration, and in 20 years 20,000 people had left. With the disruption of society and with long-continued emigration has gone a decline in the Gaelic language. Only about 75,000 Gaelic-speakers exist today, and of these very few speak Gaelic alone.

The clan system was well adapted to the Highland terrain. The territorial unit was the Highland glen, occupied by a unit of society. Not every group living in its glen had full clan status, but all were integrated into the system, chiefs exercising patriarchal authority over their clansmen. Order within the clan was remarkably stable, even though feuds between clans seriously reduced the united social strength of the region as a whole, and the clan system prevailed for five hundred years. When it was destroyed, the Highlands were left as low in social strength as they are poor in natural resources. The greatest damage was done in the interior, where neither fishing nor cash-cropping could provide the basis for a new social and economic organisation.

THE EAST

The eastern side of the Highland region is better placed, both physically and economically, than the west coast, and is far better placed than the mountainous interior. Most of the inhabitants of the region live on the eastern side, which contains all the towns with more than 10,000 inhabitants, the only large town, nearly all the arable land, and nearly all the farm livestock.

The essential contrasts between west and east are apparent in the land-use figures for the counties of Argyll and Aberdeen. The former has 5% of its area in improved farmland, the latter 50%.

In Buchan—the northeastern projection of the Grampians towards Buchan Ness—most of the land is farmed. Farmland stretches through the coastal belt towards Moray Firth, around which it spreads over the low ground. It becomes sparse and patchy farther to the north, but reappears in the northeastern tip of the Northern Highlands and in the Orkneys. On the farms of all these localities, permanent grass is uncommon. Rotation grass and tillage each take about half the improved land, the leading tillage crops being oats, fodder roots (mainly turnips and swedes), potatoes, and barley.

The physical and agricultural contrasts between the western and eastern sides of the Scottish Highlands resemble the differences between the south of Norway and the lowlands of southern Sweden. In Scotland, as in Scandinavia, the eastern side has the more extensive low ground, the lower total of precipitation, the less humid air and the better soils. But the comparison should not be pushed too far— the eastern side of the Scottish Highlands is subjected to very little of the continental influence which so strongly affects the Swedish climate. Its mean annual range of temperature varies between 15° and 19°F.—little higher than ranges on the west coast; mean January temperature runs at about 38°F.; the average frost-free season is six months long at places near the sea; precipitation is frequent, coming on some 200 days a year. All these are characteristics of a maritime climate. On the other hand, the annual total of precipitation is low; in the immediate neighbourhood of the coast, it ranges from 25 inches at Buchan Ness and at the head of Moray Firth to 30 inches at Wick, and remains below 35 inches throughout the farming areas. The low totals express the powerful effect of rain-shadow produced by the interior highlands. Since most of the farmland lies below 400 feet, it is not very greatly affected by lifting, condensation, and precipitation occurring when air comes in from the North Sea.

Soils and Farming

The low precipitation makes tillage possible, the quality of the soils encourages it. Around the head of Moray Firth, and in the hinterland of Wick, the land is based on Old Red Sandstone, and local glacial deposits include a high proportion of rock-waste derived from that formation. Farther east, the drifts are derived from metamorphic rocks and from granites. Throughout the coastal belt of the eastern Highlands, therefore, the parent materials of the soils developed on glacial drift are generally coarse. In the natural state the soils belonged to the podsol group, and were strongly acid in reaction. They have been much improved by heavy fertilisation and wise management during the last hundred or hundred-and-fifty years, but although they have been enriched, little can be done about their texture. They will warm up quite readily, but remain too permeable and therefore too acid to be well suited to permanent grass. Tillage and ley-grass between them take nearly all the farmed acreage. Long leys are unusual, since the quality of their grass deteriorates.

Many of the farms are too far from urban markets to rely on dairy-ing, but some kind of stock-farming is dominant in most of the district as it is throughout Scotland generally (Fig. 95). Many farms produce winter feed for sheep, but cattle are more numerous than sheep except in the hills. The main beef breed is the well-known Aberdeen-Angus. There is a rough gradation from stock-rearing on the landward side, through a broad central belt of rearing and

N

Hill sheep-Farming

Stock-rearing,
stock-rearing and feeding

Cropping with livestock,
cropping and feeding

Dairying

Market-gardening, fruit-growing,
pig-farming, poultry-farming

0   10   20   30   40   50 MILES

FIG. 95. Types of farming in Scotland. Compare Figs. 36, 43

feeding, to coastal patches where cash-cropping is combined with fattening. Tillage is best favoured around the head of Moray Firth, where the soils are developed on débris of Old Red Sandstone, and where daytime temperatures of summer, rising higher than else-where in the district, enable the long days to compensate somewhat for the typical coolness of the season. Part of the oat crop is sold for milling into oatmeal.

Part-time and spare-time farms are far less common in the east than in the west and the interior. Family labour is also less usual, although it is still used—half the farms in the entire Highland region are worked by family labour.

Settlements

Settlements in the eastern part of the Highland region are generally small and well scattered. Every town is the urban focus of some piece of lowland, but in few cases do urban influences reach far afield. Coastal settlement is inhibited by long, smooth stretches of sandy shore, and the growth of coastal towns is restricted by the lack of demand for ports. Wick is scarcely holding its own in numbers of inhabitants. Peterhead and Fraserburgh record but slight increases in the last 25 years, despite the share they take in the herring fishery. Elgin, with woollen manufacture and tanning, has outgrown Fraserburgh, where pneumatic tools are made. Inverness profits both from its industries and from tourist traffic. It stands at the northeastern end of the Great Glen, which provides by far the easiest routeway from the western to the eastern side of the Highland region, and carries pleasure-steamers in summer on the Caledonian Canal. Manufactured products of Inverness include whisky, woollens, and welded metal goods.

Aberdeen

Aberdeen is growing only half as fast as Inverness, but has a long start. Until 1350 it was the most populous town in the whole of Scotland, and still ranks third after Glasgow and Edinburgh. It is the northernmost large town of the British Isles (Fig. 69), and is alone among the towns of the Highlands in providing a full range of urban services. Not least, it is a university town.

As its name shows, Aberdeen stands at the mouth of the Dee (Fig. 96). There was formerly a corresponding settlement, Aberdon, at the mouth of the river Don, but this has been absorbed by the larger town and now goes under the name of Old Aberdeen. Aberdeen has access to the wide lower reaches of the Dee and Don valleys, commands routes along the coastland, and is the main urban focus of the farmlands from Stonehaven to Elgin. In medieval times,

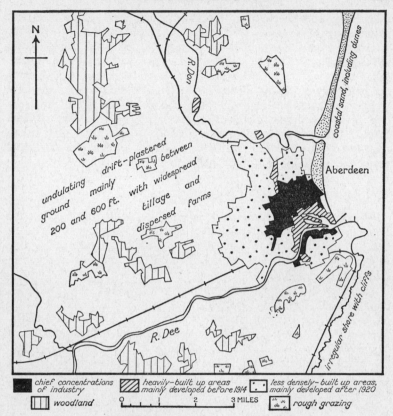

FIG. 96. Aberdeen and its local setting

Aberdeen merchants and Aberdeen ships were busy in the Baltic trade. The local shipbuilding and ancillary occupations achieved their greatest success with the construction of clippers. The change from wooden to metal ships depressed the Aberdeen yards, of which the three remaining today employ some 2,000 people. Timber-mills and paper-mills take the wood which is imported nowadays. Textile industry is represented by the working of linen and wool, hosiery and overcoating being leading products. But the textile and garment trades employ only 18% of the manufacturing workers of Aberdeen, and the timber trades only 14%, while metal manufacture and engineering employ 40%. No more than a few hundreds are directly employed in working the granites of Aberdeen and Peterhead.

Of the workers in metal in Aberdeen, about a quarter are employed in the shipyards. Three times as many are needed by the varied engineering industry, which produces oil engines, agricultural machinery and mechanical handling appliances. Light electrical engineering is tending to expand under the influence of H.E.P. generated in the Highlands. The dominance of engineering among the industries of Aberdeen brings the town into line with numerous other manufacturing centres in the British Isles, but Aberdeen is not primarily an industrial town. Dundee has nearly twice as many workers in manufacture, and Aberdeen is no more highly industrialised than is Edinburgh. Distributive trades and transport services employ twice as many people in Aberdeen as does manufacture; retail trade is vigorous, and in its functions of resort and tourist centre the town employs many people in personal service.

FISHING IN THE HIGHLAND REGION

Aberdeen is the greatest base of fishing vessels, not only in the Highlands, but also in the whole of Scotland. Nine out of every ten Scottish fishermen have their homes in the Highland region; one in every four lives in the county of Aberdeen, and one in seven in Aberdeen itself (Plate 38).

Aberdeen is the chief Scottish port for landings of white fish—cod, haddock, hake and plaice. Its trawlers go to the fishing-grounds off Iceland, the Faroes, Northwest Scotland, the Orkneys and the Shetlands. For several reasons trawling has fallen on hard times. The typical Aberdeen trawler is too small to reach far-off grounds; the high-grade white fish landed at Aberdeen is not bought by fish-and-chip shops, and in any case the town is far from the industrial towns of England.

The Scottish herring fishery, handicapped by being organised in small units, has also suffered a serious decline. Landings are shared by several little ports, among which are Mallaig, Stornoway, Wick, Lerwick, Stronsay (Orkney), Fraserburgh and Peterhead. Inshore fishing is still more widely dispersed; landings are made at very many places, mainly on the east coast of Scotland from Wick to Arbroath.

In explaining the decline of Highland sea-fishery, some allowance must be made for the effects of World War II and its aftermath. Many vessels were lost in the war years, when replacement was impossible, and post-war inflation greatly hampered recovery. The net results of the various difficulties are seen in the steep decline in numbers of fishermen—a decline amounting to 40% in the intercensal period 1931–51.

FUTURE PROSPECTS OF THE REGION

In these same 20 years, 1931–51, the Highlands as a whole provided no additional work for their inhabitants—numbers employed in

1951 were, indeed, slightly less than in 1931. Increased employment in the metal trades, building and contracting, and in professional, technical, and clerical occupations were counterbalanced by losses in fishing, farming, textile- and garment-manufacture, and in personal service. Agriculture remains the chief provider of work, taking one in five of all workers in the region. The Highlands are handicapped not only by poor agricultural resources in most parts, but also by lack of economic minerals. The metamorphic rocks of the Lewisian, Moine, and Dalradian series have little to offer except road-metal for local use. Granite from Aberdeen and Peterhead, although still much used for monumental stone, ornamental stone, and tarmacadam, is no longer required as setts for London streets. Minor deposits of metal ores, spasmodically worked in the past, are unlikely to provide much profitable mining in the future.

On the credit side stands a very great increase in the tourist trade, much of it since the 1951 census. Hydro-electric schemes have provided work for a time, and are rapidly bringing light and power to the whole region. It cannot yet be said, however, whether the Highland economy will in the long run reverse its tendency to contract.

CHAPTER 15

Central Scotland

Area: about 4,000 square miles.
Population: about 4,000,000.
Largest towns: (*a*) The Central Clydeside Conurbation (1,760,000), of
which the leading members are:—
    Glasgow (1,077,000).
    Paisley (96,900).
    Motherwell (72,750).
    Coatbridge (53,750).
    Clydebank (51,500).
    Airdrie (33,400).
(*b*) Other industrial towns located on or very near to
the coalfields:—
    Greenock (78,500).
    Kirkcaldy (52,500).
    Dunfermline (47,000).
    Kilmarnock (45,800).
    Ayr (44,500).
    Hamilton (41,600).
    Falkirk (37,600).
    Dumbarton (27,000).
(*c*) Remaining towns:—
    Edinburgh (469,500).
    Dundee (181,000).
    Perth (41,100).
    Stirling (27,100).

The average density of population outside these towns is above
225 p.s.m.

More than 60% of this region is in improved farmland, grassland
being much more extensive than tillage. The acreage of farmland
represents more than one-third of the total for Scotland.

Numbers of livestock: cattle 540,000; sheep, 970,000; pigs, 295,000.

This region, located between the Scottish Highlands and the
Southern Uplands, has several names. It has been variously called
the Midland Valley, the Central Valley, the Central Lowland, the
Mid-Lowland, the Scottish Midlands, and Central Scotland. None
of these possible titles has yet been generally accepted. The names
Lowlands of Scotland or *Scottish Lowlands* are not applied to this

40. Refinery plant for the production of high-grade motor spirit at Grangemouth.

39. A 32,000-ton oil-tanker being launched on the Clyde.

41. View across Edinburgh to the outcrops of volcanic rocks on Arthur's Seat.

42. Summer sheep fair at Rothbury, Northumberland.

region except by the misguided, for the Lowlands include the whole of Scotland south of the Highland Line. Two of the possible names have been selected for use in this book. The first of these is *The Midland Valley*, a term in general use by geologists to connote a well-defined crustal belt underlain and bounded by distinctive structures, which has already appeared in a geological context in Chapter 2. The name *Central Scotland* will be used for the geographical region.

Central Scotland accounts for about one-seventh of the total land area of Scotland, and contains some three-quarters of the total population. In many ways it compares favourably with the adjoining regions on the north and the south. Little of its land stands really high above sea-level, and the bleak mountain climates typical of the Highlands and of parts of the Southern Uplands are not widely represented. Although many of the soils were naturally poor in the uncultivated state, they do at least exist. There are large coalfields which provided one of the original bases of heavy industry, and long inlets which give access to busy sea-lanes. Central Scotland is the only one of the three Scottish regions where large numbers of people can make a living. In this region alone have numerous industrial towns arisen.

The present high total of population in Central Scotland is due mainly to natural increase within the region itself. If ever there was a time when the industrial towns owed their growth chiefly to migration from the two upland regions, that time has long since passed. During the 70 years from 1861 to 1931, for instance, the combined loss by migration from the Highlands and the Southern Uplands was about 850,000; during the same period, the population of Central Scotland rose by nearly 1,850,000. Thus, even if all the migrants from the upland regions had settled in Central Scotland, they would not have accounted for half the actual increase in population. But not all of them went to Central Scotland, and of those who did so, not all settled in the region. Central Scotland also lost people by migration, either to England or to places overseas. Perhaps a quarter of its net increase in population during the last century is to be ascribed to migration within Scotland, the remaining three-quarters being due to the regional excess of births over the combined loss by death and migration.

During periods of industrial depression in the inter-war period, standards of diet in the towns of Central Scotland were commonly lower than those on the coastal crofts of the Highlands. But there was no migration from Central Scotland to the crofting districts— rather did people leave the region for towns in England or for places overseas. The drift from the land and into towns involved far more

I

than a change of work, a choice of occupation, and—in times of prosperity—a better standard of living than the countryside could provide. Living in towns is today a firmly-rooted social habit. Consequently people will move from one town to another, but will rarely go from the town to the country. Very many, of course, never consider the possibility of moving far from the places where they were born, but, when movement occurs, the highly urbanised region of Central Scotland is able to retain many of its own natives and to attract Scots from elsewhere. Even if they were fully understood, the possible disadvantages of life in an industrial town would be unlikely to outweigh the attractions.

The greatest social and industrial resources of Central Scotland today consist in towns and industries already in being. Both the manufacturing and the farming of this region represent the results of generations of effort, during which natural advantages have been realised, and difficulties of various kinds have been overcome. Here, as in other industrialised parts of the British Isles, profound changes have occurred in the nature, aims, and economic relations of the regional industry. The story of industrial growth has been far more complex than the mere rise of manufacturing on coalfields or on tidewater. The present status of farming has been attained by adaptation to the regional climate and by deliberate improvements of the soils. Nevertheless, it was the presence of coal and iron-ore which made possible the first growth of modern industry, just as the nature of the climate and of the soil made it possible for farming to become profitable.

Physique

The Midland Valley is a structural depression, bounded on the northwest by the Highland Boundary Fault and on the southeast by the Southern Uplands Fault. The line of the Highland Boundary Fault corresponds to the Highland Edge, where a sharp descent of a thousand feet or more marks the dissected margin of the Grampian block. The Southern Uplands Fault, separating the Midland Valley from the intensely-crumpled Ordovician and Silurian rocks of the Southern Uplands, is more clearly marked on the geological map than on the ground, for the physical boundary on this side of Central Scotland is obscured by hill-masses within the region.

Between the two faulted boundaries, a strip of crust some 35 to 50 miles wide has been depressed. Sediments laid down in the sagging trough belong chiefly to the Old Red Sandstone and Carboniferous systems. Subsidence was greatest in the centre, so that Old Red Sandstone appears at the surface along either margin and Carboniferous rocks are exposed in a broad central belt. Volcanic

eruptions accompanied crustal movement, with the result that lavas
and tuffs (solidified volcanic dust) are interbedded with the sediments in many places; the outbreaks continued well into Permian
times. Generally speaking, the volcanic rocks are more resistant than
the sedimentaries, and underlie the groups of hills which diversify
the relief of the region. The Sidlaw Hills and the Ochils are based
on volcanic rocks of Old Red Sandstone age, while the Campsie
Fells, the Kilpatrick Hills, and the Renfrew Hills are underlain by
Carboniferous volcanics. These five hill-groups are aligned from
southwest to northeast across the northern part of the region,
separated from the margin of the Grampians by a long vale eroded

FIG. 97. Central Scotland, the Southern Uplands, and the Border Country:
physique and main settlements

in Old Red Sandstone (Fig. 97). Their sides rise abruptly from the surrounding lower ground, and tabular summits exceed 2,000 ft. O.D. in the Ochils.

The patterns of geology and relief along the southeastern border of the Midland Valley are complex. Here too occur outcrops of sedimentary Old Red Sandstone and of volcanic rocks, but there is no strip of lowland to define the regional boundary. The Pentland Hills rise above 1,800 ft. on lavas and tuffs, Tinto Hill reaches a summit more than 2,000 ft. high on intrusive igneous rock, and Cairn Table approaches 2,000 ft. on resistant Old Red Sandstone sediments. A dissected belt of hilly country runs northwestwards from Cairn Table between the Ayr and Lanark coalfields, crossing upfaulted Silurian rocks on to volcanics of Carboniferous age.

Between the two flanking belts lie the coalfields. Each field is a structural basin, bounded by tracts where coal-bearing rocks thin out and disappear. The older rocks surrounding the coalfields offer no prospects of concealed reserves. The structural pattern of each coal-field is complicated by minor folding and faulting, and the Fife and Midlothian field is broken across by the wide estuary of the Forth.

Little is directly known of the geological history of the region after Permian times. It seems highly likely that the Highlands and the Southern Uplands were uplifted during the Tertiary period, when volcanoes broke out in the Hebrides and basalt flows occurred in Antrim. Presumably the Midland Valley was also uplifted, but, if so, its fill of weak sediments has long been denuded away. Differential erosion during the Tertiary period produced a pattern of relief generally similar to that of the present day.

Many of the hilltops are gently-sloping and display accordant summits—signs of partial planation in previous cycles of erosion, whether the platforms represent old wave-cut benches, or whether they are the remains of old land-surfaces. Most of the ground is between 1,800 and 200 ft. above sea-level, although patches lower than 200 ft. occur near the shore and in the bottoms of large valleys. Many of the details of surface form are due to glacial and fluvio-glacial deposits, but the erosional platforms are well in evidence in a general view of the landscape, their gentle slopes impeding soil-drainage in many places.

Just as the erosional platforms truncate rocks and structures in profile, so do the main lines of drainage cut across the grain of relief in plan. The North and South Esk, the Tay and the Earn, the Teith and the Forth all emerge from the Highlands to run across the fringing belt of lowland. The Tay and the Earn empty through the Perth Gap into the Firth of Tay, where tidewater runs up between the Sidlaws and the Ochils. The Teith joins the Forth before the combined stream flows through the Stirling Gap, between the Ochils and the Campsie Fells, into the Firth of Forth. A neck of land less than 30 miles across separates the Firth of Forth from the head of the Firth of Clyde, into which the Clyde flows from the southeast. Lesser streams—the Irvine and the Ayr—drain the Ayrshire Plain, and the Almond, Esk and Tyne flow across the Lothian coastlands.

Apart from subsequent streams aligned on weak outcrops, the drainage-pattern of Central Scotland is difficult to explain. The main streams show signs of having been superimposed—hence the gaps which they cut through belts of high ground. The Perth and Stirling gaps had very great strategic importance in past times, but the gap occupied by the Clyde estuary between the Renfrew and the Kilpatrick Hills led northward routes only to the wild country of the southwest Highlands.

Glaciation and Its Effects

Ice and meltwater deposited a great bulk of rock-waste in Central Scotland. Stiff boulder-clay, up to a hundred feet or more in thickness, is widely distributed; drumlins occur on the Ayrshire Plain, on the coalfield country of the centre of the region, and north of the Tweed. Deposits of sand and gravel are well known from the eastern side of the region, where they are diversified by kettle-holes and old lake basins.

In immediate pre-glacial times the Scottish land stood higher than it does today, and rivers were cutting deep valleys in their lower reaches. The great weight of the ice-sheets depressed the land during glacial maximum; after deglaciation the land began to rise again, carrying the late-glacial beach up to 100 feet above the present shore. Post-glacial uplift, however, has not yet compensated fully for glacial depression, and in any case the general level of the sea has fallen. Thus raised beaches and river-terraces, indicating emergence of the land and rejuvenation of the streams, adjoin the drowned valleys of the Firths.

Soils

The soils developed on the various types of superficial deposit— boulder clay, sand and gravel, terrace material and raised beach— are very varied (Fig. 98). On the stiffer of the boulder clays, soils are usually cold, and in the natural state poorly drained, while the sands and gravels develop coarse-textured soils which are readily leached and tend to be podsolised. Leaching is most severe in western districts. The raised beaches—particularly well-developed on the eastern side—provide some of the most useful soils of all under heavy fertilisation.

Parent material

■	very poorly-drained meadow soil, deficient in lime	boulder clay derived from shale and sandstone
▨	poorly-drained meadow soil, deficient in lime	boulder clay derived mainly from shale and sandstone
▨	imperfectly-drained Brown Forest Soil, poor in bases	mixed boulder clay
▨	freely-drained Brown Forest Soil, poor in bases	glacial outwash
▨	freely-drained Brown Forest Soil, poor in bases	raised beach deposits

▭ alluvium   ▨ wind-laid sand

FIG. 98. Sample of soil-distribution in the Ayrshire coastland

Climatic and Agricultural Contrasts

Climatically and agriculturally the two sides of the region differ strongly from one another. Contrasts in agriculture represent adaptations to, and not the direct effects of, contrasts in climate. They are well illustrated by a comparison between Ayrshire in the west and Fife in the east. In Ayrshire less than one-fifth of the farmland is under tillage crops, in Fifeshire more than one-half; the most extensive tillage crops in Ayrshire are oats, potatoes, fodder roots and green fodder crops, in that order; oats and potatoes also lead in Fifeshire, but are followed by barley, fodder roots, wheat, and sugar beet. Permanent grass is twice as extensive as rotation grass in Ayrshire, but rotation grass occupies slightly the larger acreage in Fifeshire. The ratio of beefstock to dairy cattle is far higher in Fifeshire than in Ayrshire.

Such differences are associated with a rainier climate in the western than in the eastern parts of Central Scotland. There is little contrast between the west and the east in annual range of temperature, incidence of snowfall, or length of frost-free period, although the west is slightly more maritime and thus slightly more equable than the east. The east receives rather more frost but also rather more sun than the west. The most significant contrasts are in rainfall. Little of the west receives less than 40 inches a year, and the total rises above 50 inches on the hills west of the middle Clyde. All the lowland of the east records an average below 40 inches, the total falling to 25 inches on the coast between Edinburgh and the Tweed. Correspondingly, the number of rain-days falls from well over 200 a year in the west to 175 days on the east coast.

Types of Farming

The net results of agricultural response to these spatial variations in climate are clearly revealed in Fig. 95. Cropping with stock-farming is dominant north of the Forth, while dairying is the main interest to the west and south of that river. Hill sheep are kept on the Pentlands and other masses of high ground in the south of the region, as well as on the hills of volcanic rock in the north, as far northeastwards as the Ochils.

Grain-growing was dominant in the east until the late 1800s, when increasing imports of cheap North American grain brought about a general change. Very few farms carry no livestock at the present day, but a considerable number north of the Tay, on the peninsula between the Tay and the Forth, and along the southern coastland of the Forth estuary concentrate on a combination of cropping and fattening. Many Irish store cattle are bought for fattening, except in the northern part of the district where home-bred stores are typical. The cropping-and-fattening farms are surrounded by more numerous, but similarly distributed, farms where cropping is combined with rearing as well as with fattening.

The farms of the eastern side of Central Scotland have produced several notable pioneers of agriculture, and the area has been well in the van of agricultural advance for more than two centuries. Among the local developments were four-course and six-course rotations, which are still widely practised. In general, farming in this part of the region is notable for its high yields, which result more from good management than from any naturally favourable circumstance. The impression of prosperity and of a high standard of cultivation is enhanced rather than weakened by a scarcity of hedgerow timber and by large fields. On the wide raised beaches the land is flat, and tillage is particularly extensive.

Intensive farming of a specialised kind is localised. Pig-farms and poultry-farms occur north of Glasgow and west of Edinburgh, while market gardens are concentrated east of Edinburgh, in the Clyde valley upstream of Glasgow, and around the town of Ayr. The greatest single concentration is located on the Lothian coast-lands, which contain half the market-gardening area of Scotland and yield two-thirds of the country's production of market-garden crops. Musselburgh is the centre of a district where, on the shore of the

Forth estuary, a raised beach provides a foot of very light soil overlying shelly gravel; the topsoil has been transformed and made highly productive by heavy dunging. Deliberate improvement has also been highly effective in Strathmore and in the Carse of Gowrie. Strathmore, between the Sidlaw Hills and the Highlands, is floored by alluvium and glacial drift. The local soils are, in the main, loamy, and have well repaid the draining and fertilisation which began in the 18th century; at that time, shell-marl from the bottoms of lochs was widely applied to the lime-poor soils, and many years of wise management have converted Strathmore to a highly arable district noted for potatoes in the western part and for fodder crops in the east. The Carse of Gowrie is based on estuarine clays exposed by the post-glacial rise of the land. Until the 18th century this district was very marshy. Drainage, ploughing, and fertilisation have enabled it to gain a high reputation for small fruit, orchard fruit, and dairy produce. Cattle-fattening in the Carse of Gowrie is associated with rich grassland, but dairying, market-gardening, and fruit-growing are closely linked to the demands of Dundee. Other specialisms include the production of high-grade potatoes on the red soils around Dunbar and the growing of early potatoes on the coastal sands of Ayrshire. A different kind of specialism is exemplified by the development of the Ayrshire breed of dairy cattle, now represented in many parts of Great Britain as well as in its home area.

Industry

Although well over half the area of Central Scotland is in improved farmland, and although the average standard of farming is high, agriculture takes but 3% of the workers in the region. A high degree of mechanisation—which is particularly characteristic of eastern districts—helps to explain the fact that farm workers number no more than 55,000; but the contrast between this low figure and the total of 1¾ million at work in Central Scotland is almost entirely due to the fact that most of the inhabitants live and work in towns. Three quarters of the people live in one or other of the towns listed at the head of this chapter, and nearly half live in the Central Clydeside Conurbation. About half the people at work in Central Scotland are absorbed by commerce, finance, insurance, clerical work, metal-manufacture and engineering, transport and communication, or mining—typical occupations of an industrial society.

That industrial society, however, is in process of change. During the intercensal period 1931–51, the numbers employed in metal manufacture and engineering rose by one-fifth. At the same time the numbers engaged in mining and quarrying diminished by one-third. The trends expressed by these figures are due principally to the progress made by the steel industry and to the contrasted decline of coal-mining.

Coal, Iron Ore, and Oil-Shale

Apart from small and isolated outcrops of coal-bearing rocks, the coalfields of Central Scotland include the Ayrshire field, which adjoins a low, sandy shore with few inlets; the Lanarkshire or Central field, which straddles the middle Clyde and extends northeastwards towards the Forth at Grangemouth; the Fife and Clackmannan field, where seams in the Limestone Coal Group are exploited in the central part of the field west of Kirkcaldy; and the Midlothian field southeast of Edinburgh.

The location and extent of the working coalfields are not accurately shown by small-scale geological maps. Coal seams are not confined, in Central Scotland, to the Coal Measures. Indeed, hydrocarbons of organic origin are found low down in the local Carboniferous succession, in the Calciferous Sandstone (App. 1) which contains oil-shales. Next above this formation comes the Carboniferous Limestone Series, including the Limestone Coal Group with productive coal-seams which are much exploited. Also in the Limestone Coal Group are the clayband and blackband ironstones. Next comes the Millstone Grit, which is worked for ganister in places, and above that the Coal Measures. These are divided into a productive Lower group and a barren Upper group of beds.

Coal is known to have been worked in Scotland in the 12th century, and the export trade dates at least from the 16th century, when many shipments went to London from ports on the Forth. There was little metal-working until 1759, when the Carron Ironworks began to use clayband ore. This type of ironstone occurs as concretions in the Limestone Coal Group, and could be worked by means of colliery shafts. Blackband ironstone, a variety of clayband ore, contains enough carbonaceous matter to make it self-calcining. It came into use from 1828 onwards, with the application of the hot-blast process to smelting. These two kinds of ore supplied a vigorous metallurgical industry. The peak of extraction was recorded in 1880, when more than $2\frac{1}{2}$ million tons of ore were raised, but there was a rapid decline in later years as the richest deposits were exhausted and costs of working rose sharply. The present output is very small, and the manufacture of iron and steel in Central Scotland now relies on imports of ore and on supplies of scrap.

Reserves of coal, like those of iron ore, have been seriously depleted. The annual output of coal from the combined fields of Central Scotland reached its peak of 42 million tons before World War I. Present output runs at about 23 million tons a year, and

12

the most to be hoped from planned developments is an increase to 30 million tons. The Lanarkshire field has undergone the worst decline. Its production fell from 24 million tons in 1910 to 9 million tons in 1950, accounting for most of the total fall in regional output. Mining in the Lanarkshire field is handicapped by thin seams, water in old workings, falling productivity and rising costs. The variety of coal known as *splint*, which was suitable for charging raw into the early hot-blast furnaces, has been superseded by metallurgical coke, and Scottish supplies of high-grade coking coal are limited.

Reserves in the Ayrshire field are scattered, but new drift mines are planned to increase the output of 4½ million tons a year by more than 50%. Prospects are best in the eastern fields, where Fife and Clackmannan possess 4,000 million tons of workable reserves. The Fife and Clackmannan field produced 10 million tons of coal in 1913; the present output from its 40 working collieries is between 7 and 7½ million tons a year, and an increase to 11 million tons is projected. Since the richest reserves lie deep, large new collieries are required to work them. The most promising part of the coalfield is near the coast, with extensions of the seams under the sea, for the western part is heavily faulted and its seams dip steeply underground. Little is hoped from the 12 collieries in West Lothian, but the output from East Lothian and Midlothian, where there are 20 collieries, is planned to increase from less than 4 million to nearly 6 million tons a year. Reserves here total 1,200 million tons; however, the present state of the coal industry does not suggest a hopeful future.

In drift mining, a sloping gallery instead of a vertical shaft is driven into the ground. Drift mining has long been common in parts of the Scottish coalfields, especially where the seams are repeated by faulting—a circumstance which also favours opencast working—but opencast workings and drift mines alike have a short working life, most drifts operating for 6 to 10 years only. As deep mining in large collieries becomes concentrated in the eastern part of the region, there must be a redistribution of miners. These now number some 80,000—far fewer than in 1913; the decline in numbers has naturally been greatest in the Lanarkshire field.

The export trade in Scottish coal has suffered severely from declining output, rising home demand for certain types of coal, and a shrinking foreign market for general-purpose coals. Of the coals suited to industrial uses, a high proportion is taken by industry in Central Scotland, a quarter of the entire output of coal going for industrial use.

The working of oil-shale, like that of coal, reached its peak in 1913. Some 4,000 workers are now employed in extracting the shale, which goes to the refinery at Pumpherston; the yield of 100,000 tons of oil a year makes but a small contribution to the national consumption of mineral oil.

The almost complete exhaustion of economically workable iron ore, the serious decline in coal production, and the greatly reduced output of shale-oil contrast sharply with the progress made by the iron and steel industry. The present-day manufacturing of Central Scotland well illustrates the power of industrial momentum, for the depletion of local reserves of ore and fuel have been more than offset. Nowhere in the British Isles is the result of industrial momentum better displayed than in Central Clydeside, where industry has perforce had to adapt itself to the decline of the Lanarkshire coalfield.

The Rise of Glasgow: Industrialisation of the Clyde Valley

The rise of Glasgow to the rank of great port and manufacturing town began early in the 18th century, when trading links were forged between the Clyde and the American colonies. The political union of England and Scotland, in 1603, barely preceded successful colonisation on the mid-Atlantic coast of North America; but the English Parliament favoured English merchants to the extent of imposing restrictions on colonial trade with Glasgow, and the town did not become heavily engaged in transatlantic traffic for another century. When the restrictions were removed and Glasgow secured its commercial freedom, its merchants could freely import Virginian tobacco and West Indian sugar. Workshops in and near Glasgow produced leather goods, textiles and furniture for export to the expanding colonies.

The War of American Independence and the Napoleonic Wars hit Glasgow hard, but the bankrupted traders were soon succeeded by prosperous manufacturers of cotton textiles. Technical developments and new building provided the Glasgow area with more than a hundred cotton-factories by the early 1800s. The population of the town rose from 43,000 in 1780 to 77,000 in 1800, and by 1840 it was more than 250,000. Then came a pause in the growth of the cotton textile industry, followed by the American Civil War and by the loss of textile-manufacturing to Lancashire. Industrialists on Clydeside forsook textiles for metals, investments went into engineering and shipbuilding, textile-making machines were allowed to wear out without replacement, and the cotton mills closed one by one. Paisley alone retained the manufacture of cotton textiles as a main interest, being very well known today for its production of cotton thread. Glasgow produces cotton shirtings and muslins, but employs more people in making woollens than in making cottons; carpets, hosiery and knitting wools come from the town's mills.

Textile manufacture today employs but 2½%—1 in 40—of the workers in the Central Clydeside Conurbation. Metal-manufacture and engineering are outstandingly dominant. These two industries, in their modern form, were first established in Scotland in 1760, when James Watt joined forces with Roebuck at the Carron Works near Falkirk. The rise of metal-manufacture on Clydeside began in the early 1800s, and during the 19th century a number of shipyards were established—all the largest by manufacturers of marine engines. Heavy industry was favoured by local supplies of coal and of the economical blackband ore. It developed on Clydeside step by step with the replacement of sail by steam, the accompanying replacement of wood by iron, and the supersession of iron by steel. The Clyde was deeply dredged to make possible the launching of larger and larger ships, and the Clydeside shipyards gained a great reputation for building enormous vessels.

The Clyde now ranks an easy first in the list of shipbuilding districts in the British Isles, with about a third of the total gross tonnage launched each year (Appendix 2, Plate 39). This total represents about one-sixth of the tonnage launched from all the yards of the world—excluding those of the U.S.S.R., for which returns are

FIG. 99. Central Scotland: numbers at work. Compare the next Fig.

not available. Thus the Clyde produces some 5% of world output (U.S.S.R. excluded). But the Clyde in particular, and British yards in general, are suffering from foreign competition—especially from the competition of Japan. In 1930, British launchings amounted to more than half the world total, and were still more than one-third in 1937–38. Although post-war production is nearly half as great again as that of 1937–38, competing yards overseas have increased their output to a still greater extent. In 1956, Japan launched more than 25% of the world's new tonnage, and Germany's output was 15%. (See Appendix 3 for 1962 orders).

The present concentration of Scottish steel-making in the Clyde valley, which contains the second greatest group of steel furnaces in the British Isles, is shown in Figs. 56 and 57. Outliers of the steel industry occur at Glengarnock in the west and at Armadale in the east. Some 2½ million tons of steel are produced in Scotland each year, basic open-hearth furnaces accounting for 90% of the total output of crude steel. Heavy steel products are typical of the Scottish industry, the main demands coming from shipbuilding, marine and con-structional engineering, railway engineering and boiler-making. About one-fifth of the output is exported, with tubes, plates and other

Fig. 100. Central Scotland: manufacturing employment

heavy products providing more than half the export tonnage. It is the flourishing condition of Clydeside steel-making which, more than anything else, exemplifies the result of industrial momentum in Central Scotland.

Among the adaptations to changing circumstances has been a great reduction in the number of blast-furnaces. The peak annual production of 1½ million tons of pig-iron was reached in the early 1900s. At that time there were more than 100 blast-furnaces in Central Scotland, concentrated on the Lanarkshire (Central) coal-field. The local output of iron ore, however, was already well past its peak, and the home product was fast being replaced by imported ore. The old-fashioned, small, hand-charged furnaces went out of use. Today there are 15 large mechanically-charged furnaces, of which 10 can operate at one time. They are concentrated on the Central coalfield, mainly in the Clyde valley in and upstream of Glasgow. Their annual output of a million tons of pig cannot meet the demands of the steelworks, where large quantities of scrap are used. Because scrap metal is scarcer than it was in the inter-war and immediate post-war years, a new blast-furnace with associated coke ovens has been built near Motherwell, and new ore-handling plant installed at Glasgow Harbour; plans for a semi-continuous strip mill at Motherwell, employing 3,500 workers, were announced in 1958.

Industrial Population

Fig. 99 shows the relative sizes of the Central Scottish towns in terms of working population. The circles are proportional in area to the number of people employed in each place, the segments marked in solid black indicating the proportions directly engaged in mining and manufacture. In no town do miners and manu-facturing workers amount to half the employed population, although they closely approach that fraction at Port Glasgow. In most of the towns which are readily recognised as industrial, mining and manu-facturing take about a third of all workers. This or a greater fraction seems to correspond to deep involvement with productive industry. Ayr, Stirling, Perth and Edinburgh are alone in having 25% or fewer of their workers in mining or manufacture.

Fig. 100 shows the distribution among the large towns of people directly employed in mining and manufacture. Wheels in this map represent the solid black segments in Fig. 99. In this second map a simple analysis has been made of industrial employment. Mining and quarrying—almost wholly accounted for by coal-mining—is separately shown where it employs a sizable fraction of the labour force: that is, at Ayr, Hamilton, Motherwell, Airdrie, Stirling, Dunfermline and Kirkcaldy. The manufacture of textiles and

garments is well distributed, but the clothing trades—as opposed
to textile-milling—account for much of the employment it affords;
Paisley and Dundee, both special cases, dominate textile-manu-
facture proper. Woodworking—not separately shown—is quite well
represented in most of the large towns. Special items are the leather-
manufacture of Kilmarnock and the paper-making, printing and
publishing industries of Edinburgh. All towns record a high proportion of workers employed in metal manufacture and engineering.

TOWNS

Glasgow, Edinburgh and Dundee, in that order, have the largest
industrial populations. They are also the only towns of Central
Scotland with more than 100,000 inhabitants, despite the facts that
the region as a whole is well urbanised and that some 2 million
people live outside these three towns. It is characteristic of Central
Scotland that most of its towns are of moderate size. Glasgow, for
instance, is overwhelmingly the dominant member of the Central

FIG. 101. The Firth of Clyde; continuation in Fig. 102

Clydeside Conurbation, being more than ten times as populous as Paisley, the next largest.

Towns of the Clyde Valley

Glasgow, like Liverpool, is a major west-coast port, deeply committed to transatlantic trade. But, unlike Liverpool, Glasgow lies well inland. In this respect it resembles Bristol, but has been more successful than Bristol in developing outports—Greenock and Port Glasgow, 10 miles down the river, which are very closely linked to Glasgow by road, rail, and trading arrangements (Figs. 101–103). The central part of Glasgow is based on raised beach, terrace, and drumlins. Here the silty Clyde is crossed by the lowest bridges,

FIG. 102. Glasgow and its local setting; continuations in Figs. 101 and 103

towards which routes converge along the valley and, crossing broad saddles between obstructive groups of hills, from the east and the west.

Although the town has spread on to both flanks of the Clyde valley, its expansion has been too slow to prevent serious overcrowding in its older residential parts. During the depression years of the inter-war period there was little chance of rebuilding or even

FIG. 103. The Clyde Valley upstream of Glasgow; continuation in Fig. 102

of repairs, and urban blight settled heavily on some portions of the town. The necessary task of reconstruction will be long and difficult. Few would claim that Glasgow is a handsome town, even though its central squares and main shopping streets are spacious, but there can be no mistake about its present high level of industrial and commercial activity.

Glasgow today has more than half-a-million people at work, of whom 80,000 are employed in metal manufacture and engineering. This is the leading industrial group, taking 15% of the town's labour force and more than 1 in 2 of industrial workers. Iron, steel, ships, marine engines, aero-engines, road vehicles and machine tools are among the many metal products. Other manufactures include electrical gear, paints, rubber, brass and copper, tobacco, packages, plastics, beer, soft drinks, bottles, furniture, leather and concrete.

Motherwell, Coatbridge, Airdrie and Hamilton are satellites of Glasgow. As a group they concentrate on metal-manufacture, Coatbridge and Motherwell being great producers of steel. Coatbridge takes a minor part in coal-mining, and Motherwell has the smallest proportionate share in the making of textiles and clothing.

On the west and northwest, the tentacles of Glasgow are entangled with those of Paisley and Clydebank. Clydebank records a higher proportion of workers in the metal trades than does any other Scottish town, concentrating on shipbuilding and marine engineering. Ships and engines are also produced farther down the river at Dumbarton on the north bank, where non-ferrous metals are worked, and at Greenock on the south bank, where there are sugar refineries. Greenock and Port Glasgow benefit from deep water close inshore; a huge new dry dock is being built at Greenock.

Towns in Ayrshire

The Ayrshire coalfield has not experienced industrialisation comparable with that of the Clyde Valley. The sand-fringed Ayrshire coast provides no deep and sheltered inlets. Ardrossan and Troon, sharing with Ayr the export of coal to Ireland, have not grown large; Ayr remains a centre of coal-mining, but the export trade has declined with the decline of coal production. The industries of Kilmarnock include, in addition to leather-working, engineering and the making of carpets and blankets.

Towns East of the Clyde

Falkirk, although located on the Central Coalfield, has little importance as a mining centre. Its engineering industries take a large fraction of the industrial labour force, the Carron Ironworks having migrated to the Clyde Valley. Leading products are light castings and rolled aluminium. The ancient, strategically-placed towns of Stirling and Perth have lost all their former defensive functions and part of their practical nodality. Perth, at the head of the Tay estuary, has been deprived of railway traffic by the Tay Bridge and of road traffic by ferries from Dundee. Stirling, at the head of the Forth estuary, is bypassed by the Forth Bridges[1] and by Queen's Ferry; the mines which employ 1 in 4 of its industrial workers exploit the Limestone Coals.

Kirkcaldy and Dunfermline are the chief towns of the Fife and Clackmannan coalfield. In addition to their engineering, Kirkcaldy is concerned with the making of linoleum and Dunfermline with the production of linens. Alloa, Burntisland, Grangemouth and Bo'ness are among the small ports handling coal and suffering from the present condition of the coal export trade. Iron ore goes directly to the Clyde rather than through ports on the Forth, especially now that very large ore-carriers are coming into use, and the import of pit-props has declined both with the depletion of the Lanarkshire coalfield and with the progressive replacement of wooden props by steel. Thus in various ways the demand for port facilities on the Forth is weakened. Grangemouth, exceptionally, is expanding fast. It has acquired chemical engineering, light manufacturing, and a refinery to which oil is piped sixty miles from the west coast (Plate 40). The oil is landed at Finnart, on Loch Long, where the harbour has been extended in order to accommodate tankers of up to 100,000 tons.

Arbroath may be regarded as an industrial outpost of Dundee, sharing with that town shipbuilding, ship-repairing, and engineering of various kinds, but Dundee is best known for its manufactures of jute, which account for the very high proportion of workers employed in its textile industry. During the late 1700s the manufacture of linen spread widely through Angus and Fife, Dundee specialising in heavy linen goods such as canvas. The problems of spinning and weaving jute were first solved at Dundee, and in the second quarter of the 18th century the working of jute largely supplanted that of linen in the town's mills. The manufacture of jute bags and jute cordage was soon followed by the production of jute-backed linoleum. Although Dundee has had to face severe competition from the mills of Calcutta, jute goods still constitute the town's leading products.

Upstream of Dundee lies the Carse of Gowrie (p. 250), a low-lying belt of coastland which includes broad raised beaches and is sheltered

[1] The original Forth Bridge carries the railway. A road bridge over the Firth of Forth was completed in 1964.

from the north by the compact Sidlaw Hills. Fruit-farms from this district supplied the first jam factories of Dundee, and the preserving industry was vastly extended during the later 19th century when the import of great quantities of foreign fruit began. Dundee jams and marmalades are sold throughout the U.K., and Dundee cakes are widely distributed in Scotland. The town maintains a paper industry which serves its publishing houses and package-making works, and light industries established in the post-war period include the making of cash registers.

Edinburgh

Edinburgh (Plate 41) had emerged as the accepted capital of Scotland by 1500. Its castle on Castle Rock had great tactical importance in war between Scots and English, just as the town had great strategic value in commanding the east-coast route. The union of Scotland with England in 1603, and the union of Parliaments in

FIG. 104. Edinburgh and its local setting

1707, lessened the political significance of Edinburgh, but came too late to arrest the growth of the town, which was unsurpassed in Scotland until the early 19th century, when it was outstripped by Glasgow.

A contrast is often drawn between Glasgow and Edinburgh, the one being dominated by heavy industry and the other regarded as a centre of service and administration. Although, as Fig. 99 shows, Edinburgh employs a far smaller proportion of its workers in manufacture than does Glasgow, its total population of nearly half a million includes nearly 50,000 workers in manufacture, so that Edinburgh ranks next to Glasgow and above Dundee and Aberdeen as an industrial town. Flour-milling, brewing, distilling, textile-working, rubber manufacture, and the processing of foodstuffs are among its wide range of industrial activities. For paper-making, printing and publishing, Edinburgh is noted throughout the world. Their growth has been associated in a number of ways with the educational, administrative, and financial functions of the town. Edinburgh is expectedly a great centre of retail trade.

Leith is the port of Edinburgh, the second port of Scotland, and—like the neighbouring ferry terminal of Granton—a base for trawlers. From 1329 to 1833 Leith was administratively united to Edinburgh, and the two were reunited in 1920, the present population of Leith being included in the total given for Edinburgh. The two towns are firmly welded together by buildings and roads (Fig. 104). Leith processes an extremely varied range of imported materials, producing flour, fertilisers, sugar, tobacco, leather, paints and chemicals.

THE FUTURE OF THE REGION

Any forecast of future developments must be speculative, but two kinds of change seem likely to occur. A probable eastward shift of mining may well be followed by industrial expansion in the east, a renewal of trade through the Forth ports, and a more rapid increase of population in the east than in the west. Although it is unlikely that heavy industry will migrate from the Clyde valley, where it is so firmly fixed, the existing contrast between the eastern and western parts of the region can be expected to undergo modification. Secondly, the industries of Central Scotland as a whole will probably be diversified. Some diversification has already occurred, in the form of industries established during the Second World War and in the post-war period. In part, diversification involves the location of manufacture in new places—for instance, at the new town of East Kilbride, 10 miles south of Glasgow, where jet engines and electrical gear are made; on the Hillington, Queenslie, and Newhouse

Industrial Estates; and at the new towns of Cumbernauld (Dunbartonshire) and Glenrothes (Fife). There are now 19 industrial estates in Central Scotland. Three hundred new firms have entered the region from outside Scotland, some being financed by capital from the U.S.A. and Canada. In this region, as in the other industrialised regions of the British Isles, the rise of light manufacturing is complicating the distributional pattern of industry. The pull of the coalfields is weakening. How far the elaboration and relocation of industry will go, however, remains for the future to show.

APPENDIX 1

THE CARBONIFEROUS SUCCESSION
IN CENTRAL SCOTLAND

4	COAL MEASURES	Barren Red Measures
		Productive Coal Measures
3		MILLSTONE GRIT
2	CARBONIEROUS LIMESTONE SERIES	Upper Limestone Group
		Limestone Coal Group
		Lower Limestone Group
1		CALCIFEROUS SANDSTONE SERIES (includes oil-shales in upper part)

APPENDIX 2

SHIPBUILDING DISTRICTS OF THE UNITED KINGDOM

District	Annual average launchings, 1954–6, gross tons	Percentage of total U.K. launchings, gross tons	Approx. mean gross tonnage per ship launched
Clyde	458,135	32·2	5,800
Tyne	234,168	16·5	8,250
Sunderland ..	190,177	13·4	6,800
Middlesbrough	128,324	9·0	12,500
Belfast	112,831	7·9	11,500
Liverpool ..	78,336	5·5	7,600
Barrow	43,396	3·0	18,500
Hartlepool ..	39,491	2·8	6,200
Leith	36,310	2·6	3,400
Dundee ..	23,487	1·7	6,400
Aberdeen ..	20,087	1·4	1,250
Hull	17,916	1·3	495
Bristol	2,450	—	612
Southampton ..	2,341	—	1,000
Others	8,650	—	432
TOTAL	1,422,066		

APPENDIX 3

LEADING SHIPBUILDING COUNTRIES OF THE WORLD, 1960–62
(U.S.S.R. EXCLUDED)

Country	1960		1962	
	Orders	Percent of world total	Orders	Percent of world total
Japan	1,737,656	20¾	2,183,147	26
United Kingdom ..	1,331,491	16	1,072,513	12¾
West Germany	1,092,139	13	1,009,698	12
Sweden ..	701,659	8½	841,022	10
France	594,422	7	480,578	5¾
U.S.A.	484,978	5¾	449,050	5¼
Netherlands ..	566,993	6¾	418,494	5
Italy	433,840	5¼	348,196	4

In 1960 the U.K. was a net *importer* of shipping. West Germany in that year exported 70% of its production, Sweden 65%, the Netherlands 40%, and the U.K. only 15%. Foreign yards offered lower costs and earlier deliveries than many British yards. Tonnage under construction in Britain during 1961 was lower than at any time since 1945.

In 1964, Japanese yards received more new orders than the combined yards of Western Europe and the U.K.

CHAPTER 16

The Southern Uplands and the Border Country

Area: about 5,000 square miles.
Population: about 500,000.
Largest towns: Dumfries (27,800).
Hawick (16,600).
Berwick upon Tweed (12,250)
(on the English side of the border).
Galashiels (12,200).
Stranraer (9,100).
Outside these towns the average density of population is about 80 p.s.m., but the central districts have few inhabitants.
Some 35% of the region is in improved farmland, with grassland more than twice as extensive as tillage.
Numbers of livestock: cattle 450,000; sheep, 2,850,000; pigs, 110,000.

This region is far less extensive than the Scottish Highlands, and far less populous than Central Scotland. Much of it consists of high ground, and the region as a whole contrasts strongly with adjacent regions, even though linear boundaries are not easy to fix. On the northern side, hill-masses project across the geological boundary of the Southern Uplands into Central Scotland (Fig. 97), where the Pentland Hills form a true outpost of upland country. On the southwest, estuarine flats and coastal lowland begin on the west of the Nith, sweeping eastwards round the head of Solway Firth and linking the region with the margins of the Lake District. The political boundary between England and Scotland runs northeastwards from the Solway, placing in Cumberland and Northumberland a tract of hill country which lies north of the Tyne Gap; this tract, with the Cheviot and the Southern Uplands proper, will be described in the present chapter.

Physique

The Southern Uplands, underlain by hardened sedimentary rocks of Ordovician and Silurian age, rise well above the limit of cultivation, reaching heights of more than 2,500 ft. in places. The country is much dissected and has been heavily glaciated, but, because the rocks are dominantly fine in grain and in uniform texture, the signs of highland glaciation are not everywhere obvious. A noteworthy exception occurs west of the Nith, where a group of granitic hills culminating in Merrick (2,764 ft.) is rugged, indented with corries, and dotted with tarns. Elsewhere the main effects of ice seem to have been the enlargement and deepening of valleys, the scouring of summits, and the deposition of drift on low ground.

Much of this upland country, like the uplands of central Wales, consists of broad, subdued divides separated by steep-sided, narrow valleys—the plateau-remnants of former landscapes, dissected by young rivers. The Upper Clyde, the Doon and smaller streams escape to the north-west. The Cree, Ken, Nith, Annan and Liddel discharge to the south coast. The Tweed drains a wide valley-basin between the Lammermuir Hills and the Cheviot, receiving the Yarrow and Ettrick as major tributaries. The Nith and some feeders of the Tweed flow right through the upland region, having risen north-west of the crestal belt of summits.

The Cheviot Hills are based mainly on volcanic rocks and granite. They are complexly dissected by radial streams, two of which— the Aln and the Coquet—break through an infacing scarp of sandstone to reach the Northumberland coast. The Rede and the North Tyne collect most of the drainage of the Border hills north of the Tyne Gap, flowing in glacially-deepened valleys between sandstone-capped hills.

Climate and Vegetation

The scenery of the large dales is enriched by woods, and the basin of the lower Tweed is much diversified by widely-distributed patches of ornamental timber. The Forestry Commission has planted large blocks of conifers—for instance, in Glentress Forest, Peeblesshire, and Kielder Forest, Northumberland. The upland platforms, however, carry very few trees, and well over half the region is classed as rough pasture. The existing vegetation represents a biotic rather than a climatic climax, for it results from centuries of grazing. Sheep prevent the growth of trees, as they do in Wales and the Pennines.

There is, nevertheless, a change in the character of the open grazing-land from west to east (Fig. 20). West of the Nith, where precipitation exceeds 60 inches a year on the higher ground, a patchy combination of heather, molinia and nardus is characteristic, with peat moor on the low, ill-drained hills north of Luce Bay. Precipitation decreases to 25 inches a year at the mouth of the Tweed, and the eastern parts of the upland carry a great deal of nardus moor. Fescue becomes dominant on the Moorfoot and Lammermuir Hills, and heather on the sandstone cuesta of Rothbury Forest on either side of the Coquet.

The wind-scoured uplands are subject to frequent rain or snow, frosts in 7 or even 8 months of the year, much cloud, and mean actual temperatures which descend in January to freezing-point or below. Improved farmland is confined to the valleys and the coastal lowlands, being roughly limited by the 500-ft. contour on the west, but rising to 1,000 ft. in the rain-shadowed east. The farms near the Solway are linked with those of the Ayrshire Plain through the valley of the Nith, and tongues of improved land project into the enclosing hills from the basin of the middle Tweed.

Hill-grazing

Grazing has been practised in this region for at least six hundred years, medieval religious houses having done much to foster a pastoral economy. The presence of nearly 3 million sheep in the region shows the importance of grazing today. Blackface sheep, raised for their mutton, typical of the moorland grazings, can endure the frequent snow of the high plateaus. Cheviot sheep can be kept on the best of the hill lands, and are particularly numerous in their home area of the Cheviot and in adjacent districts. One example of the elaborate systems of cross-breeding practised in the region is the crossing of Border Leicesters with Cheviots, in order to improve the quality of wool. Border Leicester rams appear at the Kelso sales as crossing sires, while large numbers of Cheviot and Blackface lambs are bought and sold at Hawick.

A variation in the quality of hill grazing occurs in the east Cheviot, where soils deficient in the trace-element cobalt have developed on andesite lava, and the pastures have to be sprayed or the flocks dosed. The standard of pasturage can vary in time as well as in space; if heather is left a long time before being burnt-over it is slow to regenerate itself, and the grazings are liable to be invaded by bracken.

The Scottish portion of this region contains one-third of the full-time shepherds in the whole of Scotland. One in every ten of those at work on the farms is a shepherd.

Lowland Farming

Farming in general takes a quarter of all workers. The heaviest demands on labour are made by the lowland farms, with their arable fields and improved grassland. In this group a marked contrast appears between the east and the west. To the west of Nithsdale dairying is dominant, some 90 % of the farmland in the rainy country of Wigtown being in grass. In the Tweed basin, the hill-grazings overlook a belt of stock-rearing and feeding farms, and these in turn give way to farms where cropping is the main and stock-fattening the secondary interest (Fig. 105). Grassland is reduced in Berwickshire to 60% of the farm acreage; barley, oats, fodder crops and potatoes take most of the land in tillage. The difference between Wigtown and Berwick repeats the difference noted in the previous chapter for Ayr and Fife.

| Rough grazing | Woodland |
| Improved farmland | Towns |

Contour interval 500 ft.

FIG. 105. Part of the Tweed basin

Routes

There is very little settlement in the heart of the uplands, where high continuous divides limit the number of practicable routes through the region, and easy passages between industrial Central Scotland and industrial England are few. Railways make six crossings between north and south (Fig. 97). The east-coast railway between Berwick and Edinburgh keeps to the belt of coastal lowlands, except where these are interrupted by the projecting Lammermuir Hills and the tracks swing inland to take advantage of a narrow trench. The line running up the North Tyne valley joins the Liddisdale route from Carlisle, before tunnelling through the watershed and descending to Hawick in the Tweed basin; exits to the north are supplied by the valleys of the Gala and Eddleston, on either side of the Moorfoot Hills, and by the Biggar-Tweed valley which leads into the valley of the Clyde. West of the Liddisdale route lies a compact mass of upland, 30 or more miles across. Then come Annandale, giving access to the upper Clyde valley, and Nithsdale, running from the lowland about Dumfries to the Ayrshire Plain, Kilmarnock and Glasgow. Lastly, there is a connection between Glasgow and Stranraer, by way of Ayr and Girvan and across the low hills of western Galloway.

Routes between east and west are confined to the Tweed valley, the coastal belt in the southwest, and the Tyne Gap, the last-named running along the regional boundary and linking Newcastle with

Carlisle. The line across the southwest coastland terminates at Stranraer, a packet station for services to Larne. Stranraer occupies a very sheltered position on Loch Ryan, behind the hammerhead of the Galloway Peninsula. Its rail-served pier overcomes the obstacle of a shelving, sandy shore.

The West

The coastal lowland between Stranraer and the head of the Solway is highly indented by wide, sandy estuaries, which are surrounded on the landward side by patches of low ground. Drift is widespread —boulder clay, glacial outwash, river terraces, coastal deposits, and peat all contribute to the form and quality of the ground. White-washed stone farms dot the undulating, grass-clad countryside. The native Galloway cattle are kept as beefstock, particularly in exposed situations, but dairy herds of Ayrshires and dual-purpose Galloway-Shorthorn crosses are the most common.

Market towns are located at river-crossings, in central positions in small lowland basins, and at the heads of estuaries. They range in population from about 1,250 to 5,000. Some have small industries connected with the agriculture of their surrounding districts, and large seasonal sales of livestock are held at Castle Douglas and Lockerbie. Dumfries has lost its former port trade, and the lead ore of the Leadhills district of the Lowther Hills has been largely worked out, but Dumfries serves the biggest patch of lowland along this coast, and with the aid of its retail trade and industries has become the largest town in the region. A quarter of its workers are in manufacture. The largest share of industrial labour is taken by engineering, but textile-making is also prominent, hosiery for the home market being the chief type of textile product. Chemicals—including synthetic fibres—and rubber are also made here.

The Tweed Valley

Textiles for the export market are produced in the Tweed valley, where the woollen industry was established in the late 18th century. At that time the farming of the Tweed basin was entering a period of drastic change, which produced consolidated, well-managed farms and large scattered farmsteads, but reduced the rural population. The wool-working towns grew faster than the villages, until in the late 1900s the textile industry passed its peak of success. There has been very little net change in town population during the last 25 years, except at Jedburgh, which has added rayon-making to the manufacture of wool. Among the other towns there is much specialisation. Hawick concentrates on hosiery[1] for the home market,

[1] The term *hosiery* means knitwear of all kinds.

Galashiels on woollen cloth—including cloth for naval uniforms—and Peebles on tweed. Selkirk also has woollen mills, but Kelso functions mainly as a market town and a centre of livestock sales. Berwick-upon-Tweed may have suffered in the long run from the neutrality granted to it in the 16th century, for it failed to grow large either as an English outpost against the Scots or as a Scottish focus for the Tweed basin.

The prosperity of the woollen industry in general, and of the making of tweeds in particular, varies rapidly with the state of the market. There is a domestic market for tweeds which can be relied on for a minimum demand. Exports to Central Europe have fluctuated widely for many years, under the impact of economic and political changes, and the U.S.A. offers the best prospects of sales abroad at the present time. Sellers of Scottish tweeds must overcome, if they can, the effects of changing fashions, and have to meet the competition of tweed made in Ireland. The two types are now competing strongly, especially in the great fashion-houses of Europe and North America.

The Country South of the Cheviot

The area between the Cheviot, the Tyne Gap, and the Industrial Northeast of England is, as a whole, thinly peopled. In all respects it is transitional. Although it is based on rocks of Carboniferous age, it resembles neither the limestone country of the North and South Pennines nor the shale-based farmland and industrialised districts of the coalfields. Historically it was frontier land for many centuries, doubtfully held by Romans, penetrated in places by small groups of Scandinavians and Danes, and disputed by English and Scots.

The western portion, between the South Tyne and the Rede, is underlain by a shaly and sandy development of the Carboniferous Limestone Series. The broad hilltops are covered in nardus moor, interspersed with peat-bog in the hollows. There is scarcely any settlement, and the deposits of lead ore, zinc ore and barytes characteristic of the North Pennines are absent. Rough pasture used for the grazing of sheep is extensive (cf. Plate 42). Otterburn, on the Rede, produces tweeds which are well known in the fashion-trade. A recent development is the planting of Kielder Forest, where the dispersed houses first built for the foresters have been replaced by nucleated settlements.

Northeast of the Rede the rivers have cut well down, excavating a strike vale in the limestone-shale beds known as Cementstones. This vale, drained to the Coquet, the Aln, and the subsequent Till, separates the Cheviot block from the broken cuesta of Rothbury Forest. It carries scattered rural settlement and small mixed farms. The enclosing sandstone hills with their cover of moorland form the structural and physical boundary of a narrow strip of coastal lowland which, broadening southwards, merges into the coal-mining country of the Wansbeck and Blyth valleys.

CHAPTER 17

The Lake District, The Isle of Man, and The Pennines

THESE upland blocks do not constitute a single region. The Isle of Man stands physically apart from the others, while the Lake District and the Pennines, although linked by the hilly tract of the Howgill

FIG. 106. The Lake District, the Isle of Man, and the North Pennines: physique and main settlements

43. View to the west across the head of Haweswater, up the open trough of Riggindale. The tarn in the middle distance is Blea Water; High Street, immediately beyond, rises above 2,500 feet.

44. Detail of limestone surface in the North Pennines.

45. Pennine farm, Swaledale. Walls are of limestone, with cornerstones of grit roofs are of slate.

46. Cotton mills, Oldham. The pools (lodges) receive waste water from the mill which are surrounded by brick-built, terraced houses.

Fells, differ strongly from one another in landscape-texture. Pronounced internal variation is typical of each division: the Central Lake District differs from the margins, the Isle of Man contains northern lowland in addition to central and southern upland, while the Pennines are subdivisible into contrasting northern, central, and southern parts. Nevertheless, certain characteristics are common to most parts of the entire area. Much of the land is high, rainy, sparsely inhabited, and used chiefly as rough pasture for sheep. Settlement is mainly peripheral. Resources are developed partly in response to the demands of lowland regions, whose inhabitants come as tourists or utilise the abundant surface water.

The internal differences within the area are closely associated with variations in rock-type and geological structure (Figs. 106, 111). The Isle of Man is a fault-block, while the Lake District is a structural dome, deeply gouged by radiating glacial troughs. The North Pennines are based on gently-tilted Carboniferous Limestone, on which the distinctive landforms of limestone country are well developed; the lower and narrower Central Pennines are underlain mainly by Millstone Grit, while Carboniferous Limestone is again revealed in the scarp-rimmed Derbyshire Dome of the South Pennines. Climate becomes more extreme across the area from west to east, and less severe from north to south, underlining the physical contrasts between the Lake District and the Pennines and among the several subdivisions of the Pennine Upland.

THE LAKE DISTRICT AND ITS BORDERS

Area: about 2,250 square miles.
Population: about 350,000.
Largest towns: Carlisle (71,000).
　　　　　　　　Barrow-in-Furness (64,750).
　　　　　　　　Workington (29,500).
　　　　　　　　Whitehaven (27,500).
　　　　　　　　Kendal (18,500).
　　　　　　　　Maryport (12,250).
　　　　　　　　Penrith (11,000).
　　More of this region is in improved farmland than might be expected
—namely, about 45%—but only 10% is in tillage.
　　Numbers of livestock: cattle, 345,000; sheep, 1,125,000; pigs, 43,000.

Physique

Ordovician and Silurian rocks are uplifted in the Lake District dome. They consist partly of tough shales produced by the hardening of fine-grained rocks, but in the high central part of the area occurs a great thickness of volcanic rocks. These, the Barrowdale

K

Volcanics, include solidified dusts in addition to lavas, but it is particularly on the lavas that the most spectacular Lakeland scenery is developed. At one time the whole area was mantled with sedimentary rocks of Carboniferous age, and probably also with Permo-Trias, but upheaval of the dome initiated consequent rivers which flowed radially outwards and in due course stripped away a great deal of the cover. So far has denudation gone that the Carboniferous Limestone survives only in low, broken cuestas on the outer flanks of the dome, where scarps face inwards. The Permo-Trias is preserved mainly in the fault-angle valley drained by the Eden, between the Lake District and the northern end of the Pennines.

The radial consequents, cutting sharply into the dome, were incised into the older rocks of the core. Their valleys were deepened and still more firmly impressed with a radial pattern by glaciers, which hollowed out the lake-basins from which the district takes its name. Windermere, Coniston Water, Ennerdale Water, Thirlmere, Ullswater and Hawes Water are all ribbon lakes. Two former single lakes have been divided into two by lateral deltas, Buttermere being separated from Crummock Water and Derwentwater from Bassenthwaite (cf. Plate 43).

Climate

Corrie-scalloped mountains rise high between the main valleys, exceeding 3,000 ft. on Scafell, Helvellyn, and Skiddaw. The high ground is fully exposed to maritime winds from the west. and the degree of exposure is increased by the presence of wide, subdued summits, which are remnants of old erosional platforms now high above sea-level. Precipitation is heavy, annual totals exceeding 80 inches in the central parts and rising well above 100 inches at some places. The westerly location of the Lake District makes for a low annual range of temperature and for a moderation of winter cold, but these effects are offset by the height of the ground, which brings actual January means on the mountains into the region of freezing-point and at times promotes heavy falls of snow. Above the limit of cultivation, the vegetation consists principally of heather fell, grading eastwards into mountain grassland which typifies the Howgill Fells. Trees are limited to low levels, except where plantations extend up hillsides, or between Windermere and Coniston Water where deciduous and coniferous woodland are alike abundant.

The Central Districts

The open land of the Lake District is useful only for sheep-farming, tourism, water-supply, and afforestation. Rough grazing on the mountains supports large numbers of sheep (Fig. 41).

Stone-built sheep-pens and washbrooks occur high up in the valleys, but the extreme valley-heads, like the mountains, are uninhabited even by shepherds.

Private motoring in the inter-war and post-war periods has done much for tourism, although most of the Lakeland settlements famous in the tourist trade are places of very modest size. Industrial growth in other regions has led to heavy demands on Lakeland water, Hawes Water and Thirlmere both supplying Manchester, 75 miles away.

Afforestation is changing the scenery of some central parts of the Lake District. It used to be maintained that planting in catchment areas secures an increase in the supply of water, but it is now held that a forest cover tends in fact to reduce surface runoff. The degree of reduction is, however, too small to affect the Lake District at all seriously, and it seems likely that planting as well as the impounding of reservoirs will continue—particularly since forests reduce the risk of pollution.

Agriculture and Rural Settlement of the Margins

Improved farmland runs up the valley-bottoms, with hay almost the only cut crop at the higher levels. The inner fringe of settlement

FIG. 107. Land-use sample for the Eden Valley. Boulder clay, partly moulded into drumlins, is extensive in this area

consists of single farmsteads, each surrounded by little fields enclosed by stone walls. Farmsteads become steadily more numerous down-valley, where tillage crops begin to appear, and are well distributed over the margins of the Lake District region where they are interspersed with villages. Many of the village names are of Scandinavian origin, for the whole northeast of England was subject to Scandinavian penetration and settlement during the Dark Ages.

The climate improves as the mountains are left behind, but most of the farmland on the low ground is under grass—conditions are far too wet to favour tillage crops. Oats, the main cereal, is cultivated in the south, where an extension of the Lancastrian Plain lies between Kendal and the sea, and also in the Eden valley where the slopes of drumlins promote surface drainage (Fig. 107). In these two localities are also found most of the cattle of the area.

Industrial Economy: Minerals other than Coal

The Lake District proper has few mineral resources of economic quality. Copper ores were worked under Elizabeth I, but ores of other non-ferrous metals have usually proved too poor or too limited to be worth mining. The Borrowdale graphite mine, formerly the basis of pencil-manufacture at Keswick, has been worked out. Roadstone is quarried at a number of places, and Shap granite is used as a monumental stone. The Permo-Triassic rocks of the Eden valley yield gypsum—used in plaster-making—and the handsome red Penrith Sandstone, which is widely used for building. Evaporites from the Permo-Trias are also extracted near Workington (see below, p. 279).

The weakness of local industry, other than that at Barrow, Carlisle, and the coalfield towns, corresponds to the scarcity of minerals in most of the region. Penrith, the chief centre of the Eden valley, has but 11,000 people, while Kendal, with woollen manufactures and a large share in the tourist trade, has not yet reached the 20,000 mark.

Industrial Economy: The Cumberland Coalfield

The Cumberland coalfield lies on the northwestern seaboard of the region. Most of the seams on the inland portion of this coalfield have been worked out, and galleries run for as much as three miles beneath the sea-bed. The seams are heavily faulted, difficult to work, and gassy—natural methane fires the boilers at one colliery. In the 18th century there was a flourishing export of coal to Ireland, Scotland, and the Isle of Man, and iron-working was established early in the 19th century, in time absorbing one-third of the coal raised. Smelting and steel-making are still carried on, with coke ovens near

Workington taking one-third of the present-day output of coal, but the prospects of mining on this coalfield are poor. The planned annual output of coal is but 1 million tons, and there is no reasonable hope that the lengthy decline in production will be reversed.

Although their mining and engineering were very severely depressed during the Great Slump, and continue to be handicapped by the exhaustion of the most accessible coals, the small towns of Workington, Whitehaven and Maryport increased their populations by 25% between 1930 and 1955. In the years of depression some 20,000 people left the district, leaving behind them 15,000 at work and 18,000 unemployed, but industrial estates founded in the late 1930s flourished during World War II, and in the post-war period have continued to prosper so greatly that industrial and social decline have been reversed. A new manufacture is that of chemicals—including detergents—for which anhydrite ($CaSO_4$) is extracted from local deposits in the Permo-Trias.

The selection of Calder Hall as the site of Britain's first atomic power station emphasises the remoteness of the Lake District region, not the expected local demand for electric power. Calder Hall may well benefit the Lake District generally, and the coalfield in particular, by reducing the cost of electricity, but it is to be compared with the use of Hawes Water and Thirlmere as reservoirs, rather than with the H.E.P. stations of the Scottish Highlands.

Industrial Economy: Barrow and Carlisle

Barrow has done less well than the coalfield towns, its population remaining stationary. As a manufacturing centre it developed late, its main period of growth coming in the second half of the 19th century. The high-grade hematitic iron ore then discovered in pockets in the Carboniferous Limestone, and the development of the Bessemer process, made possible the rise of a steel-making industry. The paper-mills and railway workshops of Barrow are less well known than the shipyards and engineering works, where naval craft and marine engines of various specialised types are constructed. Some 11,000 people are employed at Barrow in shipbuilding and heavy engineering. Post-war launchings have included passenger liners and large oil-tankers—the average size of vessel launched at Barrow is greater than the average for any other shipbuilding centre in Britain (see p. 265)—and Barrow ranks seventh in the list, in order of gross tonnage.

Carlisle (Fig. 108), the largest town of the region, has changed hands many times. Its troubled history is a measure of the tactical advantages of its site and of the strategic importance of its situation. A Roman fort was located on the north bank of the Eden, on the line of Hadrian's Wall, but the medieval castle stood on the narrow neck of land between a meander of the Eden and the tributary Caldew, with some additional protection given by the Petteril a mile to the east. Strategically, Carlisle lay between the estuarine marshes of the Solway and the steep western edge of the North Pennines. Routes converged on it from the north, an easy passage led towards it from Newcastle on the east, and it commanded the approaches to Shap and to the west coastal route on the south. For 650 years Carlisle was involved in successive Border troubles, being last captured in 1745.

Fig. 108. Carlisle and its local setting

Its industrial development dates from the late 18th century, when manufactures of woollen, linen and cotton textiles were established. Demolition of the old walls in the early 1800s reflected the end of raids and the expansion of the town. In the mid-19th century began the mechanised production of the biscuits for which Carlisle is nationally famous, while a focal position on routes between England and Scotland made the town a great railway junction. Vehicles, cranes and metal boxes are among its modern engineering products, but manufacture takes only one-third of its workers; nearly two-thirds are employed in the service industries appropriate to a flourishing centre of shopping and marketing.

THE ISLE OF MAN

Area: 221 square miles.
Population: about 48,000.
Largest towns: Douglas (20,250).
　　　　　　　Ramsey (4,750).
Some 55% of the Isle of Man is in improved farmland, most of the remainder being in rough grazing. Improved grassland is twice as extensive as tillage.
Numbers of livestock: cattle, 26,000; sheep, 83,250; pigs, 8,500.

Most of the Isle of Man (Fig. 106) is based on the tough, fine-grained rocks of the Manx Slates, which underlie the well-dissected highland exceeding 2,000 ft. in Snaefell. Severe glaciation has deepened the valleys and scoured the mountains, without destroying the plateau-steps on the divides. Running northwestwards from Douglas, the Central Valley divides the highland into two and leads to Peel on the west coast. Coastal platforms end in cliffs at their seaward edge, and there is little low ground except in the north, where glacial drift conceals Carboniferous and Permo-Triassic rocks and ends in a gently-shelving, sandy shore.

The Isle of Man has its own legislature, the Tynwald. Its administration has evolved from that established by Scandinavian conquerors, to whom the obsolescent Manx language owes part of its vocabulary. In this the Isle of Man resembles the Channel Islands, which also have considerable independence of government and retain Norman-French *patois*. Again like the Channel Islands, the Isle of Man receives large numbers of visitors each year—more than half a million.

Economy

The tourist trade is the main basis of the island's economy, Few people are occupied in mining ores of lead and zinc, and the thousand or more farms send their summer produce to the resorts. Farming is generally mixed, although there is a complete range from very small market-gardens to very large hill-farms where sheep are grazed. The main tillage crops are oats, mixed corn, and fodder roots.

The chief port, Douglas, is located on a sheltered bay at the eastern end of the transverse Central Valley. Ramsey is also on the eastern side of the island, at the junction of the main block of highland with the patch of northern lowland. The somewhat indented coastline of the central and southern parts is dotted with smaller settlements, all taking a share of summer visitors. Climatically speaking, the coastlands are better favoured than the high ground of the interior.

experiencing far less rain and cloud and much more warmth and sun.

THE PENNINES

Area: about 4,000 square miles.

Population: about 1,000,000 (this total does not include the inhabitants of industrial regions on the flanks of the Pennine Upland).

Largest towns: (*a*) in the North Pennines:
Harrogate (56,250).
Skipton (13,000).

        (*b*) The small towns of the Central Pennines belong to the woollen-making district of the West Riding.

        (*c*) in the South Pennines:
Buxton (19,250).
Leek (19,000).
Matlock (18,500).

About one-third of the Pennine area is in improved farmland, and most of the rest is in rough grazing. Within the farmed area, grassland is more than twice as extensive as tillage.

Numbers of livestock: cattle, 360,000; sheep, 1,000,000; pigs, 200,000.

Climate and Vegetation

Although precipitation tends to decrease eastwards across the Pennines, it remains high in all parts. Cloudy skies and rainy days are not much less frequent than in the Lake District. Winters become increasingly severe towards the east, where continental influences begin to make themselves felt, with the result that the average number of mornings with lying snow rises above 40 in much of the North Peninnes. A similar total is reached in the Peak District (Fig. 12). Improved farmland is confined to the valleys in the north and centre, but spreads on to the lower plateau-tops in the south. Peat moor is common on the upland north of Stainmore Pass, where crevices in the underlying limestone are caulked with boulder clay, but on the southern side of the Pass bare limestone emerges, carrying nardus moor, which is intermixed with peat moor on outcrops of shale and on patches of glacial drift. Peat moor regains its dominance on the Millstone Grit country of the Central Peninnse, where water cannot easily soak into the coarse, well-cemented sandstones. The Millstone Grit rim of the Derbyshire Dome is partly covered by peat moor and heather moor, but the limestones exposed over the centre of the Dome carry much improved grassland of reasonable quality. All the open moorland is classed as rough grazing. It carries large numbers of sheep, particularly in the north (Figs. 35, 41). Thus in land quality and land use the heart of the Pennine Upland broadly resembles the heart of the Lake District.

Contrasts with the Lake District

Both in detail and in general appearance, however, the Pennine and Lakeland scenes are dissimilar. The Pennines were heavily glaciated, snow collecting on their high parts, becoming transformed to ice and moving downhill. Valleys as far south as those of the Aire and Ribble were somewhat widened and greatly deepened by

FIG. 109. Faults and passes in the North Pennines

the moving ice, but, as in parts of Wales, there was little development of corries or of sharp peaks. Thus the full range of landforms typical of glaciated highland country is not widely represented in the Pennines, and much of the Upland consists of plateaus standing at various levels and dissected to a varying extent by streams (Figs. 106, 111).

The North Pennines

The North Tyne drains a moorland plateau of moderate height, where extensive rough grazing links the Pennine Upland with the Cheviot. This plateau descends gradually towards the Tyne Gap—drained by the South Tyne and aligned on the Tyne Faults—where road and rail link Newcastle and Carlisle across a sill less than 600 ft. above sea-level. The remains of Hadrian's Wall and the accompanying forts show how the Romans protected this easy and strategically important cross-route against attacks from the north.

On the south side of the Tyne Gap, the North Pennines rise in high plateaus which slope upwards to the west and approach 2,000 feet in height (Fig. 109). This division is based on a rigid crustal block, the Alston Block, which terminates on the west in the fault-line scarp of Cross Fell. Cross Fell, overtopping the drumlin-strewn Eden Valley by 1,000 or 1,500 feet, is gashed by short streams flowing in narrow, precipitous valleys, between which the strong limestones form steep edges. Highly permeable limestones are marked by lines of swallow-holes at the top and by lines of springs at the base. Many disused shafts and galleries record the former mining of lead.

Eastwards from the scarp, the Carboniferous Limestone dips gently away and the height of the ground decreases, but moorland lying above 1,000 ft. extends far into the basins of the incised Wear and Tees. Settlement in this division of the Pennine Upland is restricted wholly to the main valleys or to the lower ends of tributary valleys. The upper valleys and the divides are without permanent settlement, despite the former widespread working of lead ore and the present extraction of fluorspar.

The Alston Block ends on the south at the line of the Stainmore Faults, where Stainmore Pass leads a road from the Eden valley into the upper valley of the eastward-flowing Greta across a sill some 1,400 feet high. South of Stainmore Pass, the surface features typical of the Alston Block are reproduced in the Askrigg Block, which extends from the Stainmore Faults in the north to the Craven fault-belt in the south, and which ends westwards in the Dent Faults separating the Carboniferous Limestone from the older, highly-dissected, and generally impermeable rocks of Howgill Fells.

Like the Alston Block, the Askrigg Block has been highly mineralised, and lead-mining was once common in its eastern part. Fluorspar
and barytes are the chief mineral products at the present day.

On the western side, tabular beds of Carboniferous Limestone lie
bare in places (Plate 44). Highly distinctive landforms appear—limestone pavements, dry valleys, swallow-holes, powerful springs, and
systems of underground caverns. Such features are well displayed
on the shoulders of Ingleborough, where Gaping Gill is 340 feet deep.
Ingleborough itself, like its neighbours Whernside and Penyghent,
rises well above 2,000 feet and overtops the surrounding broad
shelves of limestone by some 1,000 feet. As the main valleys deepen
eastwards, their trough-like sides become ribbed by strong out-
cropping limestones. This is part of the Yorkshire Dale country,
drained by the Swale, Ure, Nidd and Wharfe. Farther eastwards
still, the Carboniferous Limestone disappears under a thickening
cover of Millstone Grit (Plate 45).

South of the complex faults of the Craven district lies the flexured
belt of the Central Pennines. The Aire-Ribble Gap, guided by the
South Craven Fault, sets a recognisable boundary between the north
and the central divisions of the Pennine Upland.

Skipton stands in the Gap itself, commanding the approaches to
the three broad sills over which main roads run into the valleys of
the Ribble and the (Lancashire) Calder. For all its focal position,
it is no more than a small route-centre and market town. Harrogate,
on the very edge of the Pennines 20 miles to the east, gained a great
reputation as a spa with the aid of the mineralised waters which
there issue from the Millstone Grit. It is still a watering-place, but
also carries on a general resort trade and functions as a conference
centre. Among the attractions of its neighbourhood are the ruins of
the 12th-century Fountains Abbey.

The Central Pennines

The Central Pennines are traversed by flexures running from
northeast to southwest, some of them responsible for the uplift
of the Millstone Grit in Bowland Fells and Rossendale Forest.
Both of these uplands and the main mass of the Central Pennines
have been cut across by erosion in previous cycles, so that the details
of the fold-structures are concealed on the ground, and the terrain
consists of dissected plateaus. Because the rocks stand lower, formation for formation, than in the Northern Pennines, most of the
Central Pennine division is based on Millstone Grit, which reaches
great thicknesses.

River erosion, aided in the later stages of glaciation by meltwater,
has made much progress in the Central Pennines, which are quite

highly dissected. Roads and railways passing along their valleys link the industrial districts of Yorkshire on the one side and Lancashire on the other, while small industrial towns, large industrial villages, and textile mills penetrate far into the upland. In many places there is a most abrupt transition from the industrial scenery of the valleys to the moorland of the divides (Fig. 110).

Arable   Meadow (permanent grass)   Garden   Waste (non-agricultural land)
Rotation grass   Heath (all rough grazing)   Inland water   Forest (all woodland)

0   ¼   ½ MILE

FIG. 110. Land-use sample for the Pennines, on the outskirts of Huddersfield

In addition to rough grazing, the Central Pennines provide gathering-grounds for numerous reservoirs. The Pennines as a whole are of very great importance to the water-supply of the densely-peopled districts on their margins, carrying some 400 reservoirs, but it is on the Central Pennines and the extension of the Millstone Grit belt to Harrogate that the greatest demands are made. Water from the surface of the Millstone Grit is typically soft, and in consequence is highly suitable for use in the textile industries—especially in washing and dyeing. It is also abundant, since precipitation is heavy and the rocks of the Grit allow little percolation. The peat of the Grit-based moors acts as a natural regulator of runoff. About half the total area of the Central Pennines drains to one reservoir or another; Manchester draws on the Longdendale valley, while the Derwent Valley Scheme west of Sheffield supplies water to Sheffield, Derby, Nottingham and Leicester. Three dams impound the headwaters of the river, the water passing for delivery through a filtration plant with a daily capacity of 9 million gallons.

The South Pennines

Unlike the block-faulted North Pennines, the Central Pennines form an unsymmetrical structural arch, the western limb broken by step-faulting at the margin of the Lancashire coalfield. Arching of structures becomes more pronounced in the South Pennines, where Carboniferous Limestone is elevated in the centre of the Derbyshire Dome and the cover of Millstone Grit has been partly removed. Whereas in the Lake District Dome the rocks of the core are stronger than those of the cover, in the Derbyshire Dome the rocks of the core are the weaker; the plateaus cut in the Limestone of the centre are enclosed on three sides by infacing scarps etched in the Grit. The doming is possibly due to the intrusion at depth of a large body of igneous rock, with which the many mineral veins in the limestone are associated. .

The higher parts of the Grit cuestas are under rough grazing, which is however less common than in other parts of the Pennines. Grazing and rearing of sheep are the main farming activities of the Millstone Grit country, although some of the enclosed land has been ploughed, re-seeded, limed and fertilised to provide pasture for cattle, among which the hardy Galloway breed is prominent. Most of the Carboniferous Limestone country is in farms, on which sheep and cattle are reared and dairy herds are kept. These farms profited by the agricultural stimulus of World War II, but are handicapped by lack of surface water, the main rivers being deeply incised into the tabular limestone plateaus, and the water table lying well below the surface. Much of the rain which falls percolates rapidly into the permeable rock, in which underground features of limestone country are well developed.

Mineral veins include deposits of lead ore, which, like the ores of the North Pennines, have been worked for centuries. In both areas, however, the period of the most intensive mining was the 18th century. Many of the workings have since been abandoned, whether because of exhaustion, because of uncontrollable flooding, or because of too great depth. Lead ore is now a secondary product, fluor spar being of greater importance. About nine-tenths of the output of fluor spar goes for use as a flux in basic open-hearth and electric furnaces. Barytes, used in paint and as a filler, is taken from the old workings in times of need—e.g., during wartime. The limestone itself is extensively quarried; some $5\frac{1}{2}$ million tons a year are taken for use as roadstone, ballast, and aggregate, or as raw material for the manufacture of lime and cement. The metallurgical, chemical, and textile industries of nearby regions all need great quantities of lime.

The three towns in this division are very similar in size. Buxton near the head of the Wye, and Matlock on the Derwent, are watering-places and health resorts, the former possessing hot springs. Leek is a Pennine outpost of the manufacturing district of Lancs.-Cheshire, for more than one-third of its workers are employed in the textile industry; it is a noted producer of silks.

CHAPTER 18

The Lancs.-Cheshire Plain and its Industrial Borders

Area: about 3,000 square miles.
Population: about 6,500,000.
Largest towns: (a) The Southeast Lancashire Conurbation (2,500,000) of which the leading members are:
    Manchester (661,000).
    Bolton (161,000).
    Salford (155,000).
    Stockport (142,500).
    Oldham (115,500).
    Rochdale (85,750).
    Stretford (60,250).
    Bury (60,000).
    Middleton (56,750).
    Sale (51,250).
    Ashton-under-Lyne (50,250).
    Cheadle & Gatley (45,500).
    Eccles (43,250).
    Altrincham (41,000).
    Swinton & Pendlebury (40,500).
    Prestwich (34,000).
    Chadderton (32,500).
    Hyde (31,750).
(b) Towns of the Ribble Valley:
    Preston (113,250).
    Blackburn (106,000).
    Burnley (80,500).
    Accrington (41,000).
    Nelson (32,000).
(c) The Merseyside Conurbation (1,400,000), of which the leading members are:
    Liverpool (747,500).
    Birkenhead (141,750).
    Wallasey (103,250).
    Bootle (82,750).
    Huyton with Roby (63,000)
    Crosby (59,750).
    Bebington (52,250).
    Ellesmere Port (44,750).

(d) Towns located between the three groups named above:
St. Helens (108,250).
Wigan (78,750).
Warrington (75,500).
Widnes (52,250).
Leigh (46,250).
Chorley (31,250).
Darwen (29,500).
Runcorn (26,000).

(e) Remaining towns:
Blackpool (152,250).
Southport (82,000).
Chester (59,250).
Crewe (53,500).
Lancaster (49,000).
Morecambe & Heysham (41,000).
Macclesfield (37,500)
Fleetwood (27,750).

Nearly three-quarters of this region is in improved farmland, grassland being nearly twice as extensive as tillage.
Numbers of livestock: cattle, 640,000; sheep, 210,000; pigs, 360,000.

The subject of this chapter is double-tiered. The plainlands of Lancashire and Cheshire constitute an agricultural region, with well-characterised landforms, climate, and land use. Superimposed on their rural pattern is highly-developed and widespread industry, with a wide scatter of towns, not all easy to separate from their rural surroundings. Both in the industrial and in the rural aspects there are contrasts between different parts of the region. Just as the several groups of towns differ among themselves, so does the countryside vary, both in its physical qualities and in its response to the demands which the towns make upon it. Population is notably concentrated in the towns, some 5½ million out of 6½ million inhabitants of the region inhabiting one or other of the towns named above. More than half the people live in one of the two conurbations.

Contrasts in Rural Areas

The region extends for about a hundred miles from north to south. Shrewsbury stands near the southern limit, and Lancaster near the northern (Fig. 111). Most of the land is below 250 ft. O.D., for it is based mainly on weak rocks. The large southern portion is underlain by Permo-Trias, which reaches great thickness in the elliptical basin between the Pennines and northeast Wales (Chap. 2). The extension of Permo-Trias across the lower Ribble probably represents the flank of another such basin lying between north Wales, the Isle

FIG. 111. The Lancs.-Cheshire Plain and its borders, the Central and South Pennines, Scarplands of Eastern England: physique and main settlements

of Man, and the Lake District. Along the eastern margin of the region, Carboniferous strata rise in the Pennines and project westwards in Bowland and Rossendale Forests. All but the lower flanks of the upland belongs agriculturally to the Pennine region, but the industrial districts overlap the physical boundary which separates high ground from low.

Large areas of the lowland are covered with glacial deposits or other superficial material. In the south there is much boulder clay, laid down by a broad tongue of ice entering from the Irish Sea, with small lakes contained in many shallow depressions which pock its surface. On the northern side of the Mersey, sandy deposits are widespread and patches of peat occur where bogs formerly grew. The soils of the lowland districts are very diverse in quality, but most of them are under improved farmland. In many places cultivation is specialised and intensive, for enormous markets exist within the region, and the local climate ensures a long growing season. .

The low ground receives less than 40 inches of precipitation a year, the 40-inch isohyet running precisely along the inland border of the plains. Rain is fairly frequent, coming on some 200 days a year, but the coastland is no less sunny than the tip of Holderness (Fig. 12). Mild air moves freely in from the sea, giving 6 months free of frost in all but the extreme south, and 7 months in the Wirral and between the Mersey and Ribble estuaries. Lying snow is infrequent on the low ground. The mean annual range of temperature is about 20°F.

Although the whole of the plains experience an equable climate, their central parts are better favoured than the north and south. The broad peninsula between the Ribble and the Mersey contains the largest block of land with 7 months free of frost, has less than 200 rain-days a year, and experiences particularly mild winters which bring down its annual range of temperature (Fig. 11). On all these counts it is the district best suited to tillage. Farther north the climate becomes wetter and cooler, while towards Shrewsbury winters become significantly cooler and more liable to frost. The climatic differences are reinforced by differences of soil, for whereas the northern and southern parts of the region have much stiff and heavy soil developed on boulder clay, the centre contains much post-glacial sand and peat. Tillage is very common upon the sandy and peaty soils between Southport and the Mersey, and also south of the Mersey, where it thins out across the patchy mosses towards Macclesfield.

Cash crops dominate the farming of this highly-tilled central district. Early potatoes on the lighter soils, and maincrop potatoes on the heavier soils, are grown in variable rotation with such crops as oats, wheat, and hay sold off the farm. Were it not for eelworm, potatoes could be grown even more widely than they are, but where eelworm damage is severe they tend to be replaced by peas. Cabbages enter some rotations, while a number of mosses support market-gardens. Farm animals are few, but poultry are extremely numerous (Fig. 41). Towns, roads, railways and waterways interpenetrate this part of the region.

North of the Ribble estuary, the emphasis of farming changes to dairying. There is some arable, mostly under fodder crops, but grass is far more extensive than tillage. Settlement is sparse in the subdued terrain running towards the sandy estuary of the Lune.

South of the Mersey valley, dairying is again the main interest, having increased considerably since 1939 at the expense of fattening. In the triangle roughly marked by Shrewsbury, Crewe, and Chester the country is unmistakably rural. Hamlets, small villages, and single farms contain much of the population, but little market towns occur at intervals (Fig. 112). This piece of country is very varied in detail,

Fig. 112. Settlement on the extension of the Lancs.-Cheshire Plain into Shropshire: a small market town, with surrounding hamlets and single farms

for its soils display abrupt contrasts in quality. Settlements are located with reference to the minor irregularities in relief and in rocktype. Seen as a whole, the area is low-lying and subdued, the most prominent set of physical features being the low sandstone hills rising above 500 ft. in Delamere Forest, between the Dee and the Weaver, where tillage is widespread around a core of woodland and patches of heath.

INDUSTRIAL CONCENTRATIONS AND INDUSTRIAL POPULATION

Urban Groups of the Ribble Valley and the Southeast Lancashire Conurbation

Two groups of manufacturing towns lie on, or near the edges of, the Lancashire coalfield. In the north, in the Ribble valley, are Preston, Blackburn, Accrington, Burnley, Nelson, and their neighbours. The denuded sandstone hills of Rossendale Forest separate this group from the towns of the Southeast Lancashire Conurbation in the upper Mersey Basin—Bolton, Bury, Rochdale, Oldham, Stockport, and their neighbours, all forming an arc with Manchester and Salford at the focus. -

Manchester is located on the Irwell, a tributary of the Mersey. Although an early foundation, the town declined in status in medieval times, beginning its effective growth during the 16th century when it was a market for wool and flax. Its industrial development came with the establishment of cotton-manufacture in 18th century Lancashire, and progressive concentration of the cotton industry benefited the town greatly. It lies on the edge of the exposed coalfield, and was well equipped to share in the conversion to power-milling, but, as its central position in relation to other textile towns became steadily more influential, its land-values rose and industry was partly displaced in favour of commerce. In round numbers, its population rose from 36,250 in 1773, to 75,250 in 1801, to 303,500 in 1851, and to 607,000 in 1901. In 1830 it was linked to Liverpool by railway, and in 1893 became a seaport with the completion of the Ship Canal.

The spread and functional change of building converted the angle between the Irwell and its tributary Medlock to the heart of a great town, with railway premises near the two rivers, and canal wharves and heavy industry near their confluence. Numerous bridges bound Manchester ever more closely to Salford, on the other side of the Irwell. Although both towns have declined in numbers of resident population since the 1931 census, the decline reflects conversion of residential property to the uses of commerce and business, rather than a weakening of urban functions.

Spreading across the rising ground to the east and north, Manchester has established physical connections with the other towns of the Conurbation. It is not, however, the only focus of the Conurbation, and the other large members still appear as thick knots in the tangled map of man-made features.

Nearly all the increase in the population of the Southeast Lancashire Conurbation took place before 1911, since when there has been very little change. The rate of increase in the last half-century has been well below that for England and Wales as a whole (p. 161). Without inward migration there might well have been a decline in numbers, for some 750,000 of the present inhabitants were born outside the Conurbation; but the large towns of Southeast Lancashire are not alone in failing to maintain their numbers without the aid of immigration, and it would be a mistake to relate their population-trends solely to the difficulties of the cotton-textile industry (see below).

Many of the buildings in Southeast Lancashire were erected in the late 19th century, when little planning was practised, although Manchester—usually well to the fore of national thought—built large numbers of municipal houses in the inter-war period. The towns merge into surroundings which can scarcely be called rural, even when buildings are few, and throughout the Conurbation there is much intermixture of old factories, new factories, and blocks of houses of varying date (cf. Plate 46). Only on the north and east is town fairly sharply separated from countryside.

Cotton Manufacture

The present cotton-textile industry of the British Isles is very strongly localised in the Southeast Lancashire Conurbation and the Ribble Valley. The general history of its localisation is well known, even though the power of some of the localising factors is often misjudged. At the end of the 18th century, cloth-making was widely diffused throughout the populated areas of the British Isles, and cotton manufacture promised to become as widespread as the spinning and weaving of wool. When powered machines capable of working cotton were invented, many small mills were established in the uplands between the Midland Triangle in the south and the Scottish Highlands in the north. Natural humidity of the atmosphere was an advantage common to all parts of a very large area, and cannot possibly be regarded as having favoured Lancashire in particular. Soft water is available in Lancashire from the surface drainage of Millstone Grit and Coal Measures, but the same formations also supply the West Riding, and soft water is also to be had in the west of the Central Lowlands of Scotland; in any event the degree of softness is relevant only to dyeing, bleaching and printing. Lancashire had no monopoly of the physical conditions which suited the early cotton industry.

When water-power was superseded by steam-power, access to coal became a locating factor. As the output of raw cotton from the U.S.A. increased, two parts of the British Isles were well placed to develop and concentrate the manufacture of cotton textiles— Lancashire and the Clyde Valley. Both had coalfields, both had west-facing ports already engaged in transatlantic trade. Lancashire achieved unrivalled supremacy for two main reasons: the export market of the 19th century demanded coarse goods, whereas fine goods were the chief products of the Scottish mills; the cotton famine of the 1860s additionally weakened the Scottish industry, and diverted the attention of manufacturers in the Clyde valley to metals.

The Lancashire cotton industry reached its peak of success in 1913, having in a hundred years secured nearly all the cotton-manufacturing of the British Isles, developing a huge output and a correspondingly great export trade. Exports were severely and progressively reduced during the inter-war period, partly by two slumps and partly by competition from foreign producers. India, China, and Japan developed large cotton manufactures of their own, Japan forcibly entering the export market. Some two-thirds of the lost exports were due to production in consumer countries, the remaining one-third to Japanese competition. The export of cotton piece goods had sunk, by 1939, to the level of 1850. The number of looms and spindles was back at the level of 1880, and would have been still smaller had it not been for the custom of short-time working adopted in the face of reduced export demand.

The chronic difficulties of the cotton industry during the last 40 years have been reflected in unemployment, which was very severe during the 1930s and still tends to remain above the national average. Conversion to other forms of manufacture has, however, been slow. It was not fully realised during the inter-war period that the cotton industry had seen its best days, partly because some sections of the industry, concentrating on fine counts of yarn and on piece goods of high quality, escaped the worst of the depression. The lost markets were those which had taken the coarser and cheaper grades of cloth. It is ironical that the least vulnerable forms of manufacture should have been those which had earlier proved a handicap in Scotland, and that one of the obvious alternatives to cotton-manufacture—metal-making and engineering—should be precisely the one chosen in the Clyde valley.

Textile manufacture today employs no more than 11% of the workers in the Southeast Lancashire Conurbation—fewer than the 12½% employed in metal-manufacture and engineering. Although the clothing trades take another 5½%, bringing the fraction employed in making textiles and garments up to 16½% of all workers, the two industrial groups employ but 200,000 in the Conurbation, in contrast to 250,000 in commercial and clerical occupations. The textile industry takes a higher share of the labour force in the large towns of the Ribble valley, with 21%—more than 1 in 5—of all workers, and nearly another 2% work in the clothing trades. Metal manufacture and engineering, the next most prominent occupational group, take but 12½% of all workers—only half as many as textile and clothing manufacture. So far, however, no more than a quarter of a million textile workers have been identified. It is true that the cotton industry employs many who are not textile operatives, and that some textile operatives live and work outside the Southeast Lancashire Conurbation and the large Ribble valley towns. Nevertheless, the figures quoted serve to place direct employment in textile-making in its proper perspective.[1]

Distribution of Processes in Cotton Manufacture

It was during the period when Lancashire was successfully over-coming Scottish competition that the contrast developed between textile-working towns in the Southeast Lancashire Conurbation and those of the Ribble valley. The former carry out most of the spinning and the latter most of the weaving. Bleaching, dyeing and printing are also located mainly on the south of Rossendale Forest, where they are supplied with soft surface water and are close to Manchester, but the works where finishing processes are carried on are mostly outside the large towns.

The concentration of spinning and weaving in two separate districts was due to technical factors operating in the third quarter of the 19th century. By 1850 or thereabouts, spinning was firmly established in the south. Powered weaving lagged behind powered spinning in its development, and, when the delay was made up, the Ribble Valley had a large number of hand-loom weavers who could be recruited for the new weaving mills. It also possessed coal to drive the machines. Thus the cotton industry in its mechanised form invaded the Ribble Valley, and a localisation of processes appeared which has been accentuated in later times.

The existing contrast between the two groups of towns is illustrated in Fig. 113. The pie-graphs in this Figure refer only to employment in mining and manufacturing industry.

The proportion of textile employment within the mining and manufacturing groups is shown by stipple; where a high proportion of textile workers is employed either in spinning or in weaving, a segment of appropriate size is marked off and the letter *s* or *w* added. From Colne to Preston, and in Rawtenstall and Darwen, weavers far outnumber spinners. In Colne, Nelson, Burnley, Rawtenstall, Darwen and Accrington they amount to two-thirds or more of all textile workers.

The concentration on spinning in the southern group of towns

[1]The number of workers in the cotton spinning and weaving industry had fallen to 215,000 by October 1958, and by October 1959 was less than 200,000— the lowest figure for more than a century.

During 1959 there was announced a Government-sponsored scheme for eliminating surplus capacity in the cotton industry. About a third of the spindles lay idle in the spring of 1959, and the weaving side also had more plant than it could use; the proposals include the scrapping of more than 13 million spindles, 15 thousand carding engines, and 100 thousand looms—that is, about half the existing spindles and looms are to go. Re-equipping is expected to take five years. The object of the scheme is to make the industry compact and efficient. Output, and demand for labour, are expected to remain at about the present level, but results up to the end of 1961 were disappointing.

is less marked than the concentration on weaving in the northern. Nowhere do spinners amount to more than a third of all textile workers, and only in Wigan, Bolton, Rochdale, Oldham and Stockport are they particularly numerous in comparison with other textile workers. This circumstance is largely due to the considerable range of the textile processes which are carried on in the district.

The garment trades are present in all towns, but are best developed in Wigan, Bolton, Stockport, Hyde, and Manchester and Salford. In Manchester and Salford they employ more than a third of all workers in mining and manufacturing, fewer than the metal industries but many more than the making of textiles. The concentration in Manchester and Salford reflects Manchester's position as the great marketing centre of the cotton industry. Bolton, Oldham, Rochdale, Blackburn, and Burnley all have more textile workers than Manchester, and even Manchester and Salford combined rank after Bolton and Oldham, for all their enormous size. In the garment trades, however, they are supreme. A quarter of their manufacturing

FIG. 113. Manufacturing employment in Southeast Lancashire and the Ribble valley

workers are employed in occupations other than the metal, textile, and clothing industries—a strong contrast with most of the other towns.

Metal Manufacture, Mining, and Other Industries of Southeast Lancashire and the Ribble Valley

The metal industries are well developed throughout the cotton-manufacturing districts, tending on the whole to be more prominent in the larger towns than in the smaller. To some extent they are associated with the manufacture of cotton, producing textile machinery for export as well as for home use, but they also turn out an enormous variety of products unconnected with textiles, with machinery more prominent than heavy steel goods.

Except for the shipbuilding industry of Merseyside (see below), the metal industries of the Lancs.-Cheshire region have been affected similarly to those of the Black Country; that is, by partial exhaustion of workable coals, by vanishing reserves of local ores, and by changes in metallurgical techniques. Smelting in the southeast is now confined to a few blast-furnaces on the outskirts of Manchester, which produce about 3% of the national output of pig iron, using Jurassic ore. There are 35 steel furnaces, mostly of the open-hearth basic type, with the main concentration at Irlam on the Manchester Ship Canal. Lying close to the southern edge of the Lancashire coalfield, these works correspond in their geological setting to the steelworks and blast furnaces on the Flint and Denbigh coalfield across the Cheshire Plain.

The industries of Lancashire consume more coal than is produced from the Lancashire coalfield, where accessible reserves are limited and working costs are high. Good coking coal occurs in the neighbourhood of Burnley, but the Coal Measures there have been thinned by erosion and the output is small. Most of the present output comes from pits in the south, but little mining is done within the Southeast Lancashire Conurbation, which does not include St. Helens, Wigan or Leigh. Collieries take more than a quarter of the industrial labour force in these three towns (Fig. 113), but their demands are likely to diminish with the approaching exhaustion of the most accessible coals. The largest and most productive collieries are concentrated along the southern outcrop of the exposed Coal Measures, and on a narrow strip of the adjacent concealed coalfield. Working is not likely to spread far beyond the outcrop, for the seams are heavily faulted and dip sharply down beneath the overlying Permo-Trias.

Nearly all the coal raised is used in the Lancs.-Cheshire region. Industry takes half the output, domestic fires and thermal-electric stations nearly all the remainder, while small quantities are exported to Northern Ireland. No increase in output is expected, even with the addition of 5 new drift mines, and the projected figure of 12 million tons a year is less than that of 1949, and well below the interwar level (Fig. 45). Costs are likely to be reduced by the use of road transport over short distances, but the prospects for the field are poor. Coal is already brought in by the electrified Sheffield-Manchester railway, the trains being assembled in Wath marshalling-yard between Barnsley and Doncaster; the expected future deficiency is to be met by coal from North Staffs. and Nottinghamshire.

In the pie-graphs (Fig. 113), metal manufacture and engineering, textile manufacture, and garment-making are shown for all towns.[1] Coal-mining is included under *other occupations*, except where it takes a perceptible fraction of the labour force—i.e., at Burnley, Accrington, Chorley, Leigh, Wigan and St. Helens. At the three last-named places it is very prominent.

At Rawtenstall and St. Helens respectively, the leather and glass industries employ large numbers.

The Middle Mersey District

Among the competitors for the declining output of coal from the Lancashire field are the towns of the Middle Mersey district (Fig. 114). Warrington, the largest, employs nearly a third of its workers in the metal and engineering trades, constituting the chief link between the metal manufacturing of Southeast Lancashire and that of Merseyside. Warrington controls a crossing of the Mersey, approached by easy but well-drained routes from the south, and was a vigorous town in medieval times. The industrial revolution stimulated industries which had long been carried on there, and during the 19th century the town grew steadily in size. It is well served by waterways, railways, and roads. Its activities include the making of steel sheets, wire, and nails, the milling of aluminium, brewing and tanning.

Widnes and Runcorn on the Mersey, and Northwich (19,500) and Winsford (13,000) in the Weaver valley have between 40% and 50% of their workers in the chemical industry. Salt, coal and limestone are basic raw materials of chemical manufacture, and salt is at hand in the Cheshire saltfield where it occurs as lenses in the Triassic rocks (Plate 47). Salt was obtained by evaporating the waters of brine springs in pre-Roman days, rock-salt was proved in the 17th century, and during the 18th century great quantities of salt were shipped from Liverpool, particularly to Ireland. At the present day, salt is extracted mainly with the aid of brine-pumps; one mine, at Winsford, alone remains in work. Technical developments during the 19th century

[1] For recent trends, see bibliography at R. C. Estall.

FIG. 114. Manufacturing employment in Merseyside and
the Middle Mersey District

made possible the rise of a great and varied chemical industry, the
innumerable products of which include soaps, detergents, industrial
alkalis, suphuric acid and explosives. St. Helens belongs to the group
of chemical-manufacturing towns by virtue of its production of
pharmaceutical chemicals and glass. The geological basis of glass-
making is the wind-laid Shirdley Hill Sand.

The Merseyside Conurbation

The Merseyside Conurbation (Fig. 114), with a present population
of more than 1⅓ million people, has come into being through the
radial growth of Liverpool and Birkenhead round their nuclei on the
waterfront. The urban sprawl has involved and incorporated neighbouring settlements, which retain their municipal independence.
Unlike the Southeast Lancashire Conurbation, the Merseyside
Conurbation ends fairly sharply against the surrounding agricultural
land. Its size and its industrial and commercial vigour well exemplify
the influences of a coastal location.

Liverpool had a considerable trade with Ireland during the early
Middle Ages, but later fell into decline. Revival under the Tudors
left it still subsidiary as a port to Chester, and many of its inhabitants
had interests in farming as well as in trade, but the Irish rising of

1641 revealed its strategic importance, and after the Restoration its prosperity increased. Tobacco from the North American colonies and sugar from the West Indies supplied raw material for industry; the import of raw cotton began, salt shipped down the Weaver was bought by Liverpool refineries, and the salt export trade was extended to the Baltic and to America, where salt was needed by the cod-fishers of Newfoundland. Liverpool shared in the carriage of salt cod to the West Indies and the Mediterranean, and secured imports of coffee, wine and fruit. During the 18th century, too, the port was engaged in the slave trade. In 1715 was opened the first dock—a most useful addition to the original Pool, which was the small estuary of the right-bank tributary of the tidal Mersey.

As the fortunes of Chester declined with the silting-up of the Dee, and as transatlantic trade increased, so did the prosperity of Liverpool grow. From 5,000 in the year 1700, its population rose to some 75,000 in 1800. A hundred years later it was almost ten times as large again, totalling more than 700,000. The nucleus of the Conurbation had already appeared on either side of the Mersey by the mid-19th century, and subsequent developments have included the replacement of houses by commercial and business premises in the central area.[1]

The physical expansion of Liverpool was associated chiefly with the growth of overseas trade. By the early 19th century the town was a main importer for South Lancashire, the West Riding, and the Midlands, and by the mid-century was handling nearly half by value of goods exported from the U.K., against the quarter which went through London. The great oriental and transatlantic services of passenger liners were products of the 19th century, when the increase in the size of big ships steadily reinforced Liverpool's advantages over possible rivals. But the estuary of the Mersey is by no means without its disadvantages. It is commodious, it provides shelter from storms, and it strikes far inland; but the great tidal range of 32 feet at springs demanded docks, and docks with unusually deep entrances. The sea-bed offshore is covered with loose sand, which tends to obstruct the approaches. Work began in 1890 on the harbour bar, where the low-water depth at ordinary spring tides has been increased from 11 to 25 feet. Training walls help to maintain the approach channel, but some 10 million tons of sediment have still to be removed each year. Thus, although the port has manifest natural advantages, the facilities which it offers to modern shipping are to a large extent man-made.

[1] Liverpool, like Birmingham, turned to the Welsh massif for water. Lake Vyrnwy, in the Vyrnwy valley, was impounded in the late 19th century. Additional reservoirs in Wales have been completed since World War II, including the pumped storage works at Blaenau Ffestiniog, Merionethshire.

At the present day Liverpool functions as a general cargo port, with world-wide external connections and an enormous hinterland. The main destinations of its imports are Southeast Lancashire, the Nottingham area and the West Riding, and the West Midlands, which also supply much of the produce which it exports, but the Merseyside Conurbation also makes a significant contribution to export trade from its own factories.

The leading early industries of Liverpool dealt with raw materials from the hinterland of the port and with imported colonial produce. Other industries were added in the late 18th and 19th centuries, among them the manufacture of glass, pottery, and metal goods. Industrial as well as commercial progress was aided by the connection of the Bridgewater Canal to the Mersey in 1773, and the opening of the Leeds and Liverpool Canal in 1774. In later years came railways to provide rapid services between Liverpool and industrial areas inland, and the Merseyside area emerged as a considerable employer of manufacturing labour. Some 40% of all workers today are employed in manufacture, against 60% in service trades; metal-manufacture and engineering take some 14½% of all workers, and more than 1 in 3 of those in manufacturing employment. Some of the importance of the metal trades is due to ship-building and marine engineering, but a very varied range of other mechanical engineering and of light metal-work is also carried on.

Although a simple pattern of distribution is not to be expected from the industries of Merseyside, certain facts of location can be perceived. Heavy industry is concentrated in the port area, where goods can be delivered from ship to mill, flour milling is now located mainly on the Cheshire side, oil is refined near the seaward end of the Manchester Ship Canal, while tanning, sugar refining, the milling of oilseeds and the manufacture of newsprint are also concentrated near the waterfront.

Shipbuilding is located at the water's edge, on the Birkenhead side of the estuary. Launchings from the Birkenhead yard ran, in the mid-1950s, at 10 ships a year, the total launched (in tons gross) representing 5½% of all launchings in the U.K (p. 265). Although the average works out at some 7,500 tons gross per ship, most vessels are smaller than this; at the other extreme, Birkenhead is sharing in the construction of modern oil-tankers in the range 20,000 to 25,000 tons gross.

Industries which have been displaced from the dockside area include the manufactures of paint, tobacco, soap, bread, and biscuits, which now depend on direct access to railways as opposed to direct ship-to-shore offloading. Industrial estates, with their associated new housing, are the least closely linked to the docks.

Among their multifarious products are rubber, light metal goods, chemicals, and packages.

The industrial estates rely on roads for transport, on electricity for power, and on the large manpower reserve of Merseyside for labour. Those at Speke, Aintree and Kirkby were founded by the Liverpool Corporation, two in the inter-war period and one in 1946, in order to increase the range of local industry and to raise the level of employment. It is easy to overlook the fact that Merseyside has its own problems, which in some ways are at least as pressing as those of the coalfields; one of the most urgent is that of underemployment. For many years the Conurbation has recorded a level of employment lower than the national average, and long periods of little work or irregular work have lowered the general standard of manufacturing skill. One of the contributing factors is a high local birth-rate, another is immigration from Ireland—especially from Belfast. Their combined effects appear in the rate of increase in population, which did not fall below the national average until late in the inter-war period—an unusual state of affairs for one of the British conurbations.

Coastal Towns and Isolated Inland Towns

Blackpool, the largest coastal town, receives more than 8 million visitors a year—more than 50 for every one of its permanent inhabitants. Situated on the sandy shore north of the Ribble (Fig. 115), Blackpool has long sandy beaches lined with hotels, cafés, and places of entertainment. Its resort trade is the most highly developed in the British Isles; beginning as a seaside town frequented by visitors

FIG. 115. Form and setting of Blackpool

from industrial Lancashire, Blackpool now serves the whole country. Its success may be gauged from an increase of 50% in the resident population in 25 years. More than one-fifth of the working people of Blackpool are engaged in personal service (Fig. 70). A similar fraction is recorded at Morecambe, another seaside resort close to Lancaster, and a rather smaller fraction at the third resort of Southport. All three towns are located on stretches of open shore on a low, drowned coast where inlets are lined by salt-marsh.

The population returned for Morecambe includes the inhabitants of Heysham, the two places having been merged in a single borough in 1928. Heysham proper is a terminus of shipping services to Northern Ireland and the Isle of Man, and a centre of oil-refining. It is accessible at all tidal stages, for an extension of the Lune Deep runs close to its shore. Fleetwood also maintains Irish and Manx services, operates coasting services, and engages in fishing. Its older rail-served quays and the layout of its central part were built to a plan of 1836, but the docks subsequently have been greatly extended.

The situation of Lancaster on the Lune is similar to that of Preston on the Ribble. Each stands at the head of tidewater, at the inner edge of the coastal plain, and at a point where main north-south road and railway cross. Until the late 18th century Lancaster remained a market centre, assize town and seaport. A limited port trade is still maintained, but the former shipbuilding for the West Indian trade has gone, and the leading single industry is now the manufacture of linoleum, which has succeeded the making of sailcloth. Other occupations are ship-repairing and the production of rayon, plastics, and chemicals. Lancaster remains a county town— a fact which recalls its former strategic importance on the westcoast route; it is comparable with Durham on the east-coast route.

Lancaster was once a bastion against the Scots, Chester against the Welsh. The core of Chester occupies a sandstone hill above the incised Dee—a tactically advantageous site which commanded routes into North Wales. The same routes contribute to the town's present importance as a tourist centre. Chester's port trade was destroyed by the silting-up of the Dee estuary—where additional large-scale reclamation is projected—but it has become a centre of inland transport both by road and by rail. Personal service, retail distribution and local government employ many people in Chester, where manufacturing industry includes light metal and engineering work, as well as the processing of lead which depended originally on lead ore from North Wales.

Chester and Lancaster were Roman foundations; Crewe is a product of the 19th and 20th centuries. Its central position in relation to the lines of amalgamating railway companies led to the establishment of railway works, on which the town is still partly dependent. For a period it was almost exclusively a railway town, but has been adding to its range of occupations for some time. Its direct links with the industrial districts of Lancs.-Cheshire and the Midlands enable raw materials and semi-finished products to be brought together, and Crewe has been able to attract light industry and rolling-mills.

Macclesfield stands at the very edge of the Pennines, south of Manchester and on the eastern edge of the Cheshire Plain. Long reputed as a centre of silk manufacture, it has been changed technically by the 20th-century growth of the synthetic textile industry, although silk goods are still produced there. More than a quarter of the town's workers are employed in making textiles or clothing. Similar conditions obtain in Congleton (16,750). Leek, which is located in the Pennine Upland (Chap. 17), belongs industrially to the same group as Macclesfield and Congleton—all three towns are specialised outposts of the textile industry of Lancashire.

CHAPTER 19

Industrial Northeast England

Population: about 1,500,000.

Largest towns: (*a*) The Tyneside Conurbation (850,000) of which the
leading members are:

Newcastle upon Tyne (269,500).
South Shields (109,500).
Gateshead (103,250).
Tynemouth (70,000).
Wallsend (49,750).
Longbenton (44,750).
Whitley Bay (36,500).
Jarrow (28,750).

(*b*) Large industrial towns on the estuaries of the Wear
and Tees:

Sunderland (189,750).
Middlesbrough (157,250).
Stockton on Tees (81,250).
West Hartlepool (77,000).
Billingham (32,250).
Thornaby on Tees (22,750).

(*c*) Remaining towns:

Darlington (84,000).
Consett (39,000).
Blyth (36,000).
Bishop Auckland (35,000).

Much of this industrial region lies within that part of England
described under the title *Scarplands of Eastern England*, in Chap. 21.
Details of land use are therefore not required. The population given
here for the Industrial Northeast is additional to that quoted elsewhere for the Scarpland region.

Physically, most of the Industrial Northeast belongs to the drift-
plastered lowlands of the eastern side of England. Even in the west,
where it overlaps the flank of the Pennines, it consists of scarpland
country. Sandstones of Carboniferous age form scarps which face
towards the Cheviot or merge irregularly into the moors north of the
Tyne Gap. Thick boulder clay obscures the solid rocks which underlie the low ground, extending across the eroded Coal Measures and

306

48. Boldon Colliery, Northumberland. Contrast the design with that of Kinneil Colliery (Plate 14).

47. A Cheshire salt-works, with evaporating-tanks.

49. Chemical works at Billingham-on-Tees.

50. Interior of a woollen mill, West Riding, showing hopper feed of cardin
machines.

the Magnesian Limestone on to the Trias near the mouth of the Tees (Figs. 106, 111).

Beyond the inland limits of mining, nucleated and dispersed rural settlements are intermingled, with market towns occurring at intervals. Signs of industry appear towards the east, in the form of collieries, mining settlements of varying size, and manufacturing towns, becoming more and more noticeable with the approach to the great industrial and commercial centres on the coast.

THE COALFIELD

The Northumberland and Durham coalfield, which was the original basis of heavy industry in Northeast England, is the counterpart of the Cumberland coalfield on the west coast and the complement of the Yorkshire, Derby and Notts. coalfield farther south. Its seams dip eastwards off the flank of the massif, being worked beneath the sea, as in Cumberland, and beneath a cover of Permo-Trias, as in the Trent valley (cf. Plate 48). Coal was taken from the exposed field as early as the 13th century, and coastal shipments to London reached ¼ million tons a year by 1600; a hundred years later the figure had been doubled, and collieries large by the standards of the time were at work along the Tyne. Wooden rails came into use in the 17th century for bringing coal from mines a few miles inland to the staithes (jetties) on the incised Tyne. The seam chiefly exploited was the High Main, trucks running downhill from the collieries to the river.

Water became troublesome as the mines went deeper, and steam pumps were installed in the 18th century. Development on modern lines began in the period 1820–1850, when locomotive transport was introduced to the railways, deeper shafts were sunk, and the demand for industrial coals increased. Blast-furnaces were working at Consett by 1840 and at Bishop Auckland by 1846; smelting in the Middlesbrough district increased rapidly from about 1850. Ten million tons of coal were raised in 1860, but the greatest expansion of mining still awaited the rise of the steel industry and of the coal export trade. Shafts were sunk into the concealed coalfield through the cover of Permo-Trias, and concentrations of heavy industry appeared about the mouths of the Tyne, Wear and Tees.

The present output of coal is well below the peak reached in 1913 (Fig. 45). In south Northumberland and in the exposed field in County Durham the deposits of coal have been much depleted, but large reserves of general-purpose coals exist north of Blyth, where planned improvements include a new colliery and a number of drift mines. Transport from pit to port is cheap in this area, and nearly three-quarters of the coal raised goes coastwise to London and other parts of southern England, where it can compete with railborne coal from the Midlands. The bulk of the shipments goes from ports on the Tyne and from Blyth, power stations taking two-fifths of the shipments to places in the U.K. Farther south, in County Durham, occur high-grade gas and coking coals. Some two-thirds of the coal raised in Durham is used in the production of gas and

FIG. 116. Manufacturing employment in Industrial Northeast England

coke, but reserves are limited, and some of the most useful lie beneath the sea. The modest increase in output which is planned for Durham will take place in the east, working costs in the west being high. On the coalfield as a whole, mining is now concentrated mainly in a coastal belt about 5 miles wide, stretching from the mouth of the Wansbeck in the north to beyond Seaham Harbour in the south, the largest collieries occurring near Blyth and on the concealed coalfield south of the Wear. Annual output from the whole field is planned to rise to about 42 million tons a year.[1]

Blyth at the mouth of the river Blyth, and Longbenton just outside Newcastle, employ more than half their industrial workers in coal-mining, which also takes more than a third of the industrial workers at Consett, near the western edge of the exposed coalfield, and at Bishop Auckland, on the Wear (Fig. 116). At Consett, which is a centre of steel-making, the metal trades employ almost as many as mining does, but the other three are dominantly mining towns, with only a quarter of their industrial workers in metal manufacture and engineering.

METAL MANUFACTURE AND OTHER HEAVY INDUSTRIES

The five basic industries of the region are the manufacture of iron and steel, shipbuilding and ship-repairing, engineering, chemical manufacture, and coal-mining. In combination, they employ more than two-fifths of the regional labour force. They are somewhat localised within the region, as is partly shown by Fig. 116.

The Chemical Industry

The chemical industry is concentrated on Teesside (Plate 49), where it employs considerable numbers at Stockton and Billingham. It was first established on the Tyne, however, where the LeBlanc process was introduced early in the 19th century. Chemical works were set up at Jarrow after the salt duty had been removed in 1823, and by 1870 or thereabouts the Tyneside works were producing half the national output of industrial alkali. So long as the works prospered they were not modernised, remaining rather small, rather crude, and inefficient, discharging harmful fumes over their surroundings. They began to fail in the face of competition from other producers and other processes—in particular, the chemical works of the Middle Mersey and the Solvay process. Tyneside factories today make fertilisers, especially sulphate of ammonia and superphosphate,

[1] Under the revised plans for the mining industry, announced in 1959, the level of production is likely to decline; see footnote, p. 110.

the demand for which rose very sharply during World War II. Paint, soap and detergents are manufactured at Newcastle, and heat-resisting glass at Sunderland.

The chemical works at Billingham are ultimately a product of World War I. The blockade imposed on Britain in 1917 stopped the importing of organic nitrate from Chile, and the Billingham works were hastily developed to use the underlying deposits of anhydrite and the nearby rock-salt which occur as lenses in the Permo-Trias. Atmospheric nitrogen and hydrogen separated from steam combine to form ammonia, which can be processed with anhydrite ($CaSO_4$) to produce sulphate of ammonia, while a different process yields the basic industrial chemical sulphuric acid. The chemical industry of Billingham has become extremely varied since 1918, including at one time the hydrogenation of by-product creosote to make petrol. There is a wide overlap between the chemical and metallurgical industries through coke-making, and between the chemical and textile industries through synthetic textiles.

Non-ferrous Metals

Despite the vigour of the chemical industry, the industrial treatment of non-ferrous metals is not strongly represented in this region. Lead-smelting continued in and near Newcastle for some time after most of the Pennine mines had fallen derelict, but has now almost died out. Magnesia is extracted from sea-water at Hartlepool, but the processing of barytes, copper, and zinc has been wholly annexed to the chemical industry. Against the decline of smelting, however, must be set the increasing use of non-ferrous metals and their compounds in the varied light industries located on the industrial estates.

Heavy Metal Manufacture on Teesside and at Consett

No distinction is made in Fig. 116 among the production of unfinished metal products, engineering, and shipbuilding. In combination with other forms of metal-working, these occupations employ between half and two-thirds of all industrial workers, except in the chief mining towns.

Finished metal products on Teesside, as in Northeast England generally, consist principally of steel. The chief customers of the ironworks and steelworks are shipbuilders, marine engineers, mechanical engineers, and civil engineers. Constructional engineering, shipbuilding, and ship-repairing are especially prominent among the consuming industries, sharing nearly one-third of the total output of steel.

The Middlesbrough district contains the largest single group of blast-furnaces in the British Isles, producing about one-quarter of the pig iron made annually in the U.K. Works line the south bank of the Tees and the Tees estuary, with outposts on the coast at Skinningrove (near Saltburn) and at Redcar. The West Hartlepool works may be regarded as another outpost of the Teesside group, but the furnaces at Consett stand apart. It is characteristic of the Middlesbrough district that most of the pig is made in large furnaces which form part of integrated steelworks, but steel furnaces are more widely scattered than are blast-furnaces, occurring at Consett, Bishop Auckland, Jarrow, and Newcastle as well as on or near the mouth of the Tees. The Middlesbrough district, however, has a commanding lead in the regional production of steel, and some of its works have been extended in the post-war period by the addition of blast furnaces and melting-shops.

The Teesside steel industry was effectively founded and vigorously developed during the second half of the 19th century. After the main ironstone seam in the Cleveland Hills was located in 1850, the number of blast furnaces increased rapidly, and the annual production of pig iron reached 2 million tons in the mid-1870s. The growing demand for coking coal was satisfied by the collieries of west Durham. The replacement of iron by steel as a structural material might have been a grave matter for the Teesside works, for, although the Gilchrist-Thomas process made it possible to use the phosphoric Cleveland ore in making basic steel, local shipbuilders and con-structional engineers preferred acid steel, and ore from Spain had to be imported. The steelworks were converted one by one to the use of the basic open-hearth furnaces which are typical today. Expansion continued, and the population of Middlesbrough increased by more than ten times in 50 years. In 1913 the blast furnaces of North-east England made nearly 4 million tons of pig, the steelworks produced 2 million tons of crude steel, and the industry consumed 6 million tons of Cleveland ore.

The inter-war period brought a steep decline in the working of Cleveland ore, which by that time was failing. Steel-making main-tained itself over the period, but smelting suffered heavily. During times of industrial depression the iron and steel industry, like the mines and the shipyards, lost its markets, and only in the post-war period has new investment raised the output of pig above the 1913 level. The present annual production of some 5 million tons of steel, however, is nearly twice as high as the best figures of the 1930s, and well over twice as great as the figure for 1913.

Expansion has been possible only with the aid of high-grade imported ore and various technical improvements. In terms of iron content, more than 80% of the ore smelted in Northeast England is now imported, some of the Teesside works having stockyards on the waterside, and the Consett works relying on rapid transport by special trains from the Tyne. The average size of furnaces tends to increase, ore is more and more commonly prepared and sintered before being charged, high top pressure gear has been introduced at Consett, and fuel oil and coke-oven gas are increasingly used to fire steel furnaces. By these and other means working costs are kept down—as they must be, for the main products of the regional iron and steel industry are iron, mild steel, and plain steels. Heavy rolled goods—especially plates, sections, bars and rails—account for three-quarters of the deliveries of finished steel. Unlike the Sheffield district, Northeast England makes very little alloy steel.

On Teesside as a whole, constructional engineering and the chemical industry are very highly developed indeed. Shipbuilding, ship-repairing, general engineering and the manufacture of textiles and garments are also prominent. Darlington—exceptional among the large towns of the region in lying inland—has close industrial associations with Teesside. It shares in the general engineering and the manufacture of textile and clothing which are, indeed, well dispersed throughout the region, but is known mainly for its production of locomotives and railway equipment. It was chosen as a site for railway workshops because of its strategic position with relation to the 19th-century railway system. Even in heavy engineering, however, it is by no means wholly a railway town, for it produces heavy marine castings and heavy forgings of many kinds.

Industry on Tyneside

Tyneside shared in the industrial developments of the late 18th century, and had more than 100,000 inhabitants by 1800, but the swift rise of industry in its modern form was impossible until the coming of the railways. The existing Conurbation is largely the

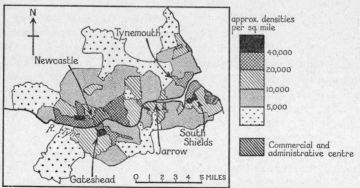

FIG. 117. Structure and population-densities of the Tyneside Conurbation

product of the half-century between 1850 and 1900. Although this is the smallest of the conurbations recognised for census purposes, having fewer than a million people, it is truly an agglomeration of towns, which have spread eastwards and westwards along the steep banks of the incised Tyne. There has been little room for expansion in the inner valley, and population-densities remain high in some central parts (Fig. 117). Similarly, there has been little scope for the displacement of industry to large vacant sites on the edges of towns, particularly since many works serve shipyards.

Basic heavy industries dominate the economy of Tyneside (cf. Fig. 116), although the manufacture of food, clothing, drink, and tobacco, timber-milling, and furniture-making are all well established. Workers employed in shipbuilding, ship-repairing, and marine engineering are mainly men. Large numbers of women find work in light industry.

Shipbuilding

Yards on the northeast coast produce some two-fifths of the annual gross tonnage launched in the U.K. (p. 265). During the inter-war period, the Tyneside shipyards rivalled yards on the Clyde in producing giant passenger liners. It is unlikely that such ships will ever again be built, but there is a marked tendency for the average size of oil tankers to rise steeply, and yards in Northeast England are taking a full part in tanker construction.[1] Marine engineering and ship-repairing, which are closely associated with shipbuilding, are well represented at all the manufacturing towns on the coast of Northeast England.

Sunderland, coming third after the Clyde and the Tyne as a producer of ships, employs about 1 in 4 of its workers in shipbuilding or marine engineering. Its textile trades include the making of ropes—a developed inheritance from the days of sailing-ships.

INDUSTRIAL ESTATES AND LIGHT INDUSTRY

A prominent feature of the geography of this region is the number and wide distribution of industrial estates. These contrast in many ways with older centres—not only in their industrial character, but also in the rate of their development. The Tyneside Conurbation, for example, recorded a rate of population-growth well above the national average for the period 1870–1900, averaging an increase of about 25% per decade, but the impetus was already weakening

[1] The Wear builds tankers of 80,000 tons; a new 58,000 ton liner is to be built on Clydeside.

by the turn of the century, and in the 30 years 1921–1951 the *total* increase was but 2½%. The trading estates, with their associated houses, have come into being since 1930.

In Northeast England, as in other industrial regions of Great Britain, the trading estates represent a response to the Great Slump. Unemployment in the Northeast reached in the 1930s levels which seem incredible today—in Jarrow, for instance, 70% of the shipbuilders had no work. This region was one of the worst distressed of the Distressed Areas. After prolonged debate, the Team Valley Estate near Gateshead was founded as a pilot scheme in accordance with the Special Areas Act of 1934; the policy adopted was to build factories to let, and thus to influence the location of industry. The new factories depended on road transport rather than on rail, and the firms likely to be attracted were those making light products. By 1939 there were already 5,000 new jobs in Northeast England, and clothing, tools, foodstuffs, plastics, safety glass, and radio components were coming from the new works. During World War II it became obvious that much existing industry could readily be dispersed, and the new industrial estates in various parts of the country developed fast.

Development has continued in the post-war period. More than 30 industrial estates are scattered through Northeast England today, in a broad crescent running from the Blyth on the north across the Tees in the south. They provide 50,000 jobs where none existed in 1930; their economic and social repercussions cannot be measured. The products of the new factories are extremely diverse, but the clothing industry, light engineering, and the making of electrical and radio equipment are especially prominent.

At Newton Aycliffe and at Peterlee, whole new towns have come into being. Newton Aycliffe, six miles north of Darlington, is meant primarily to house the workers on the Aycliffe Trading Estate, where a wartime ordnance factory has been converted to peacetime use. Its planned population of 10,000 is already exceeded by a total of 13,000; Peterlee, 10 miles from Durham, is to have 30,000, and a third new town is to be built at Killingworth, just north of Newcastle.

The development of trading estates and the growth of new towns amounts to industrial location of a new kind. Social need, labour supply, and political decisions are the locating factors, rather than lines of transport, coalfields, and access to raw materials. Nevertheless, the defects which the industrial estates are meant to remedy arise directly from the particular modes of geographical development in the past.

PORTS AND PORT TRADE

Newcastle began its rise to greatness in 1080, when the New Castle was built where firm ground closes in towards the river on the downstream side of low-lying, floodable valley flats. The full strategic value of the castle was realised when the Normans secured control of Cumberland, and when Carlisle Castle was built. Medieval Newcastle had close links with Scandinavia and the Baltic, and regular passenger and freight services are maintained today with Bergen, Oslo, Gdynia, and Danish ports; other connections include those with Canada, the U.S.A., and the Mediterranean. The chief cargoes handled at the Tyne Dock at Newcastle are coal, timber (including pit-props), and iron ore destined for Consett. Coastwise trade to and from the Tyne is large.

The harbour at the mouth of the Tyne is almost as artificial as the adjoining urban settlement. Although the Tyne, Wear and Tees all enter the sea by drowned mouths, so that their entrances are landlocked, a great deal of improvement has been necessary. At the beginning of the 19th century, the low-water depth on the bar at the mouth of the Tyne was only 6 feet; by the end of the 19th century massive protecting piers had been built on all three estuaries and channels had been dredged to low-water depths of 25 or 30 feet. Docks were constructed at Hartlepool, Middlesbrough, Sunderland and South Shields in the mid-century, either by private dock companies or by railway companies; docks on the north bank of the Tyne came rather later. In all cases, the new facilities were designed chiefly to assist the coal-export trade. As industry developed, so the docks were improved and extended, and their handling-equipment was modified and replaced.

Sunderland's docks on the Wear are equipped for handling coal, bulk cargoes, and oil. Sweden, Rotterdam, and Antwerp are the main termini of services from Sunderland, while North African ports supply a considerable fraction of total imports. Overseas trade from the Tees goes mainly to and from the Baltic and nearby Continental ports, the Mediterranean, the Far East, and Australasia.

CHAPTER 20

The Industrial Region of the West Riding: The Concealed Coalfield in Nottinghamshire

Population: about 2,750,000.
Largest towns: (a) The West Yorkshire Conurbation (1,700,000) of which the leading members are:
Leeds (510,500).
Bradford (295,750).
Huddersfield (130,250).
Halifax (96,000).
Wakefield (61,500).
Keighley (56,000).
Dewsbury (53,000).
Morley (40,250).
Batley (39,500).
Spenborough (36,500).
Pudsey (34,750).
Brighouse (30,750).
Shipley (29,750).
(b) Large towns between the Conurbation and the south end of the Pennines:
Sheffield (494,000).
Doncaster (86,500).
Rotherham (85,250).
Barnsley (74,750).
Chesterfield (67,750) (Derbyshire).

Within this region are two dense concentrations of industry. Manufacturing in the West Yorkshire Conurbation is dominated by the production of textiles and clothing, while steel-making, engineering, and mining are the leading interests of the towns in south Yorkshire and in adjacent parts of Derbyshire and Nottinghamshire. Thus this industrial region is subdivided into two parts, each containing a town with more than half-a-million inhabitants—Leeds in the north and Sheffield in the south. The concealed coalfield in Nottinghamshire is discussed separately at the end of the chapter.

The Setting

Lying on the flanks of the Pennines, the region includes land which is described either in Chap. 21 (Scarplands of Eastern England)

316

or in Chap. 17 (the South and Central Pennine divisions). Industry runs westward up the Pennine valleys between the tongues of moorland which cap divides; industrial outposts on the east are set amid the farmland of the Trent vale. Agriculturally as well as physically, the region overlies the passage from upland to lowland, the agricultural transition being well expressed by an eastward increase in the proportion of tillage to grass.

This transition corresponds to an eastward decline in height, a reduction in rainfall, and an improvement in soil quality. It is complicated, however, and to some extent blurred, by the effects of the large towns on their surroundings. The land use and farming practice of the region have been modified in four main ways by urban influences. Firstly, much land has been lost to non-agricultural use, in addition to the land occupied by the towns themselves, for collieries and tip-heaps are numerous, both along the outcrop of the Coal Measures and on the concealed coalfield to the east, while opencast working of coal removes large areas from agriculture for a period of years. Secondly, pollution of the atmosphere by industrial smoke and fumes reduces the amount of sunlight, and some of the falling dust is capable of damaging crops and harming livestock. Thirdly, damage by trespass occurs frequently, as it usually does on the outskirts of large towns; it includes trespass by dogs, which strongly discourages the keeping of sheep. On the other hand, the large towns provide enormous markets for farm produce, and their proximity stimulates intensive cultivation, especially in the forms of market gardening and dairying. Although the modern practice of transporting fresh milk over long distances has reduced the advantages of local dairy-farmers, dairying is still dominant on the flanks of the high ground in a belt which runs northwards by Chesterfield, Sheffield, and Barnsley, and on past Wakefield between Leeds and Bradford. Towards the east of the exposed coalfield, mixed farming becomes common, with its emphasis on tillage crops and beef and store cattle. Still farther eastward comes the Magnesian Limestone belt, which is mainly arable (Chap. 21). In the northeast of the region the eastward changes are obscured by the presence of Leeds, by the development of low ground about the Aire and the Calder, and also by the intensification of market-gardening. Market-garden produce from the area south of Leeds includes half the rhubarb grown in England.

The transition across this region from Highland to Lowland Britain is well shown by the location of its towns. The westernmost of these lie well within the margin of the Pennines, while those in the southeast are equally clearly in the Trent lowland. Halifax is set some 15 miles inside the limit of the uplands, no more than 16 miles in a direct line from Burnley or 14 miles from Rochdale, and

Sheffield is notoriously compressed in the valleys of the Don and its tributaries. At the other extreme, Doncaster lies east of the Magnesian Limestone belt. The wideness of the urbanised belt is associated with the gentle dips of the Coal Measures which, exposed in a broad strip of country running from Leeds and Bradford southwards past Chesterfield, sink slowly eastwards beneath younger rocks, where they can be reached by colliery shafts. The passage from upland to lowland occurs mainly on the exposed coalfield, but the boundary of the industrial region does not coincide with the physical boundary between plateau in the west and scarpland in the east.

The Pennine flank is deeply cut by eastward-flowing streams running in incised valleys. The intervening divides typically have the subdued tops which result from planation in previous cycles of erosion, but complications are produced by the etching into relief of west-facing scarps. The Wharfe, Aire and Calder in the north retain some parts of their west-east consequent lines, trenching the high ground in markedly incised valleys which provide routes through the upland block. Many small dip-streams come off the upland farther south, but the Dearne alone maintains its easterly direction across the exposed coalfield. Much of the surface water is collected by the Don, which is fault-guided across the coalfield below Sheffield and receives the upper Don and the Rother as subsequent tributaries. In the south of the region there are no deep valleys leading towards the west; the upland rises above 2,000 ft. in the Peak District and broadens in the Derbyshire Dome. Sheffield is isolated in comparison with Leeds; Leeds, moreover, had ready access to the sea— by way of the Humber—when need arose, whereas Sheffield was partly enclosed on the east by the little-inhabited Sherwood Forest and by the ill-drained lowland of the Trent valley. Although the two towns are very similar in population at the present day, the industrial neighbours of Sheffield are fewer and smaller than those of Leeds. Doncaster, Rotherham and Chesterfield have a total population of some 239,500, whereas Bradford, Huddersfield and Halifax together contain more than 520,000. But the relative degree of isolation cannot by itself explain the contrast in respect of population and number of towns between the north and south of the region. The essential reason for that contrast is to be sought in different modes of industrial development.

THE WOOLLEN TEXTILE INDUSTRY

Origins and Growth

The ultimate origins of woollen manufacturing in the West Yorkshire Conurbation are hard to define. Sheep-farming and the making of woollen cloth were largely controlled by monks during the Middle Ages, many monastic flocks being kept on the Pennine uplands. Sheep-farming and the crafts of spinning and weaving survived the 16th-century dissolution of the monasteries, but subsequent development of the local textile industry involved far more than the taking-over of land and craft by laymen. The industry was certainly encouraged by the strength previously attained; it had already been able to attract refugee textile-workers from Europe in the late 1400s, but still in 1500 Yorkshire ranked a rather poor third among the woollen-producing areas of England, coming after the West Country and East Anglia. The great advantages of West Yorkshire, in the days before the industrial revolution, lay far less in local supplies of wool than in water-supply.

In early modern times, textile working in west Yorkshire was mainly a family concern, combined with rather unproductive small-scale farming. Family labour was cheap, and production costs were further kept down by the making of coarse cloths, but the local wool was adequate neither in amount nor in quality. It was too coarse even for many of the locally-produced cloths, and during the 16th and 17th centuries, raw wool was brought in from the Midlands and Lancashire. Worsted manufacture, introduced by powerful clothiers towards the end of the 17th century, brought changes into the industrial structure, but much domestic craft persisted for many years afterwards. Defoe in the early 18th century named Leeds, Bradford, Wakefield, Huddersfield and Halifax as the chief centres of the clothing trade, but also made clear the importance in the neighbouring valleys of small and thickly-scattered manufactories, each with its own water-supply from stream, gutter or pipe. In the days of hand-craft and small machines, very many single sources of water were needed for washing, fulling and dyeing. West Yorkshire had the benefit of multitudinous streams of soft water, either from the Millstone Grit or from the Coal Measures, and of an annual rainfall in the headwater basins ranging up to some 60 inches.

As the use of machinery became steadily more extensive, the area profited at the expense of its rivals who were less well supplied with sources of power. Spinning was mechanised first, and west Yorkshire supplied much yarn to East Anglia and the West Country during the 18th century. When steam-power was applied to textile manufacture, the advantages of West Yorkshire over the two other areas became overwhelming. Mechanisation of the woollen industry was slow, however (Chap. 6), and the benefit of local coal produced only a gradual and incomplete concentration of that industry in West Yorkshire. Within West Yorkshire, complete concentration on the coalfield did not take place. Numbers of the worst-placed water-driven mills were abandoned; others, nearer to the mines, were converted to the use of steam, and new steam-driven mills appeared throughout the district, but even today the textile-manufacturing towns do not all stand on the Coal Measures (Fig. 118).

Although the total number of sheep in the British Isles is not by any means negligible, the domestic clip could not supply the present Yorkshire mills with wool, even if there were no mills in other parts of these islands. Similarly, the output of cloth and clothing far outstrips the needs of the home market. Importing raw wool from abroad—especially from Australia, South Africa and New Zealand —and exporting part of the output of its textile and clothing industries, West Yorkshire provides an excellent example of the results of industrial momentum. Textile manufacture gives employment to no less than 16%—more than 1 in 6—of *all* workers in the West Yorkshire Conurbation, and the clothing trades take another 6%. In combination, therefore, the two industrial groups require more than one-fifth of the total labour force—a higher fraction than the one-sixth recorded in the Southeast Lancashire Conurbation.

Localisation within the Industry

Within West Yorkshire, there is much localisation of certain types of textile manufacture. It takes a different form from the spatial separation of spinning and weaving which typifies Lancashire, for the main distinction in Yorkshire is between the making of worsteds and the making of woollens. Worsted manufacture is concentrated in the north and west of the textile district, in and beyond Huddersfield, Halifax, and Bradford. Within the worsted industry there is much specialisation by single mills either in spinning or in weaving, particularly in the larger towns. Woollen manufacture, located chiefly in the south and east of the district, is characterised by integrated mills where both spinning and weaving are carried on (cf. Plate 50).

Some of the reasons for the distinction in practice between worsted spinning and worsted weaving are historical. The worsted industry did not evolve directly from local woollen manufacture, but was superimposed on it. Worsted manufacture was, from the outset, in the hands of concerns or individual mill-owners who specialised in a single process—or, at most, in a limited range of processes. In addition, there are technical reasons to encourage the separation of worsted spinning from worsted weaving—for example, the fact that a large variety of yarns is used in weaving, and that yarn is produced for use outside West Yorkshire.[1]

[1] This matter is discussed in Wilfred Smith: *An Economic Geography of Great Britain* (Methuen, London).

A number of successive processes were performed in the original small woollen manufactories, in many of which the raw wool was received and finished cloth produced. The industrial structure typical of craft industry was retained in the early days of powered machinery, and has persisted subsequently. Firms producing woollens tend to be smaller than those producing worsteds, even though spinning and weaving are both performed in many single woollen-mills.

The partial separation of worsted making from the making of woollens reduces the significance of separation between spinning and weaving. Some small centres do, however, specialise either in spinning or in weaving, and weavers are at least twice as numerous as spinners in Huddersfield and Dewsbury, and five times as numerous

FIG. 118. Manufacturing employment in the Industrial West Riding

in Batley, while spinners outnumber weavers in Bradford, Shipley, Keighley, and Halifax. The finishing trades are well represented in all the large towns, and especially so in Bradford, Batley, and Halifax. Garment workers are highly concentrated in Leeds. Despite its huge size, this town has but one-third as many textile operatives as Bradford, half as many as Huddersfield, and fewer even than Halifax, which is but one-fifth as populous as Leeds. Leeds, on the other hand, employs more than 80% of the clothing workers of the whole Conurbation—a figure representing a far higher concentration than is found in Lancashire, where the corresponding figure (for Manchester and Salford combined) is 66%.

THE WEST YORKSHIRE CONURBATION

Industrial Employment

Since the woollen textile industry (including the making of worsteds) is so prominent in the West Yorkshire Conurbation, part of what follows refers directly to the previous section. The proportion of industrial workers taken by the textile and garment industries runs at about 55% in all the large towns but Wakefield. Wakefield apart, the extremes are found in Leeds ($44\frac{1}{2}$%) and Batley (67%). Leeds has more than a third of its industrial workers in the garment trades alone; it records, however, a high level of employment in occupations other than industrial, as would be expected from a town of its size and complexity (Fig. 118).

Wakefield has more than a third of its industrial workers in the metal trades, and more than a quarter in coal-mining. With this exception, coal-mining is not prominent in the Conurbation, but metal manufacture and engineering are well distributed, taking up to one-third of industrial workers in the largest towns of all. Smelting is not practised, the 20 steel furnaces depending on local scrap and on pig-iron and crude steel from elsewhere. Although engineering products include machines for the textile and clothing factories, the metal industry is only partly dependent on the regional production of textiles and garments. Leeds especially has acquired a very large range of engineering, producing aero-engines, aircraft, motor vehicles, and foundry products.

Character and Connections

Many of the great towns of the Conurbation are cramped in smallish tributary valleys. Whereas Leeds and Wakefield stand respectively on the Aire and the Calder, where these rivers emerge from their Pennine trenches, Bradford is crowded into the narrow valley of a tributary of the Aire, Halifax into that of an equally small feeder of the Calder, and Huddersfield is located on the Colne three miles above its confluence with the Calder. Belts of building run up and down the valleys, and the largest towns have spread up the valley-sides to develop suburbs on the hilltops. Large towns, small towns, and swollen industrial villages are all bound together by strings of houses and factories and by a tangle of roads, railways, and canals.

Between a quarter and a third of all the people in the Conurbation live in Leeds, which is the greatest centre of wholesale trade, shopping, and finance. It is not however the only centre, Bradford being a vigorous and neighbouring rival. The West Yorkshire Conurbation resembles the Southeast Lancashire and West Midland Conurbations in lacking a single focus.

The West Yorkshire Conurbation developed mainly during the 19th century. In 1801, Leeds had but 53,000 people; like its neighbours, it expanded rapidly with the growth of the wool textile industry, but already by 1900 the rate of growth in this area had fallen below the average for England and Wales. Little increase has taken place in the last 25 years. A great many of the buildings in the Conurbation are constructed in the styles of a hundred years ago; the town centres have been progressively transformed by reconstruction, but the old residential parts still include back-to-back houses. The tasks of re-planning and rebuilding are made difficult by the intermingling of settlements, and also by the problems of maintaining the basic industry. The manufacture of woollen textiles is holding its own, just as the population of the area is not falling. Wool does not yet suffer the severe competition of artificial fibres which afflicts the cotton industry, nor has it great tropical and oriental markets to lose; but the textile industry of West Yorkshire has no prospect of further growth in the spectacular manner of the 19th century.

The overseas connections of the Conurbation in general, and of the woollen textile industry in particular, are provided mainly by Liverpool and Hull. Connections with Liverpool are but slightly handicapped by the Central Pennines, which are crossed not only by a generous number of roads and by several railways but also by three canals. The Leeds and Liverpool Canal, bending far to the north through the Aire-Ribble Gap, still carries some traffic (see Chap. 9), but the canals running up the Calder and Colne towards Southeast Lancashire were from the outset encumbered by too many locks. All the same, it is significant that canals across the Pennines should have been built at all. They show an appreciation of Liverpool as an inlet and outlet for West Yorkshire, and emphasise the fact that land routes can cross the Central Pennines without undue difficulty. The Aire and Calder Navigation remains successful, with single trains of compartment boats carrying up to 700 tons.

COAL-MINING

Local coal greatly aided the textile manufacturers of West Yorkshire in the early days of industrialisation. No large mines operate today in the textile-making district, where the total output of coal is small, and where Wakefield alone has a high proportion of industrial workers in coal-mining. Barnsley records 51% of its industrial workers in mining, and Pontefract 43% (Fig. 118), but these towns are outside the Conurbation. The chief coal-mining district does not overlap with the main concentration of woollen manufacture (cf. Plate 51), and penetrates the West Yorkshire Conurbation only in the southeast. The large collieries occur in a belt stretching from the Aire valley below Leeds on the north to beyond Nottingham on the south (cf. Fig. 120). The western limit of this belt runs through Wakefield, a little to the west of Barnsley, through the eastern fringes of Sheffield, and past Chesterfield to Nottingham. Its eastern limit projects down the Don valley below Doncaster, and, farther south, runs well to the east of Mansfield.

The great absolute and relative importance of the Yorkshire, Derby and Notts. coalfield to the English economy has been made clear in Chap. 7. That part which is defined by the National Coal Board as the Yorkshire Coalfield has a very long history of coal-working. Digging was recorded as early as the 14th century, and by the 16th century many collieries were in work. At that time Wakefield was the chief mining centre, but coal was already cheaper than local wood in Sheffield. There are 40 coal seams, of which 32 are at present worked. Outcrop mining along the western fringe has largely ceased, except for opencast working, and in this field, as in Northumberland and Durham, there has been a shift of mining down the dip of the Coal Measures. At one time about half the coal raised came from the Barnsley (or Top Hard) Seam, which, providing a workable thickness of some 6 ft. of coal, is the seam chiefly worked in the concealed coalfield, where 2 in every 5 of the large collieries are located. But although the easterly dip of the concealed measures is generally slight, workings tapping the Barnsley Seam have reached depths of 3,000 feet, where roof pressures are severe and the dangers of fire and gas are great. The Parkgate Seam, some 750 feet deeper still, sets great problems of mining.

Reserves are great, being estimated some 10,000 million tons of workable coal in the whole Yorkshire, Derby and Notts. coalfield.

This total, however, is less than previous estimates, for the concealed seams are now known to thin eastwards, and some to have been eroded away before the Permo-Trias was deposited. Prospects are best in the north of the concealed field.

A wide range of coals is produced—household and industrial coal, locomotive coal from the Barnsley and Parkgate seams, and gas and coking coals which are extracted mainly from the northern part of the coalfield. Large reserves of coking coal justify a planned increase in output for the steel industry. Since many working pits are fairly modern, less reconstruction of collieries is necessary than in some other coalfields.

THE SHEFFIELD DISTRICT

The presence of gas and coking coals in South Yorkshire is an obvious benefit to the industries of the Sheffield district, but, as in the West Midlands, the local industries were founded centuries before the industrial revolution. The early iron-workers used Coal

Fig. 119. Sheffield and its local setting

Measure ores and smelted by charcoal, combining farming with metal-work during the Middle Ages. Many small smithies operated in the 16th century, when local water-power and local millstones were being used in the making of cutlery. The effects of industrial momentum were already evident, for steel was then imported from Sweden, Russia and Spain. The two outstanding early advantages of the industry were the local iron ore which gave iron-working its start, and the supply of power from the Pennine streams: significantly enough, the last water-driven forge ceased work as late as 1955.

Huntsman laid one foundation-stone of Sheffield's present greatness when, in the 18th century, he produced crucible steel which could be cast. Bessemer opened his own very successful works in Sheffield in 1858. During the late 1800s the town's steel-making industry profited from changes in the construction of war-ships and from the development of alloy steels.

From a total of some 2,000 in 1600, the population of Sheffield grew to 3,500 in 1700, to 35,000 in 1800, and to 400,000 in 1900. In each of the 18th and 19th centuries, that is to say, its numbers increased tenfold, but it was during the 19th century that Sheffield became a huge industrial town. Since 1900 its numbers have continued to increase, but less rapidly than before; indeed, there has been a slight tendency to decline during the last 40 years, which is concealed in the census figures by the effects of boundary changes. The built-up area, however, is still expanding, for, like many other great towns, Sheffield is experiencing the so-called flight from the centre.

For all its numbers, Sheffield is not the overwhelmingly dominant town that might be expected from its size. Wedged uncomfortably in the narrow valleys of the Don, the Sheaf and their tributaries, its central part is not very easily accessible from surrounding areas (Fig. 119). Rotherham and Doncaster grip their environs as tightly as Sheffield grips its own surroundings. As an industrial town, however, Sheffield deeply overshadows its neighbours. Some two-fifths of its employed population works in steel-making or in engineering, and 3 out of every 4 industrial workers are in some metal-manufacturing trade (Fig. 118). In the Sheffield district is found the greatest concentration of steel furnaces in the British Isles (Fig. 56). Acid open-hearth furnaces produce steel which is particularly suitable for large forgings, while electric furnaces make highly alloyed steels. The local blast-furnaces cannot supply all the needs of the steel-works, for which high-grade pig-iron, scrap, and alloying metals are brought in. Most of the steelworks are independent of the blast-furnaces—i.e., there is little integration of the iron and steel industry.

Lack of integration would be a handicap in producing large amounts of the standard steels, but the Sheffield district concentrates on special orders and on short runs (Plate 18). It makes much alloy steel for use outside the district, in addition to precision tools and a very wide variety of highly specialised machinery. The centuries-old lighter trades of Sheffield are still pursued. Their main products are metal tableware, cutting tools, and hand tools, in the making of which Sheffield is the leading centre of the British Isles.

Sheffield is one of the main producers of refractories in the British Isles. Local fireclays and ganister were originally used, but nowadays Magnesian Limestone is worked into linings for basic steel furnaces, and ganister for making silica bricks comes from South Wales and Durham.

Rotherham, at the confluence of the Rother with the Don, has two-thirds of its industrial workers in the metal trades and one-fifth in coal mining, its chief manufactured products being machinery and heavy iron and steel. More than half the industrial workers of Mexborough (17,000) are employed in collieries, but Doncaster, which has replaced Barnsley as the principal mining centre of the Yorkshire coalfield, still has more than half its industrial workers in the metal trades (Fig. 118). Doncaster possesses large railway workshops, makes mining and agricultural machinery, and is a producer of nylon. Industrial estates on the outskirts of Sheffield, Rotherham, and Doncaster include light-engineering works.

Chesterfield, although in Derbyshire, has close affinities with the Sheffield district. Rapid industrial growth began when the railway, by-passing Sheffield, gave access to the local coals, and Chesterfield today possesses blast-furnaces—some supplying its iron-founding industry—and makes mining machinery, furnaces, and tubes.

THE CONCEALED COALFIELD IN NOTTINGHAMSHIRE

Towns and industry on the southern concealed portion of the Yorks., Derby, and Notts. coalfield show well the difficulties of regional subdivision. The area belongs physically to the Scarplands of Eastern England (see following chapter); its mining links it with the exposed coalfield, while textile and leather industries associate it with Nottingham. Mansfield (53,250) makes hosiery, footwear, and metal goods; Sutton-in-Ashfield (40,500) has textile works and produces steel alloy castings; Worksop (34,250) has interests in engineering, brewing, and furniture-making. All these towns, like Hucknall (23,250) and Kirkby-in-Ashfield (21,750) include large numbers of miners. Mansfield in particular is surrounded by dis-

FIG. 120. Industrial and mining settlements in part of Nottinghamshire, on the concealed coalfield. The former limits of Sherwood Forest closely resembled the outcrop-boundaries of the Bunter Pebble Beds

tended settlements, including mining villages, and by collieries where huge tips rise above the discontinuous remnants of Sherwood Forest (Fig. 120). Mining has indeed reached, and passed, the eastern limit of the Forest; the newest colliery hereabouts is but 8 miles west of the river Trent. Farther south, another new colliery lies on the far side of the river, 5 miles southeast of the centre of Nottingham. Mining thus invades not only the eastern Scarplands but also the Midland Triangle.

CHAPTER 21

Scarplands of Eastern England

Area: about 6,000 square miles.
Population: about 1,000,000: but see note below.
Largest towns: Hull (303,250).
   York (104,500).
   Grimsby (96,750).
   Lincoln (77,000).
   Scunthorpe (67,250).
   Scarborough (42,500).
   Cleethorpes (32,750).
   Bridlington (26,000).
   Goole (18,750).
   This list excludes (i) members of the Tyneside Conurbation, (ii) large industrial towns on or near the Wear and Tees, (iii) members of the West Yorkshire Conurbation, (iv) large industrial towns on the Pennine flanks south of that Conurbation. The population for the region is obtained by subtracting the combined population of these four groups from the total numbers of inhabitants, and rounding-off the resulting figure.
   Some 80% of the region is in improved farmland, with tillage and grass roughly equal in extent.
Numbers of livestock: cattle, 875,000; sheep, 1,850,000; pigs, 450,000.

The regional unity of this region is imposed by the scarpland character of the terrain, and by contrasts with adjacent regions. Regional boundaries, however, are largely transitional. In the south, the boundary runs along the margin of the Fenland, crosses the Jurassic cuesta where this widens into the Leicestershire Wolds, and crosses the Trent valley at the exit from the Midland Triangle. In the west, hills increase rather slowly with height as the Pennines are approached; the Magnesian Limestone, with a west-facing scarp at the boundary of the exposed coalfield, blurs the passage from vale country to hill country, and a concentration of mining and manufacture tends to obscure the physical boundary. There is, nevertheless, a fundamental difference between the Pennine plateaus and the lower valley of the Trent. In the north, again, the scarpland country reaches into the Industrial Northeast of England, but beyond the industrial region the terrain belongs to the Border country (Figs. 106, 111).

Climate

Although the North York Moors receive up to 40 inches of precipitation a year, and suffer heavy falls of snow in some winters, most of the scarpland region lies in the strong rain-shadow cast by the Pennines. Annual precipitation declines from 30 inches on the west to less than 25 inches on the lower Tees, at the mouth of the Humber, at the head of the Humber and on the lower Trent. Mean annual range of temperature is lower, at about 21°F, than in the fruit-growing districts of Kent; the frost-free period exceeds 5 months in all lowland parts and rises to 6 or 7 months in Holderness and along the Lincolnshire coast. Actual January mean temperature is below 38°F in all parts, but winter cold of this order is in no way a handicap to arable farming—indeed, the most highly-tilled parts of England are roughly enclosed by the 38° sea-level isotherm for January. The practical benefit of moderate frost, capable of breaking up the soil but not of killing autumn-sown crops, is an important one.

Physique and Agriculture: The Western Districts

The Magnesian Limestone belt is dominantly arable. Its sheep-farming has declined somewhat in recent years, partly because of sheep-worrying by dogs from the industrial towns, and cash cropping of potatoes, sugar beet, and grain is on the increase. Cash-cropping has also been established on the lime-poor soils of the adjacent Sherwood Forest district, which is based on permeable sandstones and conglomerates. The stronger of these rocks rise in a low, broken scarp along the west of Sherwood Forest; the eastern side is bordered by a second line of equally low, equally broken scarps where weak sandstones come to the surface. Between the eastern side of the Sherwood belt and the terraces which border the Trent comes a broad strip of low hills, where mixed farming is widely developed on loamy soils. Fruit-farms occur in patches round the small market-towns.

From the mouth of the Tees to the Trent below Nottingham—a distance of more than a hundred miles—stretches a strike vale, eroded in weak marls in the upper Permo-Trias (Fig. 111). The vale lies almost everywhere less than 200 feet above sea-level. Its drainage is dominated by strike streams—the lower Tees, the middle Swale, the Ouse, and the lower Trent. These rivers collect the waters of the upper Tees, the upper Swale, the Ure, Nidd, Wharfe, Aire, and Calder, which in their Pennine reaches retain elements of a former west-east consequent system. The competing rivers were dismembered by successive captures, and the number of outlets to the sea reduced to two—one at the mouth of the Tees, where the weak rocks reach the coast, and the other at the Humber, where scarp-forming Jurassic rocks are at their thinnest and weakest. Glacial deposits in the Vale of York—including end-moraines—obliterate the details of the immediately pre-glacial surface.

There is much arable land, for tillage is encouraged by nearby concentrations of industrial population and by the rain-shadow of the Pennines, with the result that parts of the vale were able to resist the reversion to grass which typified the inter-war period. The same factors which favour tillage also favour dairying and market-gardening. In detail, however, land-use distributions are very variable, partly because of variations in soil, and are liable to change from year to year on a single farm (Fig. 121). Flood-plains are mainly in permanent grass, which is extensive on the wide alluvial flats of the Humberhead levels.

Physique and Agriculture: The Eastern Districts

East of the Trent lie four cuestas, two north of the Humber and two south of it. The North York Moors and Lincoln Edge are based on Jurassic limestones and sandstones, while the Yorkshire Wolds and the Lincolnshire Wolds are cut in Chalk.

The North York Moors rise well above 1,000 feet in tabular, windswept crests, their backslope deeply gashed by young valleys. Large areas are in rough pasture, with heather moor extensive at the highest levels. The Vale of Pickering, the strike vale between the Jurassic and Chalk cuestas north of the Humber, was the site of an ice-dammed lake during the Ice Age, when the Derwent was diverted westwards from its original direct course to the sea. Its floor is covered by glacial deposits, lake-sediments, and peaty alluvium. The Vale is enclosed at the eastern end by a terminal moraine, and at the western by the low Howardian Hills, where the Jurassic rocks are thin. Uplift caused the Jurassic sediments to be eroded, and allowed the succeeding Chalk to overstep them to the west, so that the Chalk downs of the Yorkshire Wolds, swinging round to the south, pass across the Jurassic scarp-formers and conceal them.[1] Tillage and grassland are patchily distributed on the floor of the Vale of Pickering, in accordance with the poor drainage of some valley-bottom sites.

The Yorkshire Wolds, rising little above 800 feet, are extensively in tillage. Farms here profited from their generally light soils when the sheep-barley combination paid, and even today, with dairying handicapped by the same light soils and by a rainfall little greater

[1] Compare the way in which the Greensand oversteps underlying formations in the Blackdown Hills (Fig. 145).

Key to
soil
plan :-

Parent material	Soil
Alluvium	clay
Silt and Clay	grey-brown clay with stones
Boulder clay	brown loam with stones
S/G ..... Glacial sand and gravel	brown sandy loam with stones
Red Sandstone	red and brown sand

0   ¼   ½ MILES

FIG. 121*a*. Soil map of the Home Farm, Hutton Wandesley Estate, Vale of York

1951

For key see 1956 map

FIG. 121*b*

1952

For key see 1956 map

FIG. 121*c*

1953

For key see 1956 map

FIG. 121*d*

954

'or key see 1956 map

FIG. 121*e*

56

A	Asparagus	L	Linseed	r/g	Rotation grass	S/W	Spring wheat
B	Barley	M	Meadow	S	Seeds	W	Wheat
G	Grazing	P	Potatoes	S/B	Sugar beet	W/W	Winter wheat

FIG. 121*f*

s. 121*b-f*. Cropping plans for 1951–4 and 1956, Home Farm, Hutton Wandesley Estate than 30 inches a year, sheep are still quite numerous and barley is still the main tillage crop. To the south, in Holderness, tenacious soils developed on thick boulder clay are widely planted to wheat, and market-gardens take advantage of the long growing-season to produce vegetables in large quantity.

South of the Humber, Jurassic rocks form a low but well-marked cuesta in Lincoln Edge, the crest remaining below 400 feet as far as the neighbourhood of Grantham (cf. Fig. 122). The strike vale east of Lincoln Edge, the diverging Lincolnshire Wolds, and the coastal lowland, are all thickly overspread with boulder clay. Broad alluvial flats occur in the Louth and Grimsby marshes, and in the valley of the Ancholme between the two cuestas. Agricultural statistics for Lindsey

FIG. 122. Land-use sample for Lincoln Edge. The top of the low cuesta is almost wholly in tillage, the scarp-face in permanent grass

give a fair summary for this portion of the region. In Lindsey, as a whole, wheat and barley between them take half the area under tillage crops. Potatoes and oats are the next most extensive crops, followed by mangolds, which are grown in unusually large quantities. Lincoln sheep are folded on arable land, still in considerable numbers. Beefstock—purebred Lincoln Reds or Lincoln Red crosses—are fattened, but the production of fat cattle has tended to decline for many years, lessening the demand for summer pasture on the coastal marshes. Dairying is well established.

Settlement

With the vigorous farming of this region goes a considerable rural population. Scarp-foot and dip-foot villages line the margins

of the North York Moors, the Yorkshire Wolds, the Lincolnshire Wolds, and Lincoln Edge, many place-names bespeaking a
Danish origin (Fig. 123). In parts of the vale country, rural settlements are irregularly distributed in accordance with variety in minor
detail of terrain, but a distinct band of villages appears along the
western boundary of the region between Doncaster and Harrogate.
Beyond these towns the rural pattern has been overlaid by industry.

FIG. 123. Nucleated scarp-foot and dip-foot villages, Lincoln Edge

Country towns are few, considering the size of the region. They are
more widely spaced than in East Anglia, and far more widely so
than in the Borders of the West Country (Chap. 26), their sparsity
contributing to the strong social isolation typical of villages in East
Lincolnshire. Scarborough, Bridlington and Cleethorpes are the
leading seaside resorts in the region. Goole, Grimsby and Hull are
contrasted ports, and York, Lincoln and Scunthorpe rank as
industrial towns. No one town acts as the regional capital, for
the region has too little coherence to possess a single urban focus.
Hull, York and Lincoln have close trading connections with their

surroundings, but each has interests extending far beyond its immediate service area.

Towns and Industry

Hull (Fig. 124) is the fourth port of the United Kingdom, ranking after London, Liverpool, and Belfast. It seems well placed to serve the textile industries of the West Riding, but in actuality the hinterlands of Liverpool and Manchester extend on to the eastern side of the Pennines, and the two western ports compete very strongly with Hull. Liverpool and Manchester combined command a larger share of the export trade than of the import trade, having gained their success in exporting partly at the expense of Hull.

| Chief concentrations of industry | Heavily built-up areas, mainly developed before 1914 | Less densely built-up areas mainly developed after 1920 |

Fig. 124. Hull and its local setting

Textiles amount but to 0·1% of Hull's exports by weight. Coal, coke, and patent fuels provide three-fifths of total exports by weight, while coal, machinery, and miscellaneous manufactured goods are the chief exports by value. Incoming produce, destined mainly for use in the industries of Hull itself, include grain, oilseeds, timber, fruit, wool, foodstuffs, fish, and mineral oils. About three-quarters of Hull's exports go to the Continent, which supplies one-third of the imports.

Hull, in the 12th century, was a trading settlement located on a creek. Profiting by the destruction of Ravenscar, which was destroyed by wave-erosion on the Holderness coast, Hull flourished in the 14th century, establishing trade links with the Continent. It shared in the Greenland whale fishery of the 16th and 18th centuries, extending its interest in organic oils with the 18th-century import and milling of rape oil—the foundation of the processing of oils and the manufacture of paint which are prominent today. Before docks were made, deep water was ensured by the swing of the Humber against its north bank; the first dock of the present nine was excavated in the 1770s, the alluvium of the Humber offering no obstacle. In the mid-19th century began the smoking of fish, and the discovery of the highly productive Silver Pits of the Dogger Bank in 1850 greatly benefited the Hull fleet. Increasing knowledge of the North Sea fishing-grounds, the construction of docks, and the increase in the size of fishing vessels with resulting concentration on a few ports, have all been to the profit of Hull, where there are now some 160 vessels and 3,500 fishermen. Trawling is the main practice, the fish landed at Hull being chiefly of the demersal type. Growing prosperity of Hull's fishing was accompanied by the rise of shipbuilding in the yards at Beverley, where coasting vessels and power trawlers are constructed.

Hull has developed manufactures of chemicals in association with its older production of paints; sawmilling and woodworking reflect its long connection with Baltic ports, as also does flour-milling, although Russian exports of food grain ceased in 1914. The industry of mechanical engineering is partly associated with shipbuilding through marine engineering and ship repairing, but there are in addition manufactures of aircraft and excavating plant. Cement is also produced.

Hull suffered much bomb-damage during World War II, but has subsequently restored its industries and recovered its port trade. Port improvements are in hand, and much new light industry has been acquired since 1945.

Goole, more than 20 miles inland of Hull and still on tidewater, is in some ways a rival port. Whereas the port trade of Hull has developed mainly under the influence of the town's own industries, however, Goole has succeeded in establishing close connections with the West Riding. By value of trade, Goole is about the 15th port of the U.K. (p. 150), having a trade a sixth as large as that of Hull, and recording an excess of exports over imports.

Grimsby (Plate 52) claims to be the world's greatest fishing port. Silting destroyed a port trade which had flourished in the Middle Ages, increasing the social isolation of the villages of the hinterland, but the town was reinvigorated when the railway entered in 1848 and when the first dock was finished in 1854. The docks were developed by the railway companies, who provided fast trains to distribute fish. Two hundred trawlers are based on Grimsby today, and express goods trains remain vital to the fishery. Commercial docks handle timber, wood-pulp, grain and coal; the shipbuilding industry is connected mainly with fishing, and a number of ancillary industries are carried on. Reclaimed land accommodates most of the factories including those producing chemicals. Ships too big to enter Grimsby go to the docks at Immingham, 6 miles away to the northwest, where, as at Hull, there is natural deep water close inshore. The chief incoming cargoes at Immingham are grain, timber, and iron ore; coal is exported.

Lincoln was a Roman town, sited on the Jurassic cuesta above the Witham gap, and on the Roman Ermine Street which ran north and south along the dry ground of the cuesta, avoiding the forests and marshes on either side. Lincoln had considerable strategic importance, for land routes from the east were directed to it by the projecting fenland in the lower Witham valley; it was one of the five Danish boroughs, and acquired a Norman castle and cathedral. During the Middle Ages it was a great centre of the wool trade, with manufactures of woollen cloth, flour, and stained glass, but the decay of the trade in wool—well in evidence by 1500—depressed the town and recovery did not set in until the 18th century. Engineering developed during the 19th century, with agricultural machinery a leading product, but the loss of export markets in 1914 led to diversification of the industry. Diesel engines, mining gear, excavators and gas turbines are among the items produced today. Agricultural chemicals are manufactured, vegetables are canned, and grain and timber brought by barge from Hull are milled at Lincoln.

York also underwent depression in Tudor times, after having been a Roman fortress, the scene of the coronation of the Emperor Constantine the Great in 306, the capital of Northumbria, and a very great medieval market for wool. Its revival began during the 18th century, when York became a fashionable resort, and was accelerated when railways came in the 19th century. In its early days York possessed great strategic advantages, lying on the east-coast route to the north, commanding the gate between the Pennines and the Yorkshire Wolds, and serving at one time as a base in wars against the Scots. Tactically, also, the site is advantageous. York stands on one of the two moraines which, curving across the Vale of York, are bordered by marsh—marsh which, north of York, included the flood-plain of the lower Nidd, and which on the south was enclosed between the York moraine and the Escrick moraine five miles away (Fig. 125). With the effective width of the lowland gateway thus reduced, York had some natural protection both on the north

Surburban expansion of Barnsley. The pattern of streets and the design of houses are among those typical of the 20th century.

52. Docks and marshalling-yards at Grimsby.

53. Staythorpe Power Station, on the Trent near Newark. The outfall appea on the left (downstream), the intake is just outside the right of the picture (upstream

Chief concentrations of industry

Heavily built-up area, mainly developed before 1914

Less densely built-up area, mainly developed after 1920

FIG. 125. York and its local setting

and on the south, and was best approached along the hummocky moraine either from east or west.

The present nodality of York is expressed by converging roads and railways. The town has railway workshops, light engineering of various kinds, and flourishing manufactures of cocoa, chocolate and confectionery. There is a considerable tourist traffic, which the dignified ecclesiastical history of York encourages, and a large retail trade.

Both at York and at Lincoln the existence of an old-established town was a factor in attracting railways and modern industry. Scunthorpe is also an old foundation, but, lacking a high ecclesiastical status, became no more than a modest market town until the late 19th century. Industrial development began when the Frodingham ores were drawn upon in the late 1800s. Scunthorpe today ranks third, after the Middlesbrough district and South Wales, as a producer of pig-iron, with $14\frac{1}{2}\%$ of the national output. Its blast-furnaces

M

are integrated in steelworks, where the molten pig is passed directly to the open-hearth furnaces (Plate 17).

The Frodingham ores belong to the Lower Lias formation. Although their average content of metallic iron is low—20%—they are calcareous and thus self-fluxing. Most of the extraction is open-cast. Coal and coke are brought by rail from the Yorks., Derby and Notts. coalfield, and additional ore comes from the Northampton-shire Ironfield.

Unlike the Frodingham ores, the petroleum of the Trent valley has given rise to no local manufacturing industry. The output of petroleum makes a very small contribution to national supply, but has understandably aroused much interest. The main producing wells are located either in the neighbourhood of Eakring, 8 miles east of Mansfield, or near Plungar, 12 miles east-southeast of Nottingham. The Eakring and Dukes Wood oilfields are adjacent to one another, with the Kelham Hills, Caunton, and Egmanton fields lying to the east (Fig. 126). The oil is preserved in anticlines in the Millstone Grit, which is up-arched beneath its cover of Permo-Trias.

FIG. 126. Nottinghamshire oilfields

Drilling in the period 1918-1922 gave disappointing results, but oil was proved in a test well in 1939, and the Eakring field was rapidly developed under the pressure of war, peak output of 110,000 tons being reached in 1943. A rapid decline in output was checked in 1948 by the injection of water into the oil-bearing strata on the flanks of the fold, and output has subsequently been maintained. Total production from English oilfields—126,000 tons in 1962—comes mainly from the Trent valley.

During the post-war period, large power-stations have been built on the middle Trent. The stations, which are not located with reference to the needs of the region, are fairly centrally placed in the grid system. They use huge quantities of river-water in cooling, and obtain their coal from the southern part of the Yorks., Derby and Notts. field or from Leicestershire (Plate 53).

CHAPTER 22

The Midland Triangle and Its Northern Borders

IT is far from easy to define the Midlands with any precision. They merge through the Welsh Borderland with the plateau country of Wales; the southern apex of the Midland Triangle projects far down the lower Severn towards Bristol; and while the vales containing Oxford, Aylesbury, and Bedford belong indisputably to the Midlands, the neighbouring Chilterns may be regarded either as the most southeasterly Midland cuesta or as the northwestern flank of the London Basin. East of the Hitchin Gap, at the extremity of the Chilterns, it is especially difficult to discern a rapid change of regional character amid the low, irregular, drift-covered hills, where the Midlands, the London Basin, and East Anglia fade into one another. The boundary of the Fenlands is, indeed, clearly marked by the break of slope at the landward edge of the peaty levels, but farther north the low ground of the Trent valley continues unbroken towards the head of the Humber. The southern end of the Pennines and the towns which have arisen there lie too far south to be placed in northern England, although two hundred years ago it was the Trent above Nottingham which divided the north from the south. Between the Pennines and the Welsh Border, the Midland Gate links the Midland Triangle with lowland south of the Mersey (Figs. 83, 127).

Doubtful though their boundaries may be, the Midlands are separable from surrounding regions. They are also themselves divisible into two distinct regions—the Midland Triangle and the Scarplands of the South Midlands; the former will be described in the present chapter, the latter in the next.

The Midland Triangle and the Scarplands of the South Midlands resemble one another only in extent. They differ especially in their richness in large towns. Some 4,000,000 people living in the Midland Triangle inhabit one or other of the largest towns; if the Potteries are taken into account, the figure rises well above 4,000,000 and relates to 80% of the total population. The local accents in nearly all these towns are of the northern kind; accents differ from town to town, but in the southern ear all vowels are unmistakeably northern. In the Scarplands of the South Midlands no more than two-thirds of a million—less than a third of the population—live in towns

342

FIG. 127. The Midland Triangle and its northern borders; Scarplands of the South Midlands: physique and main settlements

with 30,000 or more people. The largest town in this region is but a tenth the size of Birmingham. Only in quite recent years have towns large by modern standards developed in the Scarpland region, and even in these, the local speech has a strong rustic flavour—if it has escaped the influence of London.

THE MIDLAND TRIANGLE AND ITS NORTHERN BORDERS

Area: about 4,250 square miles.

Population: about 5,500,000.

Largest towns: (a) The West Midland Conurbation (2,350,000) of which the leading members are:—
Birmingham (1,105,750).
Wolverhampton (150,500).
Walsall (117,750).
Solihull (96,000).
West Bromwich (96,000).
Sutton Coldfield (72,250
Smethwick (68,250).
Dudley (61,750).
Brierley Hill (56,500).
Oldbury (54,000).
Rowley Regis (48,250).
Halesowen (44,250).
Stourbridge (44,000).
Wednesbury (34,500).

(b) Towns with close links to the Conurbation:—
Coventry (305,000).
Nuneaton (56,500).
Cannock (42,250).
Kidderminster (40,750).
Bromsgrove (34,500).
Redditch (34,000).

(c) Towns of the Potteries:—
Stoke-on-Trent (265,500).
Newcastle-under-Lyme (76,500).

(d) Towns of the Middle Trent Basin:—
Nottingham (311,750).
Leicester (273,250).
Derby (132,250).
Beeston (56,750).
Burton-upon-Trent (50,750).
Hinckley (41,500).
Loughborough (38,500).
Ilkeston (34,750).
Coalville (26,250).

(e) Remaining towns:—
Cheltenham (72,000).
Gloucester (69,750).
Worcester (65,750).
Rugby (51,750).
Stafford (47,750).
Leamington (43,250).

About three-quarters of the region is in improved farmland; grassland is about twice as extensive as tillage.
Numbers of livestock: cattle, 775,000; sheep, 775,000; pigs, 325,000.

The large towns of the Midland Triangle and its northern borders
are highly industrialised, contain one out of every ten inhabitants
of England, and are complexly interrelated. While some of them fall
into well-defined groups, dominated by a single class of industry,
others stand apart, displaying in many cases industrial affinities
with more than one neighbour. They are widely distributed—
although not evenly distributed—throughout the region.

Around them, and in places merging with their patchy outskirts,
stretches extensive farmland. Although the character of farming is
affected to some extent by the demands of the great urban markets,
well-defined agricultural contrasts still separate one part of the region
from another.

Physique and Soils

The Midland Triangle is largely underlain by rocks of Permo-
Triassic Age, which abut against the Pennines on the north and
the Primary rocks of the Welsh Border on the west (Fig. 127). Coal
Measures rise from beneath the Permo-Trias on the western boundary and on the extremities of the Pennines, and have been
revealed by erosion in the uplifted Black Country, Warwickshire,
and Leicestershire coalfields. Extremely ancient volcanic rocks
protrude through the Permo-Trias in Charnwood Forest. Along
the southeastern margin of the Midland Triangle, the weak Triassic
marls vanish beneath the thin Rhaetic limestone, which is followed
by the thick clays and clayey limestones of the Lower Lias—the
lowest part of the Jurassic system. Being for the most part clayey,
the Lower Lias has been deeply eroded, and its claylands are included in the Midland Triangle.

Large parts of the region have been reduced below 400 ft., falling
to 200 ft. or less in the wide, gently-sloping valleys of large streams.
Post-glacial erosion has been severe throughout, but has not succeeded in removing all the thick and extensive deposits of boulder
clay, which covers much ground in the basins of the Avon and the
Soar.

Drainage in the north is to the Trent, which is fed by the Dove,
Derwent and Erewash from the Pennines and by the Penk, Tame
and Soar from the south. In pre-glacial times the Soar used to rise
somewhere near Evesham, but a lake impounded between the ice-
front and the Jurassic scarp first found an outlet to the southwest,
and the Warwickshire Avon came into being. The Severn was
lengthened during the Ice Age by the diversion of its upper reaches

through the Ironbridge gorge; the large and ramifying Severn-Avon system, which now drains so much of the Triangle, is thus mainly a product of glaciation.

Soils in the Midland Triangle are very varied, as would be expected of a region where patches of glacial drift occur on a varied array of solid rocks. Many belong to the group of Brown Forest Soils, but soils developed on certain permeable rocks of the Permo-Trias are liable to be podsolised. A noticeable feature is the reddish or reddish-purple colour of fresh ploughing both on the Permo-Trias and on the drifts derived from it, but soils become darker and duller along the eastern margin, where they are formed on the Lower Lias or on heavy boulder clay. All the rivers have been intermittently rejuven-ated, and on the light well-drained soils of their terraces market-gardens are numerous near the towns, but the highest development of intensive cultivation is found in the south-west of the region, where the orchards of the Evesham district are planted mainly on patches of sludge-gravel. All the flood-plains have developed meadow soils.

Climate and Agriculture

In climate and in farming, as in the pattern of rural settlement, the Midland Triangle is transitional, in the sense that its western parts belong to western England, while the northeast is allied to eastern England, and the southern extremity has strong affinities with the Borders of the West Country.

Annual precipitation ranges from about 35 inches in the north-west of the region to little more than 25 inches in the northeast. Liability to thunder, and the proportion of total precipitation coming in summer, both increase from west to east across the region. There is a very slow eastward increase in annual range of temperature which varies about 21°F., and the frost-free season is below six months except in the lower Severn and Avon valleys. Climatically, this southern part is the best-favoured part. Warm air can come in from the Bristol Channel, not bringing heavy rain, but noticeably moderating winter cold, reducing the frequency of snow, extending the frost-free season to more than 6 months, and raising the January mean temperature to 40° or above—a high figure for this inland region where winter chilling of the land-surface is pronounced.

The southern extremity of the region contains part of the second greatest concentration of orchard fruit in the country (Fig. 40); the fruit-growing district overlaps into Herefordshire (Chap. 13), but the production of small fruit and especially of vegetables is located mainly within the Midland Triangle. Brussels sprouts, cabbages, cauliflower, onions, peas, beans and asparagus figure in the long list of market-garden produce, and currants are the most extensive kind of small fruit. Orchards are most continuous in the Vale of Evesham, which is famous for its eating and cooking apples, but are also to be found scattered throughout the countryside. Not much more than half the farmland of Worcestershire is in grass. The leading crops, in order of extent, are wheat, orchard fruit, oats, and vegetables (excluding potatoes); potatoes and sugar beet are also extensive. Stock-farming is varied, but dairying receives increasing attention. The wide extent of tillage, the colourful soils, the many orchards, and the abundant hardwood trees combine with rather scattered settlement to make the countryside look rich and attractive.

In the northeast of the Midland Triangle there is more grass than in the south—grass still takes two-thirds of all farmland in Leicestershire, despite the recent extension of tillage. Permanent grassland becomes particularly common in the east of the county, where heavy boulder clay spread over the subdued Wolds gives rise to heavy soils, and where the boundary between the Midland Triangle and the adjacent scarplands is masked by drift. Fields are divided by sturdy well-kept hedges which contain the numerous livestock. For centuries this area has been noted for its sheep, and it was among those parts of England where villages were depopulated to make way for medieval sheep-farms, but sheep today are no more numerous than cattle, and require far less land than cattle do. Dairy cattle and followers outnumber beefstock, but fattening is still widely practised. The most extensive tillage crop is wheat, but next after this cash crop come oats and mixed corn; green fodder crops and fodder roots are also widely grown.

Leicestershire lies well within the belt of originally nucleated villages (Fig. 25), and the Saxon pattern of settlement was little disturbed by Danish occupation. Nucleated villages are still typical today, although outlying farms have been added, and some villages have swollen greatly as a result of sharing the hosiery industry of Leicester.

The character of agriculture in the northwestern part of the Midland Triangle is roughly indicated by Staffordshire, where 70% of the farmland grows grass, cattle far outnumber sheep, and a high proportion of the cattle are dairy animals. Grassland generally, and dairying in particular, are favoured by rain entering through the Midland Gate. Tillage crops are prominent mainly on the gently-undulating land south of the Pennines, where they include wheat, oats, mixed corn, potatoes, and forage crops. Staffordshire is not a wholly satisfactory sample of this part of the region, as can be seen from a comparison of county with regional boundaries;

its differences from Worcestershire and Leicestershire are, therefore, all the more impressive.

TOWNS AND INDUSTRIES

There is a most remarkable industrial contrast between the eastern and western sides of the region. Manufacturing industry in the west is dominated either by the metal trades, which take more than 25% of all the people working in the West Midland Conurbation, or by pottery, which takes more than 25% of the workers in Stoke-on-Trent. In Nottingham and Leicester the leading occupation is the making of textiles and garments, which takes 15% of all workers in Nottingham and 17% of all those in Leicester (Figs. 128, 135). Leather-working ranks second in Leicester, with 8% of all workers, while 35% of those employed in Hinckley are in the textile and clothing trades, and an additional $13\frac{1}{2}$% are in leather factories. Both the metal manufacture and the pottery-making of the west were founded in pre-industrial days, but have become concentrated on coalfields. The textile and leather industries of the east, developing from medieval crafts, have been industrialised without transference to coalfields.[1]

Industrialisation of the Black Country

The Black Country forms a low plateau, where productive Coal Measures are exposed. Industrialisation has produced an agglomeration of manufacturing towns, which have merged with Birmingham in the West Midland Conurbation.

Coal in the Black Country was worked for use in local smithies as early as the 13th century, and the production of bar-iron—accompanied by the clearance of woodland by charcoal-burners—is attested by documents of the 14th century. Iron-working in South Staffordshire thus long pre-dates 18th-century industrialisation, and its strong medieval development is, in fact, one of the leading objections to the term *industrial revolution*. The best ores, found in the neighbourhood of Walsall, were much worked. Forges, requiring water-power, were sited on streams, but the charcoal-using blast-furnaces introduced in the 16th century were located with reference to fuel-supply. Production of iron goods—edge tools, cutlery, and nails—was typically scattered.

In the 18th century came the conversion from smelting with charcoal to smelting with coke, and the thick coal of the Black Country, with its underlying ironstone, was widely mined. Local fireclay served the Stourbridge glassworks, and was distributed to the new

[1] The leather industry is dominant in and near Northampton: see Chap. 23.

blast-furnaces. Reserves of iron ore were still less adequate than they had already proved, and by 1788, when the last charcoal furnace was finally extinguished, pig-iron was being brought from the Forest of Dean up the Severn and along the new canals. Towns and villages were expanding fast by 1800, when the industrial pattern of the Black Country was already evident. Between 1800 and 1860 there was a great increase in coal-mining and in smelting, large quantities of ore and pig being brought in as soon as railways were built. By 1865 there were 172 blast-furnaces in the Black Country, concentrated mainly in a belt from Wolverhampton to Oldbury, and in and near Dudley and Brierley Hill. The two concentrations were separated by an upfaulted strip from which Coal Measures are missing.

Industrial devastation of the Black Country was severe during the first half of the 19th century, and continued into the later 1800s, combining with the intense activity of heavy industry to give the district its traditional name. Pronounced changes were, however, already in progress by the mid-19th century, and the stereotyped concept of the Black Country is a century out-of-date. Some of the best workable coals were exhausted by 1860, when the peak of iron-smelting had already been passed. The numbers of active mines, blast-furnaces, and coke-ovens had fallen greatly by 1900 and continued subsequently to fall. The demand for wrought iron lessened as steel—produced elsewhere—came in quantity upon the industrial market; iron making, tinplating, galvanising, and the light metal trades were all involved in a progressive decline. Two active blast-furnaces survive today on the western edge of the coalfield, but most of the pig for the steel furnaces now comes from the Jurassic ironfields.

By contrast with its heavy industry and primary processing of the 19th century, the Black Country's later-developed finishing trades prosper (Plate 54). Bicycles, cars, arms, machine tools and aero-engines are prominent in the list of products, but no short list can give any idea of the enormous range of modern products (App. 1).

In turning to the complex processes of the finishing trades, which absorb much non-ferrous metal, the Black Country has successfully overcome the difficulties of industrial setbacks, scarcity of raw material, and exhaustion of local fuel. Its factories, moreover, lie far inland, away from the ports through which raw materials come and produce goes. It is impossible to judge the extent to which the conversion of industry was enforced by the failure of local mines, by the declining demand for iron, or by the need for goods which could bear cost of transport. The maintenance and expansion of metal-manufacturing supply an outstanding example of the results of industrial momentum.[1]

Industrial Employment in the West Midland Conurbation

In the West Midland Conurbation there are more than a million people at work, and more than a quarter of these are employed in some type of metal manufacture and engineering (Fig. 128). The relevant trades are prominent in very many towns throughout Great Britain, but in the West Midland Conurbation they employ twice as many people as in Southeast Lancashire, two-and-a-half times as many as in Central Clydeside, three times as many as in West Yorkshire, four-and-a-half times as many as on Merseyside, and five times as many as on Tyneside. Only the Greater London Conurbation, with its enormously greater total population, has more workers in metal and engineering than has the West Midland Conurbation.

Birmingham

Within the West Midland Conurbation, an important distinction must be made between the Black Country on one hand and Birmingham on the other. Birmingham is a manufacturing town in its own right, but, although it has merged with the Black Country towns, it does not stand on the coalfield. It did not take part in the earliest iron-working of the West Midlands, and its accession to the rank of regional capital is as difficult to explain as is the medieval success of Coventry.

The rise of Birmingham as a market centre, and later as a centre of industry, was at first slow but persistent. The place was recorded as a tiny settlement in Domesday Book, but in the 12th century the de Bermingham family secured a market charter for it. Market rights and freedom from gild regulations seem to have been beneficial, for '. . . in the thirteenth century a man was more likely to be attracted to Birmingham . . . by the prospect of a burgage tenure

---

[1] The expression *inherited skill* is often used when *industrial momentum* is intended. Industrial skill cannot possibly be transmitted by inheritance. How the social and psychological pressures of industry can be measured is not clear, but children often tend to follow occupations which their parents have found rewarding. Before 1939, and still more before 1914, social mobility was but slightly developed in the British Isles; members of a given generation had little prospect of rising above their parents in the social scale. Similarly, there was not a great deal of interchange of people among manufacturing industries. This state of affairs can aptly be called *social inertia*. Its influence reinforced the economic influences of industrial inertia, which resisted tendencies to transfer established industry.

FIG. 128. Manufacturing employment in the West Midlands

for which he could pay rent in cash rather than in labour services, or the privilege of setting up as a free and independent craftsman . . . than by any consideration of a good water supply, a sandstone ridge or a bridge over a local brook.'[1] By whatever means, Birmingham secured expanding control over local trade. Its anti-Royalist sympathies and its production of sword-blades for the Parliamentary forces provoked an attack by Prince Rupert in 1643, but by 1650 the recovering town had between 1,500 and 2,000 inhabitants. Birmingham tightened its grip on the developing industries of the Black Country, and also established manufacturers of its own. Manufactures of guns, buttons, toys, trinkets, and small brassware

[1] R. A. Pelham.

were set up in Birmingham during the 17th century, with jewellery and precious-metal working following in the 18th. Boulton's engineering works were founded in 1761, and the new canals of the late 18th century encouraged great progress in brassworking and mechanical engineering generally. As the town expanded, the functions of its inner districts were modified, and its industry also changed, for Birmingham tended to lead the advances forced upon the Black Country by changing circumstance. Its mechanical engineering is extremely varied; the town is one of the greatest centres of retail trade in the British Isles, and employs many workers in woodworking, building, contracting and transport as well as in commerce, finance and clerical occupations.

Birmingham's municipal history illustrates a number of the social and administrative problems which pressed hard upon the rising industrial towns of 18th-century and 19th-century England. Although its population exceeded 100,000 in the early 1800s, Birmingham was not directly represented in Parliament until the Reform Act of 1832 came into force, it was not incorporated as a borough until 1838, and responsibility for civic affairs was still divided until 1851. Unified control was urgently needed, for polluted wells and lack of drainage promoted much disease. In the mid-19th century the town suffered from 'unpaved streets, confined courts, open middens and cesspools and stagnant ditches, and crowded lodging-houses'.

Reorganisation of local government made possible a number of far-reaching schemes of public work. Extensive slum clearance and improvements to roads began in 1875, the first of the drastic changes in the face of Birmingham. Enlargement of boundaries first occurred in 1891, city status was conferred in 1899, and the university received its charter in 1900. Partly because of its growing involvement with commerce and administration, Birmingham suffers the congestion which typifies the conurbation as a whole, and which has led to proposals for new towns near Wellington and Ludlow, and to schemes for overspill, e.g., into the East Midlands.

Modern Birmingham obtains much of its water from Wales. The watershed of the Black Country Plateau discharges modest streams which, even with the aid of wells and reservoirs, were clearly inadequate by the end of the 19th century. Three reservoirs were impounded in the Elan valley by 1906, with a total capacity of 11,000 gallons, and another 11,000 gallons of capacity have been added since the end of World War II by the Claerwen Dam.

Coventry and other close neighbours of the West Midland Conurbation

Coventry was the fourth largest town in England at the end of the 14th century—only London, York, and Bristol had more people than Coventry's 7,000. Coventry's medieval greatness cannot be explained by any physical advantages of site or situation. The foundation of a well-endowed priory in 1043, followed by the building of a Norman castle, undoubtedly contributed to its urban importance. During the 12th, 13th and 14th centuries the town secured various rights, among them freedom from toll for Coventry merchants in all parts of the kingdom. Coventry was able to become a very great merchant town, illustrating the principle that '. . . a site which may not be richly endowed by nature may nevertheless be made an important focus of human activity under the guidance and stimulus of able men during the critical early stages of its development.'[1] 14th-century products included wool, soap, needles and leather. The manufactures of woollens and leather link medieval Coventry to medieval Northampton, Leicester, and Nottingham.

There is some reason to infer that Coventry suffered from the rigid control imposed on craft and trade by its highly-developed gilds, for by 1650 it was little, if any, more populous than it had been in 1500, although it remained a great producer of woollen cloth into the 1700s. Weaving cellars in the surrounding settlements testify to the former presence of the old domestic craft. The emergence of Coventry as a modern industrial town was associated with the technical developments of the late 18th century and later times.

Purely by an accident of siting, Coventry found itself with local supplies of coal. The manufacture of watches and sewing-machines was followed and eclipsed by the production of cycles, motor-cycles, cars, car and aero engines, electrical apparatus, tractors, machine tools, and viscose yarn. Population rose from 70,000 in 1901 to 167,000 in 1931, increasing by 140% in the 30 years, and has further increased by over 80% since the 1931 census. The great industrial growth of modern Coventry was made possible by the development of the internal combustion engine and applications of electricity. Thus Coventry as an industrial centre belongs to the late 19th and the 20th centuries. With nearly 1 in 3 of its workers engaged in metal-work and engineering, Coventry today has little interest in textiles, clothing or leather. Its old manufactures of wool and silk have either been replaced by mechanical engineering, or superseded by the production of viscose yarn—a type of manufacture which belongs to industrial chemistry and the plastics industry.

Coventry suffered very heavily from bombing during World War II. Extensive rebuilding in the heart of the town has made it

[1] R. A. Pelham.

even more attractive than formerly as a centre of shopping and entertainment, but its urban strength was already strongly felt before 1939 in the districts to the south.

Nuneaton is a far smaller town which stands on the exposed Warwickshire coalfield. 19th-century industrial growth is recorded here in terraced houses of brick. Tamworth (13,500), smaller still, was once the capital of Mercia. To the southwest of the West Midland Conurbation, Kidderminster has nearly one-fifth of its workers in textile manufacture and is well known for its carpets; Bromsgrove and Redditch are dominated by engineering. Cannock in the north has more miners than metal-workers, for the Cannock coalfield still produces well from concealed seams. Stafford, a county town far surpassed in size by other towns within its county boundaries, commands the route between Cannock Chase and the Pennines; it is a railway centre, with well-developed electrical engineering and leather industries.

The Potteries

In the Potteries of North Staffordshire occurs a unique concentration of British manufacture. No other industry of comparable size is so strongly localised—the Pottery towns contain four-fifths of all pottery workers in Great Britain. Local potting began at least as early as the 14th century, in the then hamlet of Burslem, where it supplemented farming. It spread slowly through neighbouring settlements, until the 18th century brought tea- and coffee-drinking into fashion; the demand for elegant tableware then made it profitable to bring in clay from Devon and flints from Dorset, in the small quantities which pack-trains could carry, and lead from the Derbyshire Pennines was available for use in glazing. The leading improver was Josiah Wedgwood, who was born at Burslem in 1730 and opened his own works in 1769. His overwhelming success with fine china and new designs was a powerful factor in stimulating the industry, and one of the justifications for the Trent and Mersey Canal which, finished in 1777, enabled raw materials to be imported cheaply and in quantity. But even before the canal was made, the use of materials produced outside the region had reduced locating factors to two: the momentum of success, and the presence of long-flaming coal particularly suitable for firing the kilns.

The factories and the houses of the workpeople were built on the coalfield itself (Plate 55). All the older parts of the Pottery towns were in time undermined, and subsidence became serious, while large open pits bit deeply into the marls used in the making of bricks, tiles, and saggars (containers for pottery in the kilns). The towns are congested, for they had little room to spread in the narrow valleys of the Trent headstreams or on the narrow divides. Many of their streets have steep gradients, and collieries, marl-pits, derelict land, terraced houses, canals, railways, and pottery works are knotted in a confused tangle.[1] Only in the inter-war period did road transport begin to encourage much house-building at a distance from the works.

Chief concentrations of industry

Heavily-built up areas mainly developed before 1914.

Less densely built up areas, mainly developed after 1920

FIG. 129. The Potteries and their local setting

The county borough of Stoke-on-Trent, including the formerly separate units of Stoke, Burslem, Hanley, Longton, Fenton, and Tunstall (Fig. 129), employs more than a quarter of all its workers in the pottery industry, with another 15% in metal manufacture or mining. In Newcastle-under-Lyme, the three types of work employ roughly equal numbers.

In its widest sense, the pottery industry includes not only the making of household china, ornamental china, and earthenware, but also the production of goods made from the local marl—bricks,

[1] For census purposes, however, the Potteries do not rank as a conurbation.

roofing tiles, and drainpipes. Most of the work in potting, however, is light, and some two-thirds of those employed in the pottery works are women.

Mining and the metal trades take, between them, far more men than does the pottery industry. Heavy metal manufacture is represented by smelting and steel-making, and engineering is firmly established. There are still useful reserves in the North Staffs. Coalfield, particularly in the centre and south, even though parts of the field have been extensively worked.

The Trent and Soar Valleys

Although Nottingham and Leicester have highly-developed textile and garment industries, they resemble a number of other large Midland towns in combining industrial activity with cattle-marketing, produce-marketing, and a retail trade which serves an area varying with the size of the town. The leading group of industries benefited greatly from the local invention or improvement of machinery—particularly the stocking-frame; it is difficult to judge, however, how much the industry owed to invention and how much invention owed to industry which already existed. The stocking-frame was invented in the 16th century, other textile inventions came early into favour in this district, and by the end of the 19th century a third of the knitting-frames in use in England were to be found in Nottinghamshire alone. The chief group of products today is knitwear of all kinds.

Nottingham and Leicester, the main centres of the industry and the largest towns in their part of the Midland Triangle, display many similarities to one another. Both county towns, both university towns, they were both (with Derby, Lincoln and Stamford) Danish boroughs. Each lies in a valley, overlooking a broad flood-plain from a patch of terrace, and each commands a crossing.

Leicester was a Roman town on the Fosse Way, and retained a rectangular plan within its square medieval walls. An outbreak of plague caused the gates to be shut, and traffic to pass round the outside of the walls on the eastern side; on this diverted line the main modern shopping street now lies. The town has spread far beyond its medieval limits, losing its walls but retaining a produce market in its centre. Outlying settlements, such as those on the Soar terraces to the north, grew into compact and remarkably large villages during the late 19th century, when hosiery factories and terraced houses were built. Modern industries of Leicester, additional to the making of hosiery and footwear, include engineering, mainly of a specialised kind—the production of hosiery machinery, typewriters, and instruments. The hosiery industry merges into industrial chemistry through the production of nylon stockings. Leicester's industries offer a wide range of employment to women, and in some households all but the children and the very old are in work.

Nottingham's rock-based Castle, founded in Norman times, dominates the valley-bottom of the Trent, where a long causeway and a bridge provided a crossing in pre-Conquest days. A mile of flood-plain separates the channel of the river from the firm ground on the north bank where the town centre is located (Fig. 130). Under the protection of the castle, Nottingham during the Middle Ages acquired a manufacture of cloth, dyeing, tanning, brewing, and iron-working. It was of considerable importance as a market centre, being on or near the limits of contrasting pieces of country—the hills of the southern Pennines, the partly-wooded lowland of the Trent valley, and the dense woodland of Sherwood Forest based on the permeable outcrop of Bunter Pebble Beds. The Trent was navigable for the craft of the time.

Lace-making, for which Nottingham is famous, was originally a domestic craft, widely practised throughout a large area—indeed,

FIG. 130. Nottingham and its local setting

hand-made lace was still being made in the villages of the eastern Midlands in the inter-war period. Machine-working became possible in the late 18th century, was greatly developed during the 19th, and now accounts for the total output of Nottingham lace.

Nottingham's engineering industries are partly associated with the manufacture of hosiery, for machines for spinning, weaving and knitting are made here, as at Leicester. Typewriters are also made at Nottingham, and marine engines and a wide range of other machinery are produced. The manufacture of cycles began in the late 19th century and is still expanding—Nottingham has recently taken over part of the cycle-manufacture hitherto located in Birmingham. The making of pharmaceutical products, again established in Nottingham during the late 19th century, is flourishing, the factory being associated with a nation-wide chain of chemists' shops. The cigarette and tobacco industry, of earlier standing, greatly expanded in the late 19th century and subsequently.

In their modern industrial development, Leicester and Nottingham have been assisted by coal mined nearby. In the Leicestershire Coalfield the seams lie close to the surface in a double syncline. Coal is of medium or indifferent quality, but mining costs per ton are lower than anywhere else in Britain. With two new surface mines and reconstruction of old pits, the field is expected to increase its output to 7 million tons a year; at the present time most of the product goes to the Midlands and the south of England, some 30% being sold as domestic fuel and a similar amount going to power stations. The mining towns are Coalville (26,250), which looks industrial, and Ashby-de-la-Zouch (7,500), which does not.

Nottingham is readily supplied from the southern end of the Yorks., Derby and Notts. coalfield, which is separately distinguished by the National Coal Board as the North Derby and Notts. field. There was much early working in the western part, where the seams are exposed, but coal was kept out of the southern English markets by high cost of transport. The proved reserves are large, even though the seams thin underground towards the east as they do in Yorkshire, and the largest mines occur in the east and southeast. Working costs are already low, and may be further reduced by reconstruction, new pits and new surface mines intended to raise output to 40 million tons a year. Over one-third of the coal raised is at present consumed in the Midlands, and another quarter goes by rail to London; increasing output will serve not only London and power stations in the East Midlands, but also the industries of Lancashire.

Beeston, southwest of Nottingham, has recently expanded in engineering rather than in hosiery, but hosiery is still prominent, as at Ilkeston. Ilkeston, on the incised Erewash, is the largest of the indus-

trial settlements strung along valleys cut through the Coal Measures and linking Nottingham and Derby with Chesterfield and
Sheffield.

Derby is less than half as populous as Nottingham. Its more
modest prospects were foreshadowed when, in Norman times, it
was not heavily fortified—perhaps because its routes to the north
led but to the Pennine upland. Derby secured borough status
during the Middle Ages, however, and became famous for malting
as least as early as the 17th century, when coke instead of the customary straw was used in the kilns. By 1693 there were no fewer than
76 malthouses in a town of 4,000 people. Hosiery-making was established during the 18th century, and silk-weaving was added when
designs for silk-making machinery were stolen from the Italian
Piedmont. Pottery, begun in 1750, flourished with the later transfer
of the famous Chelsea works. Until the 19th century, however,
Derby spread little beyond the medieval site between the incised
Derwent and a small right-bank tributary.

The first of its chief present industries was established in the mid-
19th century, when the town was linked by railway to Leeds and
London, and locomotive workshops were built. At a later date,
one man selected Derby for the site of a car-factory because the
town offered cheaper electric power than did Leicester. The making
of rayon and plastics began with the production of cellulose acetate
(used on aircraft fabric) during World War I. Thus the three leading
industries of modern Derby—manufacture of locomotives and rolling stock, manufacture of engines for cars and aircraft, and production of rayon and other plastics—result from deliberate acts of
location on the part of the railway companies, a single individual,
or the government. In combination, they take nearly a third of the
town's workers.

Burton-on-Trent is internationally famous for its brewing.
Monastic brewhouses gained a high reputation through the use of
gypsum-bearing water from local wells; the gypsum (hydrated
calcium sulphate, $CaSO_4.2H_2O$),occurring as lenses in the desert sediments of the Permo-Trias, is highly soluble in water, and improves
the quality of beer. Burton used much of the malt produced in 17th-
century Derby, but was unable to serve a national and international
market until improvements to navigation on the Trent enabled
exports through Hull to reach Russia, Germany, and India, and the
spreading railways provided easy links to the whole of the country.
A number of large brewing firms have works at Burton, buying much
barley from East Anglia, and hops from Kent. Local engineering
industries are partly allied to brewing, but constructional steelwork
is also produced.

The Severn and Avon Valleys

Cheltenham, Gloucester, and Worcester, in the south of the Midland Triangle, are much of a size. Cheltenham, which found favour as a spa in the 18th century, expanded rapidly under the Regency and acquired large, well-designed public buildings. On the map, it seems an obvious urban addition to the area formerly served by Gloucester alone; it shares with Gloucester industries introduced, or greatly stimulated, in time of war—especially the aircraft and aero-engine industry. Clock- and instrument-making were assisted by a Government grant-in-aid in 1945. The handsome town-centre, however, looks anything but industrial, and is an asset to Cheltenham's functions as a centre of social and cultural activities.

FIG. 131. Gloucester and Cheltenham, and their local setting

Gloucester was a flourishing civil town under the Romans, had recovered its urban importance by the Conquest, and developed ironworking during the Middle Ages. Adjoining the Severn flood-plain, on to which its factories have spread (Fig. 131), it possesses the lowest bridge across the river. Although it acquired a port charter under Elizabeth I, its rôle as a port began principally with the opening of the Gloucester and Berkeley Canal in 1827. The largest ships unload at the seaward end, where Sharpness receives oil, timber, and grain. Although there is some barge traffic from Gloucester to the Black Country, Gloucester's communications are provided chiefly by busy trunk roads, and by railways with which carriage and wagon works are associated.

The remains of a once great woollen industry survive in the scarp-valleys behind Gloucester and Cheltenham, but numbers of the old mills have been taken over by decentralised modern industry —the making of furniture, plastics, and instruments—which is concentrated in and near Stroud.

Worcester, like Gloucester and Hereford (Chap. 13), is a county town. Like Hereford, it is the centre of a topographic basin and stands on the main river, but like Gloucester it has expanding engineering industries. Its wire-making, brass-founding, and iron-founding associate it with the West Midland Conurbation, but its glove-making is of local origin.

Leamington resembles Cheltenham in having become famous as a spa, but here again, metal manufacture is vigorously developed, taking one in five of the town's workers; domestic heating appliances and automobile parts are among the products.

Warwick is related to Leamington as Gloucester is to Cheltenham, but has been far outdistanced. With only 16,000 people, it has lost much of the regional significance which it once possessed as the home and headquarters of the powerful Earl called *King-maker*. Its bridge and castle are less well known than the bridge and memorial theatre lower down the Avon at Stratford (16,750) where prosperity, founded on the name of Shakespeare, is supported by a cattle-market and a famous brewery.

Rugby, rather oddly located on a flat-topped hill, has grown rapidly in the last 75 years. Alongside its converging railways have developed electrical engineering works, similar to—and in part branches of—those at Stafford. On the outskirts of Rugby and in the area to the southwest, Portland cement is manufactured from the alternating clayey limestones and shales of the Lower Lias.

APPENDIX

The following incomplete list of products manufactured at Wolverhampton is meant to indicate something of the industrial range of a single town, and to show the complexity of detail which is omitted from summary descriptions of industry.

Advertising Signs	Arc Rectifiers	Bathroom Fittings
Artificial Eyes	Art Metal Work	Bicycles
Agricultural Implements	Axle Plates	Boilers
Aircraft		Boots and Shoes
Aircraft Components	Bar, Hoop and Sheet Iron	Boxes (Cardboard)
Aluminium Foil	Barrels	Boxes (Deed, Cash and
Aluminium Products	Barrows	Despatch)
Animal Foods	Ball and Roller Bearings	Brass
Annealing Covers	Baths	Brick and Tiles

Brewers' Apparatus
Bronze Work
Bolts and Nuts
Bedsteads
Buckets
Builders' Ironmongery

Cabinets
Carpet Sweepers
Castings
Carburettors
Chains
Chemicals
Chromium Plate
Cisterns
Coal Hoppers
Coal By-products
Coffee Mills
Confectionery
Copper Stampings
Conveyor Belts
Concrete
Corrugated Iron
Cranes
Cupolas
Cylinder Blocks

Dairy Utensils
Drain Pipes
Dry Batteries
Drop Forgings
Drugs

Earthenware
Edge Tools
Elevating and Conveying
    Plant
Electrical Equipment
Electro Plate
Enamelled Ware

Fencing
Fenders
Fire Brasses
Files
Fire Screens and Coal
    Boxes
Flanges
Forgings
Furniture

Galvanised Iron
Galvanised Hollow-ware
Gas Cookers

Gas and Steam Tubes
Garden Furniture
Gauges
Gates and Railings
Gear Boxes
Girders
Grinders
Gun Barrels and Locks

Hammers
Hardware
Hay Barns
Heat Exchange
    Equipment
Hinges
Hollow-ware
Horse Shoes and Nails
Hospital Furniture

Ice Cream
Internal Combustion
    Engines

Jigs and Fixtures
Joinery

Lathes
Leather Belting
Leather Goods
Lighting Buoys
Lamps
Locks and Latches
Lubricating Oils

Machine Tools
Magnetos
Medicinal Products
Motor Car Frames
Motor Omnibuses
Motor Lorries
Motor Cycle Accessories
Motor Car Accessories

Nails and Rivets

Oxygen

Paints
Patterns
Paving Slabs
Pit-head Frames
Perambulators
Pipe Lines
Presses

Pulleys
Pumps

Rayon
Radios
Refrigerators
Ropes
Rubber Soles and Heels
Rubber Transmission
    Belts
Rubber Mouldings

Safes
Sanitary Pipes
Scythes
Shafts and Axletrees
Shipping Tackle and
    Rigging
Soaps
Spades, Shovels and Forks
Springs
Stampings
Steel
Steel Castings
Steel Convertors
Steel Ladles
Steel Range and Knobs
Steel Stampings
Steel Flooring
Strong Rooms
Stove Grates
Structural Steel
Switchgear

Tanks
Tapestries
Tarmacadam
Tiles
Tools
Toys
Trolley Buses
Trunks
Tubes and Fittings
Tyres

Varnishes
Vices

Wagons
Water Softeners
Water Tanks
Window Gear
Wire
Wrought Ironwork

CHAPTER 23

Scarplands of the South Midlands

Area: about 4,000 square miles.
Population: about 2,500,000.
Largest towns: Luton (131,500).
    Oxford (106,000).
    Northampton (105,250).
    Cambridge (95,250).
    Swindon (91,750).
    Bedford (63,250).
    Peterborough (62,000).
    Kettering (38,750).
    Corby (36,500).
    Wellingborough (30,500).
    Aylesbury (28,000).
    Banbury (21,000).
 This region is generally in farmland, with something like 90% improved. Grassland is rather more extensive than tillage in the region as a whole.
Numbers of Livestock: cattle, 640,000; sheep, 670,000; pigs, 280,000.

The grain of structure and relief in this region runs from southwest to northeast (Fig. 127). Until the present century the region was too distant, both from London and from the industrial districts of the Midland Triangle, for its towns to be stimulated into rapid growth, and even at the present time nearly all parts of it retain strong rural characteristics.

These scarplands possess no exposed coalfields, and if hidden seams are present they have still to be proved. The coasts are distant and not particularly accessible by the routes which have developed. In most parts of the region the open-field system of agriculture persisted for a long time—as long as anywhere in England—enclosure not being completed until the early 19th century, and compact villages and well-knit village communities remained typical. Secondary dispersion of settlement—recorded by isolated farms, many of them built in the mid-19th century—weakened but did not break the ties of village life. In the early years of the present century it was still usual for people to find wives or husbands either in their own village or in the next village; travel was slow, and carriers' carts were not replaced by motor-coaches until the 1920s. Small village shops and small market towns met the commercial needs of the region.

Rural Depopulation

The drift from the land began in the 19th century, but it was not until the 1930s that disintegration of village communities became really severe. At that time a great deal of ploughland was put to grass, in response to agricultural depression, when farmers decided to reduce costs and the demand for labour fell. Rural bus services increased contacts between town and countryside, making obvious the difference between rural and urban standards of living. The limited number of scholarships and free places in grammar schools diverted some of the most intelligent children from agriculture into work in the towns. For all these reasons the village populations declined. The largest towns profited the most from townward migration, for small towns tended to lose their cattle-markets as road transport became cheaper and more readily available, and also to lose their industries as factories closed during the Great Slump.

Except for council houses, villages in this region contain few dwellings built after 1900, and many of the cottages date from the early 17th century. Some of the villages display all the charm of antiquity, combining it with a high degree of domestic inconvenience. Council-house building began shortly before 1939, but dates mainly from 1945 or later. It represents an attempt to arrest the decay of village life, as do rural electrification—already well under way in 1939—and the post-war supply of piped water. It remains to be seen what the result of these attempts will be.

THE MAIN JURASSIC CUESTA

Southwestern Part

Although rural character and scarpland terrain give the region a certain homogeneity, internal contrasts are easily perceptible. They are associated with differences in altitude and texture of relief, which depend in turn upon geological structure and the history of dissection. The region can be subdivided into belts running from southwest to northeast, some of which change in character from one end to the other.

The Cotswold Hills begin south of Bath and extend to the Vale of Moreton at the head of the Evenlode, penetrating the Borders of the West Country beyond a line from Gloucester to Swindon (Fig. 127).

Northeast of this line, in the South Midlands, the Cotswold back-slope is smooth, with broad and remarkably flat interfluves sloping gently to the southeast between the incised valleys draining to the Thames. Limestones of the Inferior and Great Oolite formations are thick and well-cemented in the Cotswolds, forming a steep and continuous scarp which, rising to 1,000 ft., overlooks the lower valleys of the Severn and Avon. Between the North Cotswolds and the head of the Cherwell lie the hills of North Oxfordshire, which are rather more dissected than the Cotswolds. The whole belt of hills west of the Cherwell has been little affected by glaciation, and carries very little glacial drift.

Before the industrialisation of the 18th and early 19th centuries, this division was noted for its sheep-grazing and its manufacture of woollens. Rich cloth-merchants have left mansions and ornate tombs as signs of their former prosperity. The woollen industry survives today only in the specialised manufacture of blankets at Witney, and in the production of serges in Stroud and its neighbours in the Frome valley.

The villages, large country houses, and small towns of the Cotswolds and North Oxfordshire are exceptionally beautiful, being very largely built of natural stone. Rich brown building-stone from the Middle Lias, which thickens and becomes the main scarp-former north of Banbury, has been much used in the Banbury district, where thatched roofs are common. Farther south, towards Oxford, the Inferior and Great Oolite formations appear, extending broadly westwards in the Cotswold Hills. Their oolitic limestones, which are often yellowish in the quarry, become creamy on exposure to the air; they have been very widely employed, and some Cotswold villages are entirely stone-built. The local roofing material is the fissile oolite of Stonesfield, which, as long as the quarries continued to produce, could be worked in large slabs. In the Marlstone country, hedgerows are typical of the countryside and stone walls of the villages, but long stone walls enclose many fields in parts of the Cotswolds, where the limestone lies very close to the surface and has been taken from long shallow pits. The pattern of large rectangular fields typical of late and wholesale enclosure is diversified by numerous plantations, small woods, and belts of ornamental timber (Plate 56).

More powerfully than any other district of comparable size, this has attracted the 20th-century equivalent of the 18th-century and 19th-century country squire—significantly enough, it repeatedly provides illustrations for *Country Life*. Its isolated farmsteads are large and substantial and its fields well managed. Although grassland is more extensive than tillage, there is a great deal of ploughland.

especially on the flat interfluves; wheat is the most extensive of the grain crops, although barley also does well and oats is widely grown for stock-feeding. Potatoes and fodder crops are also grown. In many fields the plough throws up fragments of weathered limestone, for the soils are mainly shallow, but their clay content is enough to make them retain some of the water which comes from an annual precipitation of more than 30 inches. Winter temperatures go too low, and the open plateaus are too exposed, for this to become a district of fruit-growing and market-gardening, but autumn-sown and spring-sown field crops flourish. Both fodder crops and cash crops are much more widely grown nowadays than in the late pre-war years.

The numbers of sheep in the Cotswolds and North Oxfordshire are far lower than in the great days of grazing—past now for some centuries—and also lower than in the pre-war years. Considerable numbers are still kept, however, especially on the flood-plains and walls of the incised valleys. Cattle are numerous, and the totals both of beefstock and of dairy animals have risen since 1939.

Northeastern Part

Northeast of the Cherwell, between Banbury and Grantham, the main Jurassic cuesta forms a belt of rather low hills, rising above 700 ft. in a few places and much dissected in the crestal area. Here, in the Northamptonshire Uplands and the Leicestershire Wolds, the limestones and sandstones are in general both thinner and weaker than those of the Cotswolds, while the clays are thick. The feeders of the Ouse, Nene, and Welland have excavated wide valleys between which rise irregular hills of varying height. Extensive remnants of the once-continuous mantle of Chalky boulder clay occur in this district, tending to mask the northwest-facing scarps. Large intact patches of boulder clay were at one time heavily wooded with deciduous trees; many small woods still testify to Rockingham Forest, on the broad low divide between the Welland and the Nene, and to Whittlewood Forest, Salcey Forest, and Yardley Chase, which lay between the Nene and the Ouse.

Where the Jurassic limestones and sandstones come to the surface, their soils are for the most part under the plough. Both on the solid clays and on the boulder clay there is much permanent grassland which is noted for its production of fat cattle—particularly Herefords (cf. Fig. 132). The influences of wartime and post-war years have however reduced the extent of permanent grass in favour of tillage, reversing the trend of the 1930s; numbers of beefstock tend to decline slightly, and those of dairy cattle—Ayrshires, Shorthorns and Friesians—to rise. The increase in tillage is accounted for partly

FIG. 132. Land-use sample for west Northamptonshire, on a drift-encumbered part of the Main Jurassic Cuesta: mixed farmland on soils developed mainly on boulder clay or glacial sand and gravel

by fodder crops, but cash cropping has increased greatly in the north-east, on the margins of the great arable districts of eastern England, where mean annual rainfall declines towards 25 inches.

The soils on the limestones and sandstones are warm, while those on the clays are both cold and difficult to till, being sticky when wet and hard when dry. The localised influence of soil-type disappears in agricultural statistics for whole counties, but county figures can be used to give a generalised sample of farming. In Northamptonshire as a whole, wheat is the most extensive grain—as it is throughout the division—and grain takes nearly three-quarters of the cropland. Other leading crops include roots, green crops and pulses grown for forage, maincrop potatoes, sugar beet, and green vegetables. Flax-growing for fibre was encouraged during World War II and has continued subsequently.

This division is well timbered, not only with woods but also with hedgerow trees. Many of the hedges are regularly cut and laid to form stout barriers capable of containing bullocks, and the standard of hedgecutting is maintained by competitions organised by the hunts. As in other farming country which is prospering, however, the electric fence is becoming widely used, and the need for well-kept hedges is diminishing.

Stone and thatch are the traditional materials for building and roofing, one very widely-used type of stone being the iron-bearing Northampton Sand, which has a delicate apricot tint. Very little stone, however, has been used in new building for many years, and quarrying today is almost entirely confined to the extraction of iron ore (Plate 16). The craft of thatching is vanishing; even on the farms, the use of Dutch barns and hay-balers is making it unnecessary to thatch ricks.

THE STRIKE VALES

Southwestern Part

The Strike Vales of the South Midlands lie between the main Jurassic Cuesta and the scarp of the Chilterns. They are subdivided by a discontinuous axial belt of hills running from southwest to northeast, and, like the main Cuesta, can be separated into a south-western part, which is unglaciated or which retains very little glacial drift, and a northeastern part, where boulder clay is thick and extensive. The boundary between the two parts coincides roughly with the watershed between the Thames and the Ouse (Fig. 127).

The Thames above Oxford flows in a broad strike vale—the Vale of Oxford—cut in Oxford Clay. The lowest ground consists of broad flood-plains, which are bordered by gently-undulating clayland drained by numerous small streams. Permanent pasture is extensive, and cattle-farming the dominant type of agriculture, although wartime and post-war pressures have increased tillage. Numbers of cattle of all types have increased in recent years. Villages, located on sites which are naturally well-drained, avoid the flood-plains, but many occur on the adjacent patches of terrace-gravel (Fig. 133).

The Vale of Oxford ends on the southeast against a belt of hills—the axial belt mentioned above—which crosses the Thames at the

FIG. 133. Nucleated settlements on terraces of the Thames, upstream of Oxford

town of Oxford. The much-denuded hills are based on the Corallian beds—a formation of limestone strata composed largely of Jurassic corals. Their uneven landscape resembles that of the country around Banbury, for such flat hilltops as do occur are commonly under the plough. The coral limestones thin away to the northeast, where they are replaced by clays.

Between the Corallian hills and the scarp of the Chalk lies a strike vale, known as the Vale of White Horse on the west of the Thames, and as the Vale of Aylesbury on the east. Its geological basis is the Kimmeridge Clay, a thick formation of weak rock which resembles the Oxford Clay, and this belt of vale country resembles the Vale of Oxford. It carries many surface streams, but little of it is really flat, and its scenery is varied in detail. As in the Vale of Oxford, villages avoid badly-drained sites, and those which border the Thames are located on broad patches of terrace. A high proportion of the land is in permanent pasture, and dairying and poultry-farming are particularly well developed around Aylesbury.

Along the southern edge of the Vale of White Horse and the Vale of Aylesbury, Chalk scarps rise abruptly, with spring-line settlements at their feet. On the face of the Berkshire Downs the scarp is bold and continuous, and is equally well-defined in the south-western Chilterns, where hanging beechwoods are common on its steep slope, but in the northeastern Chilterns the scarp rises in steps and is penetrated by deep gaps.

Northeastern Part

Beyond the Hitchin Gap—i.e., beyond the end of the Chilterns—the Chalk outcrop continues towards the northeast, but the main Jurassic cuesta swings round to the north in the Northamptonshire Ironstone Field, so that the belt of vale country widens towards the edge of the Fens. The main rivers are all sunk below the general level of the country, the ground is extensively covered by thick spreads of Chalky boulder clay, and relief is subdued. Most settlements are small. The villages include much lath-and-plaster work, as befits a district of clayland which was once heavily wooded, and a few mud walls can still be found. With the three exceptions of Bedford, Cambridge, and Peterborough, the towns of this division display little urban strength. Buckingham, a former county town at the western extremity, has but 4,500 inhabitants, and Huntingdon, a county town centrally placed in the east of the division, has but 8,750.

Livestock farming is far less common than might be expected of clay country. Many of the soils resemble those of East Anglia, for they are developed on identical parent material of Chalky boulder clay. Although they are somewhat heavier than the East Anglian soils, containing a higher clay fraction, they nevertheless provide a satisfactory basis for tillage.

The ratio of tillage to grassland varies. Where mean annual rainfall is above 25 inches, grass is the more extensive, but where precipitation slightly decreases, sunshine slightly increases, and slightly cooler winters reduce the growing season—i.e., towards the Fenland boundary—tillage takes the lead. It is more extensive than grassland in Bedfordshire, and more than twice as extensive at the borders of the Fens. The balance between climatic and economic influences is a delicate one, however. When farming is depressed and costs must be reduced, grassland increases; when farming prospers, tillage increases. The most marked increases of recent years have been in cash-crops, which represent an extension of the cash-cropping in solidly arable areas to the east. There are now very few sheep in this division; numbers of fat cattle are roughly stable, and dairy herds have risen in numbers.

Wheat is the most extensive tillage crop in Bedfordshire, closely followed by barley. Oats, mixed corn, and fodder crops are restricted in extent in accordance with the limited numbers of cattle. Potatoes (early as well as maincrop) and sugar beet are grown throughout the division, the acreage of sugar beet increasing, like the acreage of barley, into the drier eastern parts.

Vegetables other than potatoes are more extensive than oats in Bedfordshire, which contains much market-garden land. Some of the market-gardens are located on the light, lime-poor, but loose and warm soils of the Lower Greensand,[1] which appears as a scarp-former south of Bedford and rises in a steep, well-wooded edge above the valley of the Ouse (Plates 7, 8). Market-gardens and fruit-farms stretch northeastwards from the Lower Greensand country towards the Fenland boundary, following a belt of generally light soils which repay heavy fertilisation; leading crops include brussels sprouts, parsnips, cabbages, and onions.

TOWNS AND INDUSTRIES

Luton, Bedford, and Oxford

At the census of 1931, Luton had fewer people than either North-ampton or Oxford, and was little more populous than Cambridge. In 30 years its population increased by 100%.[2] The rapid and continuing growth of Luton is largely the effect of the location there of the motor-manufacturing industry, and engineering and

[1] At Leighton Buzzard, where the sand is particularly pure, it is worked for use in glass-making.
[2] 1931-1961; affected by change of boundaries.

54. Part of an assembly-line for car engines, at Longbridge, Birmingham.

55. Part of Burslem, in the Potteries—factories, houses, kilns. The Potteries have been declared a smokeless zone.

56. The Cotswold backslope, with farmland—arable, rotation grass, and managed plantations—enclosing the incised Dikler valley.

57. Brickworks near Bedford.

metal-manufacture take 22% of the total employed. The next largest group of manufacturing workers is found in the garment industry, which employs large numbers of women, and takes about 10% of the labour force. Among the old-established industries is brewing. The only geographical advantages for the motor industry in Luton were, at the outset, of the most general character—room for building alongside a main railway, freedom from the congestion of districts already industrialised, and the possibility of recruiting labour in the existing town. It is to be assumed that, before the industry was founded, the economic questions of costs (including the costs of transport) were examined. The industry has certainly succeeded, stimulating the town to vigorous growth and thereby increasing the fund of labour on which it can draw.

Luton is actually located in the Chilterns, high up towards the head of the Lea. It is however better regarded as belonging to the South Midlands than to the London Basin, not only because it is close to the Chiltern crest, but also because, as an industrial town, it has strong similarities to Bedford and Oxford. The central parts of

FIG. 134. Oxford and its local setting

N

these two county towns occupy terraces below which their rivers
have cut, and both towns command crossings. Each provides shops
and markets for a large rural area, and Oxford retains from the
Middle Ages a very well-known fair. In addition to being an ancient
university centre, however, Oxford (Fig. 134) is an industrial town,
for the suburb of Cowley is one of the main single producers of
motor-cars in the British Isles. Bedford also takes a share in the
motor industry and produces agricultural machinery. Engineering
and metal-work take 17% of the people employed in Bedford, and
13% of those employed in Oxford; these occupations are less dominant than in Luton, but still constitute the chief manufacturing
trades. Mainly because of the motor industry, the populations of
Oxford and Bedford have increased by a third or more in 30 years.

Cambridge and Swindon

At the extremities of the region lie two towns with markedly
different character and history—Cambridge and Swindon. Swindon
is to a great extent a product of the railway. Its great workshops
produce locomotives and rolling stock, and it is a junction for lines
converging from the west. Cambridge is a town whose ancient
university maintains a keen rivalry with Oxford's. Like Swindon,
aided by light industry, it is growing fast, having added more than a
third to its numbers since 1931; it has acquired industries mainly
concerned with electrical goods, including radio and television sets
and components. It stands on the Cam, acting as the urban focus for
a rich agricultural hinterland, with a position on the boundary
between the Fens and the Scarplands of the South Midlands which
gives it particular advantage as a market centre.

Peterborough: The Brick-Making Industry

Peterborough occupies a position on the Nene like that of Cambridge on the Cam—namely, at the edge of the Fens. In its early
days the main factor of growth was the cathedral, but a comparison
with Ely shows that more than a cathedral is required for continued
expansion. Peterborough has benefited as a market from its location
on a regional boundary. About 25% of its workers are employed in
engineering and metal manufacture, particularly in producing
agricultural machinery for use on the highly-tilled surrounding
farmland, and rolling stock for the main railway which passes through
the town.

Peterborough is prominent in the brick-making industry, producing
15 million bricks a week. The raw material of brick-making is Oxford
Clay, which is well suited to the economical semi-dry process of
manufacture. Other large brickworks occur on the Oxford Clay

belt near Bedford (Plate 57), where the output is roughly equal to that of Peterborough; near Bletchley (4 million bricks a week); and at Calvert, near Aylesbury (5 million). The combined production of the various works amounts at least to one-third of the total output of bricks in the U.K. The works are located where railways cross the Oxford Clay belt, but large numbers of bricks are now distributed by road, the markets being in the London area and in the industrial Midlands.

Northampton and the Leather Industry

Northampton grows steadily but rather slowly. It has probably suffered industrially from the lack of a trunk railway, which the town authorities rejected. The traditional leather-working long predates the railway age, and, when railways were being built, the Northamptonshire iron ores had still to be developed; thus Northampton's refusal of a main line can be partly understood. The town retains its markets of produce and stock, and has profited greatly as a shopping centre by the inter-war extension of rural bus services. It is well situated at the focus of converging routes along the interfluves and along the valleys; when castles had more than a decorative

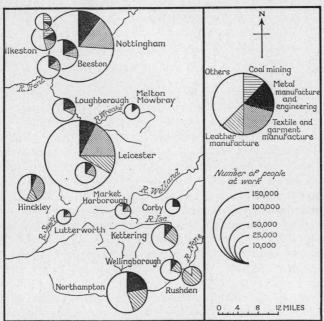

FIG. 135. Employment (all occupations) in Nottingham, Leicester, Northampton, and neighbouring towns

function, Northampton Castle guarded a crossing of the Nene, which below the town has swept out a wide meander-trough in weak clays.

The manufacture of leather remains the chief employer of labour in Northampton, taking no fewer than 20% of the town's workers (Fig. 135); the equally ancient brewing industry makes a smaller demand. Both brewing and leather-manufacture were originally dependent on local agriculture, which provided the barley and the hides and skins, while local oakwoods supplied bark for use in tanning. But barley is nowadays brought from far afield, and the boot and shoe industry supplies an international as well as a domestic market, obtaining its raw materials from abroad as well as from the home country. Numbers of smaller towns around Northampton are heavily dependent on boot and shoe manufacture; at Kettering one in every four workers is employed in the industry, and at Wellingborough one in five. Northampton, like Leicester, is surrounded by industrial satellites. Leicester, although with nearly as many leather-workers as Northampton, is a much larger town, and the footwear industry employs no more than 7% of its labour force (Chap. 22).

Nearly 10% of Northampton's workers are employed in metal manufacture and engineering. There is nothing to compare with the prominence of the motor industry in Luton and Oxford, but engineering works in Northampton are expanding both in numbers and in size. Roller and other bearings are among the goods produced.

Iron-ore, Smelting and Steel-Making

The Middle Lias Marlstone is worked in the Banbury district, much of the product being taken by rail to South Wales, while the ore of the Northampton Sand—part of the Inferior Oolite formation—is extracted from the Northamptonshire Ironstone Field to the northeast of Northampton (Chap. 8). The ore-beds are usually worked opencast, mainly where there is a thin overburden and the ore has not suffered much erosion. Huge mechanical diggers strip off the overburden; the ore is loosened by blasting, and other diggers load it into railborne hoppers. In some quarries the spoil remains in long curving ridges, some of which have been afforested; there is no prospect that the ridges can be made suitable for cultivation, but in other quarries the spoil has been spread evenly and put to tillage or grass (Plate 16).

Part of the Northampton Sand ore is smelted at the expanding town of Corby, and at Wellingborough. The economic reason for smelting on the orefield is the low grade of the ore, which is costly to transport. The same reason encouraged the development of smelting at Melton Mowbray, in Leicestershire, where Marlstone ore is used. Pig-iron is still produced for the West Midlands and South Wales, but the tendency is for local consumption to rise. Corby, increasing in importance as a centre of smelting, also has steelworks which include basic Bessemer converters. A rapidly-growing new town is being added to the older Corby, not without difficulties of retail marketing like those which trouble Oxford and Cowley.

Banbury, Abingdon, and Aylesbury

Abingdon (14,250) has acquired an outpost of the motor-works at Oxford, and there is an aluminium mill on the outskirts of Banbury. Both towns appear to benefit from their location between London

FIG. 136. Projected improvements and additions to the road-system of England and Wales.

and the highly industrialised West Midlands, sharing in the growth of metal-working typical of many old-established market centres of the Midland area. The stock-markets of Banbury are at present booming, having been extended in the post-war period and very greatly increasing their turnover.

Town life of the South Midland Scarplands is being steadily transformed. For many years after the industrialisation of the Midland Triangle and the growth of modern London, this remained a region apart, traversed by main routes but not greatly affected by their traffic. Far more than railways, road transport and electric power lines are enabling industry to locate itself in ancient country towns. Many of the new factories produce goods of the kind made in the West Midlands, but the influence of London is also strongly felt—for instance, in the selection of Aylesbury to receive an over-spill of 15,000 people from the metropolis.[1] With the completion of new motorways across the region, the former isolation of the South Midlands must be still further reduced (Fig. 136).

[1] See p. 455.

East Anglia and the Fenlands

EAST ANGLIA

Area: about 4,000 square miles.
Population: about 2,000,000.
Largest towns: Norwich (120,000).
Ipswich (117,500).
Colchester (65,000).
Harlow (53,500).
Yarmouth (52,750).
Chelmsford (49,750).
Lowestoft (45,750).
Clacton (27,500).
Bury St. Edmunds (21,250).
More than 75% of this region is in improved farmland, and tillage is more than three times as extensive as grassland.
Numbers of livestock: cattle, 350,000; sheep, 130,000; pigs, 420,000.

East Anglia consists largely of low plateau country. It is dominantly rural and dominantly arable, with less than half the population living in towns, and more than half the total area under the plough.

Regional Boundaries

Along the edge of the Fens the land rises in a low, dissected, but noticeable scarp based on Greensand. The break of slope, separating the flat alluvial ground to the west from the subdued sandy hills to the east, fixes the regional boundary. Farther south, East Anglia merges into Midland England along the belt of low Chalk hills which leads southwestwards past Newmarket. There is no physical feature on which to locate the boundary between East Anglia and the London Basin; a gradual transition occurs from the one region to the other, but a boundary can probably be drawn at the outer limit of the transport services which are used by numerous commuters. In Fig. 83 it has been traced between Chelmsford, which is included in East Anglia, and Southend, which is allocated to the London Basin. Thus East Anglia is made to comprise all but the westernmost part of Norfolk, the whole of Suffolk, a small part of Cambridgeshire and about two-thirds of Essex.

Regional Unity

The physical unity of this region is due to the wide spread of glacial drift. A very broad strip, amounting to about half the total area, is mantled with chalky boulder clay (Fig. 137), the product of successive advances and meltings of Pleistocene ice-sheets. It is likely that the original surfaces of the sheets of boulder clay were irregular in detail, but there has been time since the last deglaciation for running water to model the terrain into a continuous system of gentle slopes. Most of the streams drain eastwards to the North Sea—the Bure, Wensum, Waveney, Orwell, Stour, Colne and Chelmer—but the Little Ouse takes the drainage of the sandy Breckland westwards into the Fens. The interfluves are low and the valleys shallow, for the land rises generally to little more than 300 feet.

FIG. 137. East Anglia and the Fenlands: physique and main settlements. The Fenland boundary is marked by a heavy line

Where the boulder clay has been eroded away, in the northeast and southeast, the divides between the valleys are capped by glacial sand and gravel which, in the centre of the region, still lie hidden beneath the boulder clay. Where the sand and gravel has also gone, rocks of Pliocene and Pleistocene age are revealed. These, the Crags, are for the most part shelly limestones.

The regional unity of East Anglia has roots in history as well as in physique. A large part of it formed, during part of the Dark Ages, the kingdom from which the regional name is taken. The contrast between this and adjacent regions was recognised in practice; before the damp forests of the clay lowlands were cleared, East Anglia was hemmed in by thick, tangled wood on the west and south, and fringed by the undrained Fens on the northwest. Within these limits lay a reasonably homogenous piece of country, where gentle slopes led down into shallow valleys, and where marshes were uncommon except along the coast; the coastal marshes, fringing the very inlets which gave the Saxon and Scandinavian settlers access to the land, did not obstruct penetration (cf. Fig. 138, Plate 4).

FIG. 138. Coastal terrain and coastal settlement: sample from Essex

Soils and Climate

Being rich in fragments of Chalk, the boulder clay tends to give rise to a lime-rich soil. Although part of the Chalk content has been leached out during the development of soil on the surface, much is still retained at shallow depth, well within the reach of the roots of plants. In the northeast and the southeast of the region, the pattern of soils is broken and complex; generally speaking, the sands and gravels provide rather light but warm soils, while the soils developed on the Crags are light and rich in lime.

Precipitation is low for Britain—about 25 inches a year. The slight approach to a continental régime in East Anglia (Chap. 3) brings the total for the summer half-year up to, or even above, that for the winter half. The summer fall is beneficial in a region where evaporation is quite powerful in the warmer months, when the water need of the soil tends to exceed the supply. Convectional showers in the early summer aid the growing crops; if they come late, when the ears are heavy and the straw is drying out, they are capable of lodging the grain, but the risk is far less than in the wheatlands of Canada. Mean July temperatures rise above 60°F. The January mean falls below 38°, for this is the most extreme part of the British Isles, with annual ranges generally above 22°F. The frost-free period, however, is well over 5 months in length, and rises to 7 months along the coast; and in any case winter frosts are an advantage, for they break up the soil and help to prepare it either for ploughing or for rolling. The low rainfall is associated with frequent and prolonged sunshine. The eastern fringe of coast is especially sunny in summer, and the whole region averages more than 4 hours of bright sunshine a day throughout the year.

Agriculture

Tillage is extensive, both the low plateau and its eastern borders being very widely under the plough. The general maps (Figs. 35, 37) indicate that in much of the region more than three-quarters of the countryside is in improved farmland. More than half is in tillage crops, which are more than three times as extensive as improved grassland. Next to the Fenland, indeed, this is the most highly tilled region in the British Isles. Tillage in all but the extreme south of the region was strong enough to resist that conversion to grass which, in the inter-war period, seriously reduced the extent of cropland in Britain, and remained so markedly dominant that there has been little scope for its expansion in wartime or in post-war years.

Internal and marginal contrasts in land use are in consequence all the more remarkable, especially since some of them are very sharp. For instance, the valley-bottoms of the Broadland district in the Bure valley are very largely in permanent pasture, which occupies the flat alluvium and ends abruptly against the tillage of the low divides. Drainage of the flood-plains of Norfolk and Suffolk is hampered by the effects of longshore drift, which has extended bars across the drowned inlets and has bent some river-mouths south-wards, lengthening the stream-courses and reducing the gradient. Flood-plains also run inland from the still open estuaries of the Essex coast, and here too are commonly under permanent grass. It is on the flood-plains that cattle are chiefly pastured. Sheep are also kept on the flood-plains in the summer, when the water-table is low, but are frequently folded on arable land at other times.

The patchy distribution of sandy soils in the northeast and south-east of the region is underlined by the alternation between highly intensive cultivation and low-grade grass. In the southwest the Chalk rises to the surface, but the extensive permanent grassland of the Newmarket district is very largely fictitious. Tillage, especially for cash crops, is now the leading interest of many farms around Newmarket, where Scots pine planted in numerous hedges and belts gives the countryside an oddly alien appearance. The lime-poor soils of the Breckland, farther north, carry 30,000 acres of the Forestry Commission's conifers (Plate 5). On the margins of the Breckland appear patches of the native birch, amid which are specialised farms of various kinds, including duck-farms. Northward again, the soils of the Lower Greensand belt are partly under cultivation, but patchy woodland and heath are quite extensive.

Barley and wheat are the most extensive tillage crops of Norfolk and Suffolk. No less than one-third of all cropland is under barley, and nearly one-fifth is in wheat, the two crops covering between them nearly a third of the surface of the two counties. Oats, potatoes, and sugar beet are also common. Some districts have developed specialised market-gardening, particularly in the margins of the region where soils are warm and crops mature early. Vegetables, small fruit, and orchard fruit are grown for sale, especially near the edges of the Fenland, on the loams of North Norfolk, and in the south and southeast of the region where highly intensive cultivation is encouraged by the nearness of London. Some farms in the south concentrate on producing flower seeds.

Poultry are numerous throughout the region, and poultry-farmers raise table birds in addition to keeping laying stock, Norfolk turkeys having a high reputation in the Christmas market. East Anglia, however, displays no such concentration of poultry-farming as is to be found on the Lancs.-Cheshire Plain (Fig. 41). Pigs are fairly numerous, but the number of cattle is low, and that of sheep very low indeed.

Agricultural Change

The present scarcity of sheep represents a very great change from the farming of the Middle Ages, when East Anglia was famous first for its raw wool and later for its woollen manufacture. When the great agricultural improvements took place in the 18th century, experimenters in East Anglia were well to the fore. They succeeded brilliantly in producing a beneficial scheme of crop-rotation—the Norfolk four-course rotation of seeds, wheat, roots, barley. The folding of sheep on arable land ensured that the soil would be well dunged and trodden. But the folding of sheep has very little significance today, since there are so few sheep in the region, and the four-course rotation is practised on scarcely any farms.

The four-course rotation was common right up to the early 1920s, when it lost favour during a time of agricultural depression. With this rotation, only half the land is under cash crops. Sugar beet was already being grown in East Anglia before World War I; the seeds (hay) course has been largely replaced by vegetables, including peas; the powerful demand for barley has led to the introduction of a second barley course at some point, and sugar beet is often followed by winter wheat on the best soils. Sugar beet itself has displaced the turnips and swedes which were formerly grown as food for sheep, and in terms of gross yield is the leading crop of Norfolk. During the last 20 or 30 years East Anglian farms have become more highly arable than ever, the large grain-growing farms changing faster and more markedly than smaller farms. The acreage of barley has doubled in 20 years; the yield per acre of barley, sugar beet and oats has increased by a quarter or more, and the yields per acre of potatoes and wheat by a third. Grassland has been driven into the valley-bottoms, some of which have been improved by drainage works and by re-seeding with grasses and clovers produced at the grassland research station at Aberystwyth. Consequently, more stock per acre can now be kept than was formerly possible. Red Poll beefstock are less common than dairy herds of Friesians and Ayrshires, but dairying in East Anglia has not advanced so rapidly as that of some other regions—always excepting the southern districts close to London.

The modern arable farming of East Anglia is as much a response to demand as it is to environment. Given the demand for grain, East Anglia is the region best suited to barley-growing, and one of the best suited to wheat. British wheat grown for sale, however, is generally unsuitable for the making of bread-flour, unless it is blended. It yields excellent soft flour for biscuit-making, but bread made from it alone would not sell in the peace-time market, where the demand for white bread made chiefly from hard-wheat flour is very strong. The traditional esteem of wheat-growing is firmly rooted in human history, and its emotional associations are powerful;

but bread is no longer a staple food in Great Britain, any more than potatoes are in Ireland. Barley is the great East Anglian crop. Except in the south of the region it takes more land than the other grains combined, and even in the south it is the most extensive grain. The principal buyers of barley are the large breweries. Both barley and wheat are grown mainly for sale off the farm, while oats is meant for the livestock kept in the region.

East Anglia's high success with arable farming has been achieved, despite the fact that many of its soils are no more than moderately fertile in the natural state. Farming in this region has been deliberately designed, ever since the 18th century, to keep the land in good heart; and this it has done, and done well, in addition to responding readily to changing circumstance (Plate 58). Increases of yields, improvements in the scheme of cropping, and more effective selection of strains, are recorded on farms of all kinds—on fruit- and vegetable-farms no less than on those producing grains, sugar beet and potatoes.

Settlement

Apart from the increase in arable, and the changes in type of crop, the texture of the essentially rural scene of East Anglia is slow to alter. The region remains one of nucleated villages, isolated farmsteads, and small market towns. At one time the villages were more numerous than they are today, for parts of East Anglia suffered very severely from the depopulation which made room for sheep-farms (Fig. 29); from place to place a ruined church tower rises amid the ploughland, marking the former site of a vanished village. In the present-day villages can be seen attractive examples of half-timber, lath-and-plaster, and brick building; Finchingfield in Essex is commonly reputed to be one of the finest villages of all, and has attracted a number of artists, but it is difficult to judge the claim that this is the most beautiful village in England. The rural character of the regional landscape is enhanced by the rather open spacing of main roads and the irregular courses of minor roads; East Anglia stands largely apart from the skein of busy routes which connects London to the industrial North, and some of its railways have become butts for humour.

Most of the small towns have little tendency to grow, partly because they are small, but also partly because they are no longer required for stock-marketing. The buying and selling of sheep has almost disappeared with the animals themselves, while cattle-marketing has, in the usual way, become concentrated in a few large centres. The former network of market centres, each serving a limited area, is now too fine.

Norwich

The largest town in the region is Norwich, the regional capital (Fig. 139). Standing on the Wensum a little way above its confluence with the Yare, this town acts as the principal shopping centre of an area with 250,000 inhabitants (Plate 59). Its medieval history was distinguished; a cathedral was founded shortly after the Conquest, a Norman castle was also built, and the medieval trade fair was famous throughout the country. The huge and numerous flocks of sheep grazed in East Anglia enabled Norwich to be the greatest weaving town in Britain from the early 14th to the late

Heavily built-up areas mainly developed before 1914   Less densely built-up areas mainly developed after 1920   Marsh   Permanent grass on flood-plains

FIG. 139. Norwich and its local setting

18th centuries, and it has been estimated that in the early 18th century there were more than 100,000 spinners and weavers in Norfolk and North Suffolk. Weaving survives in Norwich today only in the form of specialised silk-working, the manufacture of wool having been lost to the West Riding during the 19th century. At the same time that woollen manufacture was lost, the manufacture of footwear was established, and 30 footwear factories in Norwich now employ 10,000 people. The great expansion of this industry occurred after World War I. To the mustard-milling started early in the 19th century has been added the production of flour and starch. Agricultural and structural engineering have developed from local ironmongery and from the employment of out-of-work weavers in the making of wire netting. Chemical manufacture is a recent development, printing and the making of foodstuffs and confectionery are older-established. Norwich retains its status as a centre of cattle-marketing, and has a large banking and insurance business.

Colchester, Ipswich, and Chelmsford

Colchester commands a crossing of the Colne, inland of a muddy estuary which is noted for its oysters. The place was a major British centre under Cunobelinus, one of the few large pre-Roman settlements built on low ground, and became a colony for retired Roman veterans. The Normans built a castle to defend the town, which at that time had not spread beyond the patch of terrace gravel where the core of Colchester still lies. Craft drawing 10 feet navigate the Colne to Colchester, which formerly had a noticeable port trade. There is no sizable town within at least 15 miles which can compete with Colchester as an urban centre, and its markets handle large quantities of cattle, eggs, poultry, and market-garden produce.

Colchester is too small for its industries to range widely, and some of them consequently appear distinctive. The same could be said of many moderate-sized towns, numbers of which are engaged in manufacturing of some unusual kind. This matter needs to be seen in proper perspective, however; an unusual but long-established industry, such as the making of mustard at Norwich, is likely to be accepted without question simply because it is well known, whereas the production of photographic equipment at Colchester is less familiar merely because it has developed more recently. Other industrial activities, also without an obvious geographical basis, are the manufacture of diesel engines and electric motors, and the printing of books and periodicals.

Ipswich stands at the estuary-head of the Orwell, Chelmsford on the diminutive Chelmer is some way inland. Both have a general resemblance to Colchester in their location on the route between London and Norwich, in their functions as urban centres for their surroundings, and in their industrial structure. They are concerned in the processing of the agricultural produce of their hinterlands, in the engineering which is common to very many towns, and in some distinctive kind of production. Ipswich, with access to tidewater, is a minor port, produces farm machinery, and processes sugar beet. Chelmsford's large cattle-market handles many dairy animals; its industries include flour-milling, brewing, and malting, the making of electrical equipment of various kinds, and the production of soft drinks for the post-war market.

Other Inland Towns

Of the East Anglian towns which lie well inland, Bury St. Edmunds is the third largest. It occupies a situation in West Suffolk comparable to that of Norwich in Norfolk, but is much the smaller. Once the capital of the kingdom of East Anglia, it is now a small administrative, shopping and market centre compactly built alongside the few remains of its former huge abbey. The second largest inland town is Harlow, one of the new towns built to drain off people from London (Fig. 161). Braintree (20,500), 11 miles north-northeast of Chelmsford deserves special mention for its steel furnaces which are most unexpected in the East Anglian countryside. The locating factor is the successful conversion of 18th-century ironmongery to 20th-century manufacture of metal windows. The ancient textile industry of East Anglia has been succeeded at Braintree by the working of synthetic fibres.

Lowestoft, Yarmouth, and the Herring Fishery

Lowestoft and Yarmouth, located on the sandy east coast of the region, are both resorts, Yarmouth receiving half-a-million visitors a year. Other and smaller resorts dotted along the coast from Hunstanton to Felixstowe share the seasonal trade, which depends on the frequency of summer sun rather than on sandy beaches—certain flourishing resorts on both sides of the Thames estuary show that sand is not an indispensable asset. A specialised form of the resort trade appears in the sailing and cruising of the Broadland.

Yarmouth and Lowestoft have long histories as fishing ports, connected chiefly with the fishery of the North Sea, where herrings are caught principally by drifters. Herring shoals appear off the Shetlands and Orkneys in early spring; successive shoals of different kinds of herring are fished off the Scottish and English coasts during the summer, the season reaching its climax off the East Anglian coast in autumn. In 1951, the fish failed to appear in the numbers forecast, and catches have continued to run low since then; 1959 was a very bad year. The shortage may be due either to a change in natural conditions, or to the trawling of immature fish with the aid of echo-sounders. Whatever the cause, the shortage has depressed the fishing of Lowestoft and Yarmouth.

Lowestoft has shipbuilding yards which have been extended in recent years, and canning factories supplied by East Anglian orchards and market-gardens.

Harwich and Clacton

Harwich and Clacton in their present form are the products of modern transport. Harwich, on a promontory at the seaward end of the Stour estuary, has a long-standing connection with the Continental mainland, having been active in the French trade in times of peace and in naval matters in times of war. Its packet services began in the 17th century; today, with a 25-ft. anchorage, it is the English terminus of the train-ferry to Zeebrugge, of passenger lines to The Hook, Esbjerg, Zeebrugge and Gothenburg, and of cargo lines to Rotterdam. Local industries include the manufacture of fertilisers and cement. The population, now 13,500, is declining. Clacton, on the open coast, is entirely dependent on its resort trade, which greatly expanded in the inter-war period.

THE FENLANDS

Area: about 1,750 square miles.
Population: about 475,000.
Largest towns: King's Lynn (27,500).
                Boston (25,000).
                Wisbech (17,500).
                Spalding (14,750).
                March (13,250).
                Ely (9,750).
Much larger towns—Peterborough and Cambridge—stand on the regional boundary.
More than 80% of the land of this region is in improved farmland, and about two-thirds is in tillage.
Numbers of livestock: cattle, 115,000; sheep, 55,000; pigs, 180,000.

The Fenlands constitute the most distinctive region in the whole of the British Isles, if only because they have been most deliberately and most profoundly transformed by man. The region contains the largest expanses of continuous flat land to be found anywhere in the British Isles, the most continuous tillage, the richest agricultural soils, and the most remarkable development of rectangular patterns in the texture of its landscape.

Except in its very high proportion of cropland, in its climate, and in its generally rural character, the Fenland region contrasts very strongly indeed with the adjoining region of East Anglia. The differences can be traced to, or associated with, differences of physique, for, whereas the central districts of East Anglia are underlain by broad spreads of boulder clay, the Fenlands consist principally of reclaimed swamp (Fig. 137).

Origin and Reclamation of the Fens

Along the shallow and muddy shores of the Wash lies a wide strip of silt, much of it deposited by the sea. The fine-grained sediment was very wet in its original state, and had a low angle of rest, so that its slopes today are extremely gentle. The silt fen is too wide to be properly described as a beach bar, but its deposits nevertheless served to shut off a great lagoon from the rising sea of post-glacial times. More silt was laid down alongside the channels of the Witham, Welland, Nene and Ouse, which maintained courses across the shallow basin to the shore. Behind the widening strip of coastal silt, and between the mud-fringed rivers, reedswamp flourished in lime-rich waters, its débris accumulating thickly as mild peat, forming peat fen on the inland side of the silt fen. The permanently-flooded area became subdivided in the course of time, and the individual shallow but originally extensive meres were reduced in size. Settlement pushed inwards from the silt fen and from the landward margins, but for many centuries it was confined, in the peat fen, almost entirely to the low islands of gravel and boulder clays which projected through the swamps.

Piecemeal drainage of the Fenland and reclamation of salt-marsh along the borders of the Wash began at least as early as Roman times. The start made on Ely Cathedral in 1083 shows that the Fenlands had no little economic importance in early Norman days, and numbers of Fenland place-names date from the Dark Ages or from the early Middle Ages. Among the chief products of the undrained fens were fish and wildfowl, which for a long time were commercially important; trade in this produce was to a great extent in the hands of the monasteries up to the time of the dissolution, and monastic control over the drainage-system was at one time widespread. It was not until the first half of the 17th century, however, that a well-organised project of artificial drainage was carried out, when the Bedford Level was made available for improvement by the Dutch engineer Vermuyden. More works followed, particularly under the 18th-century improvers, and the last considerable mere (at Whittlesea) was drained more than a hundred years ago. Wicken Fen, near Cambridge, is preserved as a nature reserve.

Very little remains in the peat fen of the natural courses of the Fenland rivers, which have been diverted, regularised, and duplicated. The general problems of drainage are two—that of controlling the water-table for the benefit of agriculture, and that of preventing floods. The second is the more difficult; as long as it can be solved, the first is simple enough.

As soon as the meres were drained and the soil-water table was lowered far enough for cultivation to begin, the fen peat began to shrink. If the peat was well dried out, it became liable to wind erosion, which still occurs in some windy springs before the crops have had time to bind the soil. In places the land-surface has sunk by ten feet or more, but the rivers remained at the old levels in their silt-lined channels, and the danger of widespread floods from burst banks or from overspilling floodwater greatly increased as the peat shrank or blew away. Similarly, the cost of pumping from farm drains into the trunk channels also rose. In some parts of the Fenland, the rivers and man-made watercourses are highly embanked; their water-level at all but the lowest stages is well above the general level of the surrounding countryside, roads run along the outer foot of an embankment, and cropland occupies the lowest level of all (Plate 60).

Limits of embanking and on the cutting of large drains are set by cost and by the calculation of risk. It is simply impracticable to safeguard against great but very infrequent floods—for instance, the floods which can be expected on an average of once in a thousand years. Floods with a far lower frequency than this can be very troublesome, especially since many embankments are already as high as they can be made: added weight in some places would merely make them liable to rotational slipping, such as occurs on the sides of railway cuttings. Dredging of channels, regulation of drainage, and construction and maintenance of drainage works generally are in the hands of River Boards (formerly Catchment Boards) who are also responsible for the operation of sluices at the outfalls to the sea. Pumping is carried out by power-driven machines.

The Landscape-pattern

Straight lines dominate the map of the peat fen. Straightened rivers, artificial cuts, roads, and the field boundaries formed by minor drains, all combine in a system of elongated rectangles (Fig.

Public roads _____ Rivers and open drains ∴ Buildings

FIG. 140. Pattern of settlement, roads, and drains on part of the peat Fen

140). Nucleated settlements are rare. Where they occur, they are typically compressed into long lines of houses, by a watercourse on one side and peat fen on the other—as at Upwell, Outwell, and The Deepings. From place to place a small group of houses clusters about a bridge, but the commonest unit of settlement in the peat fen is the isolated farmstead standing back from the through road. The pale yellow brick of the farmhouses is partly hidden by the trees planted to give some shelter from otherwise unobstructed winds, and Dutch barns are usually walled-in with corrugated iron. On many farms, Nissen huts sold as war surplus in the late 1940s are used as barns.

The character of the scenery changes immediately the peat fen is left for one of the so-called fen islands. Some tendency to nucleation of settlement is to be noted on many of these, but the most striking difference from the peat fen is the appearance of sloping ground, dry permanent pasture in some of the small fields, and hedgerow timber. The fen-girt hills look like scraps of the English Midlands set down in Holland. Similar but more general differences separate the peat fen from the silt fen, with its most irregular pattern of minor roads, its belt of nucleated villages running from King's Lynn to Boston, and reddish clayey soils developed on the silt which contrast with the deep, black, rather friable soils of the peat fen.

Agriculture

The climate of the Fenlands closely resembles that of East Anglia, being only a little drier and a little less extreme. It would suit barley as well as the East Anglian climate does, but wheat is the great grain crop in the Fenlands. Barley produced in this region often falls below malting standard, and wheat takes half or more of the area given to grain, which covers some two-fifths of all farmland; potatoes, vegetables, and sugar beet are next in order of extent.

Cash-cropping is to be expected in a region which has borne the high costs of reclamation and must still pay heavily for the operations of day-to-day drainage. Livestock, with the exception of poultry, are few in number, and consist chiefly of cattle which are grazed on the permanent pasture of the worst-drained fen or on the low hills. Within the limits of cash-cropping there is much specialisation, which in a rough kind of way amounts to a difference between the peat fen on the one hand, and the silt fen and the fen-islands on the other. Grain, potatoes and sugar beet are characteristic of the peat fen. Fruit-farming and market-gardening are concentrated on the silts, where some of the soils can be worked into an excellent tilth, and where sloping land provides the cold-air drainage necessary for orchards. The general maps (Figs. 37, 38, 39, 40) record

58. Arable farmland in Norfolk—low rolling countryside, fields of cut barley, and tower of an abandoned church.

59. Stall-market and medieval buildings. Norwich.

60. Artificial river in the Fenland; view from embankment across pasture, to chimneys of brickworks near Peterborough.

61. Haytor, one of the granite tors of Dartmoor.

unrivalled concentrations of potato- and vegetable-growing in the Fenlands, a production of small fruit which is second only to that of north Kent, and a minor concentration of orchards. Wisbech is the centre of a compact block of fruit-farms where the most extensive crops are strawberries and gooseberries; a list of all small fruit and other market-garden produce grown here would, however, be very long indeed. Fruit- and vegetable-farms are also numerous around King's Lynn, while the Spalding district is noted for bulbs, flowers, peas and beans. Potatoes are as common on the silt fen as on the peat fen, their high yields and ready sales in most years enabling the growers to bear the damage done by eelworm in some districts. The leading area for first early potatoes lies in the coastal strip near Boston, where the tubers ripen a week before those in other parts of the region.

Towns and Town Sites

Urban development in the Fenland is very limited indeed. The towns already named as centres of specialised farming districts are closely dependent on the agriculture of their surroundings. They possess shops, markets, cinemas, and banks; they sell, maintain and repair agricultural machinery; and they offer some industrial employment in canning plants and sugar-beet factories. It is significant that the two largest stand on navigable water in the seaward projections of the region. King's Lynn (Plate 21), once the greatest port of England, is now reduced to a limited coasting trade in grain and sugar, but its fine guildhall and its two market-places testify to the bustling activity of former days, while 18th-century buildings record its last days of wide-reaching importance. Boston takes a small share in the North Sea fishery, and has industries of brewing, malting, and canning. After prolonged stagnation, the Fenland towns are growing anew, recording the following increases in 1951–61: Boston, 18%; Spalding, 20%; March, 14%; Wisbech, 13%; and King's Lynn, 21%.

All these towns occupy sites which, in their natural state, were better-drained than the bulk of the fen. If towns were to develop at all, it was certain that advantage would be taken of rising ground—however slightly rising—and of outcrops of gravel. Only in such places was there ground dry and firm enough for building, and room for a settlement larger than a village to develop.

CHAPTER 25

Southwest England

Area: about 4,000 square miles.
Population: about 1,150,000.
Largest towns: Plymouth (204,250).
Exeter (80,250).
Torquay (54,000).
Camborne ⎫
Redruth ⎭ (36,000 together).
Paignton (30,250).
St. Austell (25,000).
Penzance (19,500).
About 70% of this region is in improved farmland, grass being two-and-a-half times as extensive as tillage.
Numbers of livestock: cattle, 700,000; sheep, 1,150,000; pigs, 320,000.

Southwest England contains an upland block of Primary rocks, which, exceptionally in the British Isles, escaped glaciation. Erosional platforms are broadly developed across the whole rigid massif west of the Exe, and in places are largely intact. Rivers are deeply incised into the lower platforms, which fall sharply to the sea in a cliffed shoreline indented by drowned inlets. Agriculture and tourism, the mainstays of the regional economy, are favoured by a climate which at low levels is remarkably mild in winter and sunny in summer. About half the people of the region live in towns, but most of the towns are small; rural settlement is typified by hamlets and isolated farms rather than by compact villages. Regional distinctiveness is as highly developed as in any region of the British Isles, and it can be suspected that the unmeasured quality of regional consciousness is also strong.

Physique

The Carboniferous, Devonian, and older rocks of Southwest England were incorporated in the belt of Altaid folding (Chap. 2). The existing peninsula is broadly synclinal in structure, with Devonian rocks exposed in the north and south, and Carboniferous rocks in the centre. The northern flank of the syncline, represented by Exmoor and the Quantocks, is formed by resistant sandstones and flags which reach heights of 1,400 to 1,600 feet. The downbent central part is occupied by the shaly Culm Measures, of Carboniferous age. Devonian rocks reappear on the southern flank as the sandstones and limestones of south Devon, extending westwards into Cornwall, which belongs entirely to the southern limb of the fold. The structural pattern is somewhat obscured by the trend of shorelines cutting diagonally across the lines of folding, and is complicated by the six granitic masses of Dartmoor, Bodmin Moor, Hensbarrow, Carn Menellis, Land's End, and the Scilly Islands (Fig. 141). The granitic outcrops stand higher than their surroundings, but their altitude decreases westwards, so that whereas Dartmoor rises to 2,039 feet on High Willhays, the Scillies merely project above sea-level in low, ragged islands (cf. Plates 61, 63).

FIG. 141. Southwest England: physique and main settlements

Although the upland block has been severely denuded in places, it clearly forms a single massif, probably being fault-bounded and probably also having been subject to faulting during Tertiary times. On the eastern flank the older rocks are depressed, and Permo-Triassic sediments lap on to the flanks of the massif. The sandstones, marls, and pebble beds of the Permo-Trias are in general much weaker than the rocks of the massif, and have been severely eroded, mainly by feeders of the Exe. The regional boundary, running through the wide vales which border Exmoor and stretch through the Exe basin to the Channel coast, includes the plateau country of West Somerset in Southwest England, but excludes the broken hills of easternmost Devon.

The simple erosional history of the massif has produced landforms as significant to the farming community as they are obvious to the eye. Denudation is thought to have been controlled by intermittent falls in the relative level of land and sea, broad erosional platforms being cut across the strong rocks of the massif whenever that level remained stable for a long period. The platforms, whether cut by waves on the shore or reduced by rain and rivers, extend through the whole range of height from the loftiest plateaus to the tops of the cliffs, so that most of the land in the region is gently-sloping and exposed. All the rivers have been strongly rejuvenated in their lower reaches, flowing in narrow, steep-sided young valleys cut in slowly-weathering resistant rocks. The deeply-dissected coastland obstructs travel between east and west, and roads keep to the divides wherever possible. In the upper reaches, which have so far escaped most rejuvenation, the rivers occupy wide, shallow valleys merging gently into the broad plateaus.

Origins of the drainage-system are still in part obscure. The Exe, obviously superimposed across geological structures and geological outcrops, appears to represent original consequent drainage to the south, as also do the Dart, the Fowey, and the Falmouth ria. The upper courses of the Camel and Torridge may have been captured from south-flowing rivers, but their lower courses and the whole trunk of the Taw are superimposed, and the three systems are not due simply to the headward extension of rivers draining to the north coast. Whatever their mode of origin, all the main rivers are small in volume because their catchments are limited. They are useless for navigation except in their drowned lower reaches, both because they are small and also because their long-profiles are broken by knickpoints.

During glacial maximum in the Ice Age, when the sea stood lower than it does today, the rivers of the Southwest cut deeply down near their mouths. With the waning of the ice-caps and the release of meltwater, the sea rose, flooding the lower ends of all the valleys and converting them into the branching inlets known as *rias*. In the old days of sailing-craft, the sheltered harbours of the rias were much used by fishermen (Plate 62).

Agriculture

On the level platforms and flat-topped divides there is no physical obstacle to farming. No ice-caps came to scrape off the wastemantle and to remove the soil. The land of the high moorlands is admittedly poor in quality, and its climate is rainy and bleak at high levels, where actual means range from about 36° in January to 56° in July, where rainfall rises above 60 inches a year in places, and where 200 or more rain-days may be expected each year. The rest of the region, however, is almost everywhere in farms; more than half the total area is in improved grass. The region lies too far west, and is too high, open, windy and wet for its farms to be committed mainly to tillage. Except on the coast, annual rainfall averages more than 40 inches. The coastlands fare better than the interior, being sunnier and drier, and sharing the regional advantage of a mean range of temperature generally below 17°F (Figs. 11–13), but they are restricted in extent, and most of the region experiences a distinctly damp climate in which rainfall is well-distributed through the year.

A survey of land use made in a particular year—e.g., the maps of the Land Utilisation Survey—can be guaranteed to show a high fraction of arable land, but much of this arable represents the breaking of grassland. The widespread practice in the Southwest of ploughing-up and re-seeding grassland has a double origin; in part it is a sign of good farming, for the quality of ley grass is more easily controlled and improved than that of permanent pasture, but, in addition to this, ploughing-up is especially suitable to the inland farms of this region, where the gentle slopes tend to impede the natural drainage of the soil and to make any grassland sour in the course of time. Thus the pattern of land use is a patchwork of permanent grass, tillage, and ley-grass of varying age.

The relatively small part played by tillage crops in the farming of this region is clear from the general maps of agricultural distributions (Figs. 35, 37–40). Rotation grass is as extensive as tillage crops in Cornwall, and two-thirds as extensive in Devon. Some 60% of the farmland is under grass of one kind or another; the main interest lies in livestock, and especially in dairying, for some 200,000 of the 700,000 cattle in the region are cows actually in milk. Dairying is practised throughout the region, partly for the supply of local markets—including the few sizable towns—but also for London, There is some rearing and fattening of beef cattle, but fattening tend, to be concentrated in the east of the region, on the red soils of the vales cut in Permo-Trias. The Permo-Trias belt is truly Red Devon, justly noted for its native breed of beef cattle.

Sheep are fairly numerous in the Southwest, being set to graze not only on the enclosed farmland but also on the open granite moorlands and on the higher parts of Exmoor. In the hill districts the soils are much poorer than those developed on the sedimentary rocks of the centre and south. Exmoor stands high, and its rather shallow sandy soils have been made acid by leaching in a damp climate, while the slowly-weathering granites give rise to coarse, shallow, acid soils, which are made still more acid by the raw humus supplied by heather, bracken, and peat-moss. Peat-bogs occur in the shallow valley-heads high on Dartmoor, where the weather is often wet, misty, and cool, and where drainage is particularly bad. Large areas on all the moors are unenclosed. Little fields nip the edges of the unfenced country, but some have reverted to rough grazing (Fig. 142). At the present time there is little pressure of enclosure, and the boundary of the improved farmland is stable.

FIG. 142. Sample of land use and dispersed settlement, central Devon

Agriculture in Southwest England has been revolutionised in the last hundred years. In the 17th and 18th centuries its emphasis was on the growing of food grain for local use and the production of wool for manufacture within the region; Exeter at one time had a noted serge-market. Even when the domestic craft of weaving vanished with the industrial revolution, raw wool was still needed for the new mills of Yorkshire. The local demand for locally-produced subsistence foodstuffs persisted until the railway age, with the regional output rising slowly as new ideas about farming seeped in from the east. With the entry of railways, two profound changes became possible: the region was freed from dependence on its own grainfields, and had access to an enormous urban market. Cash-farming in the Southwest, with dairying dominant, is the outcome of the rise of industry and the provision of rapid transport.

Given the means of transport, the farmers of Devon and Cornwall were able to realise the potential benefits of the regional climate. Although these benefits apply most strongly to cultivation of a specialised kind, they are also advantageous to farming in general. The mild winters (Chap. 3) combine with the inflow of moist air from the Atlantic to promote a rich growth of grass and to extend the growing-season, and the problem of winter feeding of livestock is less severe in the Southwest than in any other part of Great Britain. The smallness of farms is no obstacle to dairying, while the little fields with earthen banks around them are well suited to controlled grazing by small herds, and to giving shelter from the powerful winds. Although most of Cornwall and some parts of Devon are too remote from a railway or too far from London to specialise in the production of fresh milk, they can supply butter and cheese, which are prepared either on the farms themselves or in central creameries.

Along the south coast, bordering sheltered bays and lining the edges of the larger inlets, are found patches of market-gardens. The body of the peninsula gives shelter from the north, various pieces of high ground protect the market-gardens from strong winds from the west, and raised beaches provide warm soils on flat sites. Market-gardening is helped by the generally mild winters of the region, and also by the mild spring nights when temperatures are kept up by the warm nearby sea. Among the crops are green vegetables, early potatoes, and soft fruit. The densest concentrations of market-gardens occur at the head of Mount's and St. Ives Bays, on the western sides of the rias leading inland from Falmouth and Plymouth, and around Exeter. The Scilly Islands, with a climate slightly more oceanic than that of the mainland, specialise in cut flowers, which come into bloom there in the first weeks of the calendar year. As the main markets are London and the industrial towns of the Midlands, the prosperity of flower-growing and market-gardening in Southwest England depend on the power of distant townspeople to buy early and at a high price. In recent years the growers of Southwest England have been meeting severe competition in the London market from producers in Mediterranean countries.

Farms, Field Patterns, and Rural Settlement

The layout of farms and the distribution of farmsteads in Southwest England has been scarcely affected by the conversion of regional agriculture. Farms remain small; half of those in Cornwall are no larger than 20 acres, but there is also a significant group in the range 50–100 acres. Holdings run larger in Devon, the most typical farm being in the 50–100 acre range, but more than half are still below 50 acres.

Within single farms, fields are also tiny. Their smallness results partly from piecemeal enclosure, partly from social usage, and partly from the original practice of the first settlers. In previous centuries, land has been enclosed and improved at the edges of existing holdings; fields have been subdivided between heirs at the death of the owner, as in Normandy and the Channel Islands; in the remoter parts of the region, it is possible that the present pattern of dispersed farms and hamlets is directly inherited from the pattern established by Celtic people. It used to be thought that the scattered rural dwellings of this region were all the result of primary dispersion of settlement. But though dispersion is generally characteristic of the Celtic West of the British Isles, it is known that, in some areas at least, present dispersion has replaced originally nucleated settlements (cf. Chap. 4). Admittedly, Celtic speech survived in the Southwest up to the 18th century, and Celtic customs presumably survived along with it, but Celtic survivals can throw little light on the obscurity of early settlement. Nucleated villages of the Midland sort are known to have existed in parts of Devon, surrounded by their open fields. Whatever their origins, however, hamlets and isolated farms are typical of the region today (Fig. 142), sheltering from the frequent strong winds of the interior plateaus in small folds of the ground, and lodging on the flanks of small valley-heads. Dispersed settlements are well adapted to an environment which includes few nucleating factors, and to a region where piecemeal enclosure and improvement of the formerly extensive open land was the obvious response to any increase in population.

The Resort Trade and Resort Towns

For purposes of publicity, the south coast of Cornwall is often described as the Cornish Riviera. The title is as pretentious as the claim that the coastlands of Southwest England experience a Mediterranean climate. By British standards, however, the climate on the coasts is mild and genial throughout the year, for the peninsula projects far into the warm Atlantic. Sea surfaces temperatures continue to rise after midsummer, prolonging the effective summer season, while frost and snow are rare at low levels in the winter season. Were it not for the national habit of making August the main holiday month, the resorts of the Southwest would in all probability be still more popular than they are; even now, the number of winter visitors is not inconsiderable.

The resorts themselves are mainly small. Many began as fishing villages on little inlets, and some have scarcely expanded in the last two centuries. Their smallness, their irregular houses, their air of sleepy antiquity and their little harbours contribute to the pervasive but indefinable charm of the region. Place-names of a distinctive kind, particularly common in Cornwall, are apt to impress the visitor as romantic, and romantic qualities have a cash value in the tourist trade.

As the tourist industry has grown, so fishing has declined. The coastal settlements survive and prosper, with changed functions. Tiny coves are more typical than large sweeping bays, and some of the coastal villages are huddled in the mouths of incised valleys, with little room to grow. Many, moreover, have little tendency to grow, for tourism in the Southwest is largely decentralised, most of the well-known resort towns ranging between 2,500 and 10,000 in numbers of resident population. Barnstaple on the north coast has 16,000 permanent inhabitants, Bideford 10,250 and Newquay 11,750, Bude 5,000, and Tintagel no more than 1,500. Totals on the south coast may be illustrated by Penzance (19,500) and Teignmouth (11,500); near the other extreme come Babbacombe, with 5,000, and Mevagissey, with 2,200.

The greatest exception to the small or moderate size of resort towns in the Southwest is Torquay, which is estimated to receive a million visitors a year. Its winter trade is important, but summer is by far the main season. Visitors to Torquay come mainly from the great concentrations of towns in England—London, the industrial Midlands, the Bristol area, Lancashire, Yorkshire, and the Northeast. Significantly, Torquay is located on the south coast of the peninsula, near the eastern margin of the region. It stands at one end of Tor Bay, sharing a three-mile stretch of sandy beach with the smaller but rapidly-expanding resort of Paignton.

Plymouth, Exeter, and Falmouth

Plymouth has a strong interest in the resort trade, but is far too complex to be classed merely as a resort town. It is the regional capital of the Southwest, even though Exeter possesses both the cathedral and the university. Plymouth, the more centrally placed, has an excellent deep-water harbour, with Saltash Bridge and the ferries increasing the nodal quality of its position. The town flourished greatly under Elizabeth I, when the Southwest supplied astonishing numbers of fighting ships, seamen, explorers, and pirates. Plymouth's lengthy association with naval affairs relates to a situation near the western end of the Channel; like Brest, on the French side, Plymouth is a port of call, but just as Brest has suffered from the competition of Cherbourg, so has Plymouth suffered from that of Southampton. Both Brest and Plymouth are somewhat remote from the national capitals of their respective countries, and are handicapped as general ports by hinterlands which are little industrialised and none too well peopled.

Exeter, commanding the southern approaches to the region, lies inland of the silty ria-head into which the Exe discharges. The heart of the town occupies a patch of terrace alongside the incised Exe, and adjoining a hill cut in tough igneous rock where the Norman motte-and-bailey castle was built. Exeter is approached from the north along a valley cut through fairly resistant rocks by the superimposed Exe; hills on the north, and the floodable, broadening valley to the south, helped to direct routes to the town (Fig. 143).

Although the Exe is small, it was navigable up to Exeter until the 13th century, when the Countess Isabella had the river obstructed

FIG. 143. Exeter and its local setting

by a weir below the town. A canal which by-passes the weir has not enabled Exeter to develop much port trade. Commercially, however, medieval Exeter enjoyed much prosperity as a great centre of the wool trade, and serge-making and tanning were established in the 17th–18th centuries. Manufacturing activities—brewing, printing, paper-making, garment-making, and engineering—are subordinate to clerical and service occupations and distributive trade. Exeter's retailing may well expand in the future, for the shopping district has been reconstructed on the site cleared by concentrated bombing in World War II.

Falmouth (15,500) is located similarly to Plymouth, on the edge of a large ria. Standing nearer to the open sea than does Plymouth, and with less of the available land built over, Falmouth has recently acquired an enormous dry-dock capable of accommodating modern oil-tankers—great vessels ranging up to 850 feet in length, and some exceeding 65,000 tons deadweight. The repair-yards at Falmouth are already well reputed for work on tankers, and the new dry-dock is expected to ensure additional employment, despite possible competition from Milford Haven.

Inland Towns

The inland centres of Southwest England are mostly market towns. Many of them have developed industry of some kind—in connection with local farming, in response to the trend of industrial dispersal, or as the result of local enterprise—but there is no single industrial pattern. A common type of siting is exemplified by Newton Abbot (18,000), Totnes, and Truro (13,500), which command relatively easy crossings of incised valleys. Camborne, Redruth, and St. Austell are special cases; the first two formerly prospered as centres of ore-mining, while the latter is now the chief centre of kaolin-working.

Mining, Quarrying, and Fishing

Metal ores in Southwest England include ores of tin, copper, lead, zinc and iron. They are concentrated in a belt about ten miles wide, which runs across the northern part of the Land's End and Carn Menellis granites, cuts squarely across Hensbarrow, and tips the southern extremity of Bodmin Moor. The ores were emplaced when the granites were intruded and volatile gases cooled in fissures, depositing metal compounds. Stream tin was probably exploited as long as 4,000 years ago, and the mining of tin ore was probably carried on in Roman times. Mining was deliberately fostered by Elizabeth I, and output was high during the 18th and the 19th centuries, the chief products being ores of tin and copper sent to smelting-works in South Wales. Mining eventually declined as reserves were depleted, mines were flooded, and oversea producers came to the fore. Copper ores from the U.S.A. undercut the Cornish product, and Cornish tin was unable to meet the competition of stream-tin from Malaya. Flooding of abandoned mines made recovery less and less possible, and the economic fluctuations of the inter-war period almost extinguished mining at times, the maximum annual output of tin ore between 1919 and 1939 being but 5,500 tons. World War II brought about the hasty re-opening of some mines and the expansion of output from others, but the current annual output yields only 1,000 tons of pure tin, and represents but 5% of national consumption. Camborne and Redruth remain centres of mining technology and of the manufacture of mining machinery.

The kaolin (china clay) of Southwest England is the result of the metamorphism of granite. The alteration took place at the same time that the mineral lodes were formed, and was due to the same kind of agency—hot volatile gases emanating from the cooling granites. The potash-felspar of the affected granite was changed into kaolin.[1] Kaolinisation was most pronounced in the St. Austell district, where china-clay workings are mainly concentrated. Par is the chief exporting port. Hydraulic working is practised in the opencast pits. Jets of water are directed against the working face, breaking up the altered material and roughly separating the kaolin from the mica and quartz which are also present. Final separation takes place in tanks, where part of the mica is recovered, the rest going to waste with the quartz grains. Quartz and waste mica are dumped in conical heaps which glitter white in the sunshine.

The rise of kaolin-working in Southwest England was intimately associated with the growth of the pottery industry of North Stafford-shire (Chap. 22), and the Potteries take part of the present output, but much kaolin is used as filler for paper and cloth. Output of kaolin from Southwest England has increased since the inter-war period, running at about 1,500,000 tons a year at the present time, against some 600,000 tons a year in the 1930s; part of the increase corresponds to the increased consumption of high-grade glazed paper in North America.

At Bovey Tracey, on the flank of Dartmoor, kaolin is worked in conditions which contrast with those of the St. Austell district. The kaolin of Bovey Tracey was brought down by streams from Dartmoor and deposited in the Tertiary lake which occupied a rift-valley. Lignite in the lake-deposits is of great geological interest, but of no commercial value except in times of extreme need—as, for

[1] For example, the felspar $K_2O.Al_2O_3.6SiO_2$ became $Al_2O_3.2SiO_2.2H_2O$.

62. A Devon ria—drowned mouth of the incised Dart, at Dartmouth.

63. China-clay workings, Cornwall. The generally subdued terrain belongs to erosional platforms.

64. Bradford-on-Avon, Wiltshire. Parkland occurs on the near side of the town, with fields established by parliamentary enclosure on the far side.

65. Cottages at Wareham, Dorset, with stone footings, pug walls, and low thatched roofs.

example, the immediate post-war period, when it was sold in the Channel Islands for heating glasshouse boilers. Part of the output of kaolin from the Bovey Tracey basin is locally manufactured into chinaware, glazed pipes, and tiled fireplaces.

Other extractive industries of Southwest England include the quarrying of slate and of granite. The chief producer of slates is the locality of Delabole, while granite is taken from a number of accessible places on the blocks of moorland. Demand for slates has been seriously reduced by competition of asbestos and earthenware tiles, while granite has been largely replaced, for some purposes, by concrete and by tarmacadam in which stone of other kinds is used. Employment in granite-quarrying has been reduced by the introduction of machines—as, for example, at Newlyn, where granite from the Land's End mass is loaded into coasters by conveyor-belt.

In the whole region, no more than 5,750 people are employed in mining and quarrying Fishing takes even fewer, with 1,750. Mining, quarrying, and fishing together employ fewer than one in sixty of the regional working population. They have suffered not only an absolute decline, but also a far greater relative decline, particularly by comparison with the tourist industry. The reduction of fishery has occurred despite access to contrasted bodies of water which used to supply a varied range of fish including mackerel from the western Channel; the Southwest, handicapped by small harbours, lack of capital, inflexible customs, and railway connections inferior to those of the great centralised fishing-ports, has abandoned part of its maritime tradition.

O

The Borders of the West Country : The Hampshire Basin and Its Borders : The Channel Islands

THE Borders of the West Country consist partly of scarplands which prolong the Scarplands of the South Midlands (Chap. 23); they also include the Plain of Somerset, the Mendips, and the environs of Bristol—three districts which are structurally allied to the Midland Triangle. The Hampshire Basin constitutes a structural as well as a topographic depression. Each region contains a great port, but the links of each regional hinterland with its port are far weaker than the corresponding links in the London Basin. Consequently, the geographical unity displayed by each of the two regions is not fundamentally due to the presence and size of Bristol and Southampton, and the regional economies are in some measure detached from the trade and manufacture of the ports.

Physique

In the Hampshire Basin the Chalk has sagged deeply downwards, the resulting hollow receiving the sediments which now form Tertiary strata. Along the southern edge of the Basin the almost vertical rim of Chalk has been disrupted by erosion, and the Isle of Wight detached from the mainland. On the north, the Chalk rises in the broad structural arch of Salisbury Plain and the Hampshire Downs (Fig. 144), where the crestal belt, planed off by erosion in a previous cycle, rises flatly to 700–800 ft., a very few small hills alone protruding and rising above 900 feet. Farther north still, the Chalk is downfolded under the western tip of the London Basin, rising again in the cuesta of the Berkshire Downs to above 800 ft. and forming a north-facing scarp.

The whole belt of Chalkland surrounding the Hampshire Basin is traversed by Tertiary folds which run east-west and die away at their ends. Most of the folds are quite modest in size, and have little effect on relief, but anticlines on the western margin have been eroded to form the Vales of Pewsey, Warminster, and Wardour. The Chalk has been stripped back, forming infacing scarps above the older rocks in the floors of the Vales.

FIG. 144. Borders of the West Country; the Hampshire Basin and its borders:
physique and main settlements

Southwards from the Vale of Wardour, the edge of the Chalk
becomes less and less marked, for the Chalk formation has been
thinned by erosion; Chalk hills reappear northwest of Weymouth,
and continue into the Isle of Purbeck, ending in a cliffed coast
embellished by buttresses and stacks.

Part of the Borders of the West Country is composed of cuestas
facing some westerly direction, with backslopes descending towards
the east, southeast, and south. The scarp-forming rocks are limestones and sandstones of Jurassic age, and the Greensand which
belongs to the Cretaceous system. Clays tend to be rather thin, so
that the strike vales developed on them are narrower than those
of the South Midlands or Southeast England, and in any case the
structural pattern is confused by faulting and minor folding.

On parts of the boundary between the rim of the Hampshire
Basin and the Borders of the West Country, the thickening Greensand forms a steep, tree-clad, west-facing scarp which is even more
prominent than the edge of the Chalk. Thickening still further, the
Greensand protrudes far to the west in the Blackdown Hills, a well-
dissected tabular block with summits rising very gently to more

than 1,000 ft. The Greensand oversteps the eroded edges of under-lying formations, passing in turn across the Jurassic and Permo-Trias towards its outpost in the Haldon Hills beyond the Exe (Fig. 145).

FIG. 145. Block-diagram to show westward overstep of
Cretaceous rocks in Dorset

The narrowing Cotswolds enter the Borders of the West Country from the north, declining in height towards the incised valley of the superimposed Avon at Bath, and breaking down into irregular hills between the Avon and the Mendips. South of the Mendips comes more broken hilly country, which continues beyond Yeovil to where the Jurassic rocks pass beneath the Greensand.

The Mendips rise above 1,000 ft. in a steep-sided, flat-topped and compact line of hills in which Carboniferous Limestone is brought up by sharp folds. In the south they overlook the Somerset Plain, where eroded folds in Jurassic rocks form little lines of hills projecting into the peaty and alluvial flats of the Somerset Levels. North of the Mendips, the Avon has been superimposed across a district where folded and faulted rocks form hills of no great size, and where Carboniferous rocks, including productive Coal Measures, project through the Permo-Trias.

THE BORDERS OF THE WEST COUNTRY

Area: about 2,000 square miles.
Population: about 750,000.
Largest towns: Bristol (436,500).
     Bath (80,750).
     Weston-super-Mare (44,000).
     Taunton (35,250).
     Bridgwater (25,500).
     Yeovil (24,500).

Three-quarters of this region is in improved farmland, with grassland three times as extensive as tillage.
Numbers of livestock: cattle, 425,000; sheep, 285,000; pigs, 175,000.

Climate and Agriculture

The Borders of the West Country receive some 35 to 40 inches of rain a year—about 10 inches more than the South Midland Scarplands. The former region is slightly more sunny if slightly more equable, and quite noticeably warmer in winter than the South Midlands, with mean January temperatures about 40°F. Lying snow is infrequent, and the frost-free season exceeds 6 months. All these conditions promote the growth of grass, and the grazing of stock is so firmly established that tillage has not been much extended since 1939. Such extra tillage as exists grows mainly fodder crops.

This region is not climatically unsuited to grain; grains take well over half the tillage of Somerset, but it is significant that oats, mixed corn, wheat, and barley are roughly equal in extent. Fodder roots (turnips, swedes and mangolds) and green fodder crops (mainly cabbage, kale, and rape) take about one-fifth of the cropland. Orchards are very numerous, covering a large total area, but most single orchards are small; their main product is cider apples.

Some parts of the region are more heavily tilled than others. The Somerset Levels and other alluvial flats, very largely in permanent grass, resemble the Fenlands in being based on the silt and peat which fills a former lagoon; but although their drainage has been improved, the water-table has not been brought under complete control, and the land remains liable to flood. On the exposed top of the Mendips there is much sheep-pasture, some of it in poor condition. The broken hilly country of the central and eastern parts of the region contains clayland in the upper valleys of the Stour and Avon, where permanent pasture is extensive (Plate 64), but there are also warm sandy loams—e.g., around Yeovil—where tillage is common and includes market-gardening.

Dairy-farming is prominent throughout this region; more than a third of the cattle are dairy animals actually in milk, and few of the remainder are beefstock. Butter, cream and cheese are the leading products of processing plants, and large numbers of eggs are prepared for market in packing-stations. Pigs are numerous, especially in the eastern part of the region, where they are closely dependent on dairying; a large farm which produces its own butter and cheese may keep as many as a thousand pigs. There is a long-established production of bacon and other pigmeat, including the pork sausages for which the small town of Calne is famous.

Settlement and Industry

Most settlements in the region are small. Villages tend to be loose-knit, and hamlets are numerous. The western part of the region lies beyond the main belt of village settlement, but well-nucleated villages become common in the east, where many of them are located at some scarp-foot.

Bristol is the great exception among the towns of the region. At the other extreme come little market towns, which are closely-spaced in all parts except the alluvial flats. Some are closely associated with a particular district—Devizes with the Vale of Pewsey, Gillingham with the Vale of Wardour, and Sturminster Newton with the basin of the upper Stour. Many have long held official town status, without displaying much tendency to expand, and with their irregular, small, colourwashed buildings lining the incoming roads, represent the little English country town in all its architectural attractiveness.

Miscellaneous light industry has been added in places to the widespread processing of dairy produce, particularly during World War II. Woollen-manufacture and flax-milling developed in the region itself. Frome on the river Frome, and Bradford-on-Avon near the Frome confluence, retain elements of the Cotswold woollen industry, having specialised in serges. Flax-milling is not concentrated in towns,[1] the mills occupying riverside sites although they are now worked by steam or electricity; the limited and scattered flax industry, long in grave decline, was revived during World War II.

Yeovil, Bridgwater, Taunton and Bath have had more success than most other towns of the region—Bristol always excepted. Yeovil has a prosperous manufacture of leather, particularly of gloves. Skins (including furs) are mainly imported. Some of the manufacturing processes cannot easily be mechanised, and a great deal of hand-work is still carried on. The other leading industry of Yeovil is mechanical engineering, of which the best-known products are helicopters and small power plant.

Bridgwater has a minor port trade. Ships pass up and down the tidal Parret, and there is a canal connection to Taunton, but navigation is hampered by silting, and the canal basin needs frequent clearance. Bridgwater stand where the Parret swings against firm ground on its left bank (Fig. 146). The town has no near rival, and has secured a firm grip on the retail trade of its surroundings. Some of its activities are closely linked to local farming—e.g., brewing, malting, and agricultural engineering; clay is worked for the making of bricks, pottery, and drainpipes. Signs of elaboration of industry appear in garment-making and contracting, both of which are well developed.

[1] Flax in the retting-pit emits a powerful stench.

FIG. 146. Bridgwater and its local setting

Taunton has obvious natural nodality,[1] being in some sense the gateway to the Southwest. It stands on the Tone, between the Quantocks and a northeast-facing scarp (Fig. 144). As a market town it is the focus of the rich farmland in the Vale of Taunton Deane, where high-grade soils are developed on the Permo-Trias, but also serves the country to the south.

Bath owes its location, and directly or indirectly its growth, to its warm springs, which led the Romans to construct their baths and associated buildings where the Fosse Way crossed the incised Avon. Bath shared the redevelopment of town life in England during the later Dark Ages and the Middle Ages, becoming a cathedral centre under the Normans, but much of the existing town dates from the

[1] Natural nodality due to the convergence of natural routeways should be distinguished from the man-made nodality, which all successful towns possess.

18th century; Bath's high reputation as a spa and a fashionable resort was acquired in the early 1700s, when extensive rebuilding took place. Sheltered by the steep walls of the valley, and spreading up their lower slopes, Bath at this time acquired some of the finest examples of 18th-century architecture; the stone used was the local Cotswold oolite, Bath freestone. A resort and tourist trade is still carried on, but the chief employer of male labour in Bath today is the ubiquitous metal-working and engineering. The functions of Bath have developed similarly to those of its imitators and rivals, Cheltenham and Leamington.

The custom of resorting to English spas belonged essentially to the 18th and early 19th centuries, to the days of coach travel, and to the fashionable world which lived by its landed estates. During the 19th century seaside resorts developed, first under the influence of fashion, later with the aid of railways and rising real incomes. Seaside towns involved in the resort trade are busier today than they have ever been, for coaches bring huge numbers of daily visitors, and there has been a marked redistribution of the national income since 1945. More people than ever before can afford to go to the seaside. The effects of the modern resort trade are well seen in the contrast between Bath and Weston-super-Mare: the former has increased its population by 2% since 1951, the latter by 9%. Weston has the great advantage of a sandy beach on an estuary which is mostly very muddy, and the monotonous alluvial flats which adjoin the coast are out of sight behind detached hills of Carboniferous limestone. Inland lie the Mendips, with their commercialised caves at Cheddar and Wookey, and the old ecclesiastical towns of Glastonbury and Wells. Weston is easily accessible from a large area of the Midlands, and has no near rivals of its own size.

Bristol

Bristol (Fig. 147) is to be contrasted with Bridgwater. Each stands on a navigable river and maintains a port trade, both are handicapped as ports by their location. Bristol nevertheless ranks as a great port— eighth in the U.K. by the total value of its trade—and as a very large town. It is sixth in the list of importing ports, but well down the list of exporters, handling ten times as many imports (by value) as exports (p. 150). This disparity, without parallel in the British Isles, derives partly from Bristol's commercial history, and partly from the port's failure to become a major outlet for the industrial West Midlands. The local coalfield is modest in size and output, and Bristol and its immediate hinterland have no great heavy industries; indeed, they have little exporting industry at all, their manufactured products being sold mainly in Great Britain.

FIG. 147. Bristol and its local setting

Bristol's medieval trade was principally with Ireland, Gascony, and Iberia. Fish and hides from Ireland were imported in exchange for cloth, manufactured leather, salt and iron; from the 12th to the 15th century, cloth was exported to Gascony and wine brought back, and the Gascon routes were in time extended to Spain and Portugal. Bristol by 1400 was the second greatest seaport of England, soon taking part in the Iceland fisheries, and being selected as the base for Cabot's voyages in the last years of the 15th century. Cloth exported from Bristol was made in the Cotswolds, where the water-powered fulling-mill invented before 1200 was in use at many places.

In 1552 the Merchant Venturers of Bristol received their charter, but the activities of the port were unfortunately reduced by war with Spain and revolts in Ireland. It was during the 17th century, a time of great prosperity in Bristol, that sugar-refining and tobacco-manufacturing were established, and trade with the Americas increased swiftly after 1650. Bristol's transatlantic connections were with the Caribbean and the Virginia coast rather than with New

England; sugar, rum, and tobacco were among its leading imports, and it was involved in the carriage of slaves to America, even though the slave trade had been declared illegal for Bristol merchants. The manufacture of chocolate began in Bristol during the 18th century, when the port's activities continued to increase and a large entrepôt trade developed.

By 1800, however, Bristol had been surpassed in size by Manchester and Birmingham and by their chief port Liverpool. Bristol was handicapped by high dock charges which drove away even its own ships, and its harbour was proving inconvenient. It lost its export of Welsh produce to Cardiff, and the woollen industry of its own hinterland was on the decline; its shipyards pioneered the development of power-driven craft, but they too declined in relative importance during the 19th century. When the docks at Bristol's outport of Avonmouth were opened in 1908, it was too late for Bristol to capture much of the export trade in metal goods.

The town remains a leading centre of sugar-refining and of the manufacture of chocolate and tobacco, with manufactures of leather, clothing, furniture, and paper, besides printing and contracting industries. The engineering industry has a wide range, but is especially well known for its production of aircraft which began in the early 1900s. Bristol today is firmly established as a regional capital. More than five times as large as the next town in the region, it has no rival in the wholesale and retail trades of the area which it serves, and its pre-eminent status is underlined by the presence of a university.

THE HAMPSHIRE BASIN AND ITS BORDERS

Area: about 2,750 square miles.
Population: about 2,000,000.
Largest towns: Portsmouth (215,250).
        Southampton (204,750).
        Bournemouth (154,000).
        Poole (88,000).
        Worthing (80,250).
        Havant (74,500).
        Gosport (62,500).
        Fareham (58,250).
        Weymouth (41,000).
        Salisbury (35,500).
        Winchester (28,750).
        Christchurch (26,500).
        Chichester (20,250).

Some 75% of this region is in improved farmland, with grass more extensive than tillage crops.
Numbers of livestock: cattle, 450,000; sheep, 125,000; pigs, 220,000.

Southampton, like Bristol, is a university town, a great port, and a regional capital. There the similarities end. Southampton is not the largest town of its region. It is a deep-water port with a very large passenger trade and growing connections with Midland industries. It is far more closely linked than Bristol to metropolitan England, and its immediate hinterland differs in many respects from the hinterland of Bristol. Not only are there physical contrasts— whereas towns in the Borders of the West Country are very numerous but rather small, towns in the Hampshire Basin and its borders are fewer, area for area, but some have grown very big. Despite their presence, however, the country districts of the Hampshire Basin and its borders are more markedly rural than the country districts of the Borders of the West Country (Plate 65), being less widely and less densely peopled. The difference corresponds, in part, to contrasts in geology and in soils.

The Chalklands

The Chalklands, based on a thick and permeable formation, yield water only in the valleys, and it was to the valleys that Dark-Age settlement was largely confined. Here the villages stand today, strung out along the little clear-flowing rivers. Such a distribution is better represented in the Berkshire Downs and on Salisbury Plain, where soils are developed on bare Chalk, than on the Hampshire Downs, the strip of country south of the Wylye, or the Dorset Downs, where Clay-with-Flints occurs as an extensive capping. Oakwood was formerly widespread on the Clay-with-Flints, and piecemeal clearance and the presence of groundwater have encouraged denser but more scattered settlement than on the Chalk soils proper.

The compact area of Chalkland in Salisbury Plain was, in prehistoric times, the most heavily-peopled part of the country. The two great religious centres of Avebury and Stonehenge are located centrally in two districts of Chalk soils, respectively north and south of the Vale of Pewsey, and earthworks in great number stud the undulating downlands, round barrows being especially prominent on many skylines. The British and Roman centre of Old Sarum is an obvious focus of Roman roads. Two miles to the south lies its successor Salisbury, a market centre with a famous cathedral; twenty miles to the east is Winchester, also a cathedral town, once the capital of Wessex and at times of England.

The decline in the political status of Wessex and Winchester was accompanied by a decline in the agricultural status of their land. Tilling by means of the scratch-plough may well have continued on the shallow Chalk soils well into the Middle Ages, but eventually the downland became grassed over and put to use as sheep-pasture. The location of military training-grounds on Salisbury Plain is an index of low agricultural grade as well as of lack of settlement—compare the military use of the podsolised heathland of Aldershot. Sheep-grazing on the downs was associated with irrigation in the flood-plains, where the channels of water-meadows kept the water-table high and promoted a lush growth of grass for hay (cf. Fig. 148). The 18th-century advances in agriculture introduced barley as a main arable crop on the lower slopes, and the sheep-barley combination prevailed throughout the 19th century and into the 20th.

FIG. 148. Stockbridge, Hampshire; a small market-town at a river-crossing, surrounded by Chalk downland which is partly open

This combination no longer obtains today. As Figs. 41 and 42 show, there are now few sheep. Sheep-farming was affected by the violent fluctuations in profits typical of the present century, and farming practice was modified to introduce dairying, grass and clover leys, and a variety of cash crops. Barley is still the chief grain crop, but is nowadays grown in a complex rotation. Changes in agriculture have been going on steadily since about 1900, but have been most rapid since 1939; during World War II a great deal of grassland was ploughed up, and the remaining flocks of sheep were much reduced. Tillage continues to be extensive in the post-war period, both for cash crops and for fodder crops; many of the farms are well adapted to the use of machinery, with their fields typically large and many single farms exceeding 500 acres in size, and agriculture today is highly mechanised. Where land has been returned to grass, and on the unbroken permanent pasture, dairy-farming and not sheep-grazing is the main interest. Thus, in half a century, the farming of this block of Chalkland country has been completely transformed.

The Centre of the Basin

In the centre of the Hampshire Basin, loose sandy soils of coarse texture are extensively developed on poorly-cemented Tertiary sediments. They provide the edaphic basis of the New Forest, preserved as a royal hunting-ground for a long period and still continuous enough to be represented in Fig. 20. Neither the severely-leached podsolic soils of the sandy areas nor the use to which the Forest was put encouraged settlement, which remains sparse and irregular to this day, but on the inland side, where the sandy rocks of the centre are surrounded by a belt of London Clay, dip-foot villages mark the geological junction where springs put out at the edge of the Chalk, and mixed farmland encircles the scrub and heath of the Forest. Ribbons of cultivation extend along the wide terraces of the rejuvenated rivers.

Although most of the Forest is unpromising as agricultural land, some of the sandy soils well repay intensive cultivation; highly specialised market-gardening has developed in the coastal belt, with an extension along the raised beach of the Sussex Coastal Plain as far as Worthing. The coastlands of the Hampshire Basin are sunny, receiving their 30 inches of rainfall in no more than 175 rain-days; they profit from a frost-free season 7 months in length and a January mean temperature of about 40°F. Crops include green vegetables, peas, and beans, but market-gardens in Hampshire are particularly noted for their production of strawberries, while glasshouse crops and flowers grown in the open are increasingly produced near Worthing.

Towns of the Coastal Belt

Weymouth, Poole, Bournemouth and Worthing are eminently successful resorts, linked through the last-named to the chain of seaside towns in Southeast England. The Hampshire Basin and the Isle of Wight contain many other smaller resorts, all benefiting from sunny weather, sandy beaches, and attractive inland scenery. Portsmouth, Gosport, Havant and Fareham form a distinctive group of their own, while Southampton stands apart, except for the share taken by Weymouth in port and passenger trade.

Bournemouth has merged with Boscombe along the cliffs which overlook a long, curving sweep of shore. As at Brighton, Worthing, and Weston-super-Mare—to name but three similarly-located towns —the beach is the nucleating factor. The largest and most expensive hotels, and the public buildings constructed to serve the resort trade, stand on or near the front; the size of buildings decreases inland, numerous boarding-houses marking the transition to the spreading suburban fringe. Bournemouth first became highly popular as a resort about a hundred years ago, and is still growing steadily, with 2½ million visitors a year. Poole sprang into prominence rather later; its shallow but protected harbour favours yachting, which is much practised on this coast and became a sport for the many in the inter-war period. The population of Poole has increased by 60% since 1931.

As a naval base, Portsmouth is related to Southampton and Southampton Water as Chatham and Gillingham are to London and the Thames. Its landlocked harbour, like that of Poole, is the result of the drowning of shallow valleys by a rise of sea-level; but Portsmouth's harbour is the deeper as well as the more easterly, and Portsmouth was selected as a naval centre. Naval activity in general, and the maintenance and repair of warships, were the main factors in the town's growth. Gosport on the far side of the inlet is linked by ferry and floating bridge to Portsmouth, of which it is effectively a partner and suburb. Portsmouth is congested on Portsea Island, and both Fareham and Havant, which lie farther inland at the heads of inlets, have become to some extent suburbs and dormitories of Portsmouth. The population of Portsmouth is actually less today than it was in 1931, while the combined population of Gosport, Fareham and Havant has more than trebled.

Strictly speaking, Weymouth lies outside the Hampshire Basin, but its resort trade is very similar in character to that of Bournemouth and its port activities resemble some of those of Southampton. The ships which ply between Weymouth and the Channel Islands enter a harbour protected by large breakwaters, one of which springs from Portland Island, where stone for Wren's London buildings was quarried.

Southampton

As a port, Southampton (Fig. 149) enjoys the advantages of a peculiar tidal régime which prolongs high water; tidal waves produced in the Solent and Southampton Water are considered to be responsible. Southampton has emerged as a great terminal port for transatlantic passenger services, but its other port trade and its industrial activity are also considerable; Southampton is the seventh greatest cargo port of the U.K., ranking only a little below Glasgow (p. 149). Moreover, its history as a port goes back long before the days

N

low sandy hills with woodland, farmland, and heath

Eastleigh

R. Test

woodland and arable with rural settlements tending to expand

Totton

SOUTHAMPTON

sandy heath and woodland of the New Forest

channel dredged to depth of 30 ft. or more

Southampton Water

marshy foreshore

R. Hamble

0   1   2   3   4 MILES

Chief concentrations of industry | Heavily built-up areas mainly developed before 1914 | Less densely built-up areas, mainly developed after 1920 | Alluvium

FIG. 149. Southampton and its local setting

of the railways which have contributed so much to its present greatness.

The original settlement, between the drowned mouths of the Test and Itchen, was founded early in the Dark Ages. Under the Normans the town was important enough to be walled, and during the Middle Ages it shared in the importing of French wine and the exporting of English cloth, but Southampton did not develop trading connections comparable to those of Bristol, and was even less well placed to serve the developing industries of the 17th and 18th centuries. Its modern development did not begin until 1836, when the Southampton Dock Company was founded. The railway which entered in that year took over the docks themselves in 1872. The prolonged high water—maintained for 2 hours twice daily—the railway access to the waterfront, and the room available for making and extending docks in the alluvium, all favoured the growth of a deep-water port standing in the same kind of relation to London as Cherbourg has to Paris.

The rise of passenger traffic has been due fundamentally to demand for services. Once they were provided, the services in turn encouraged the development of travel, justifying considerable improvements to the harbour works and their approaches. A channel with a minimum width of 600 ft. and a depth of 35 ft. at low water is now maintained by dredging. The New Docks were completed in 1934, and the Ocean Terminal in 1950; there are now $1\frac{1}{2}$ miles of deep-water quay, large transit sheds, 9 liner berths and 7 drydocks. Half the ocean travellers to and from Great Britain, and 80% of those going to or coming from South Africa and the U.S.A., pass through Southampton.

In its passenger trade Southampton profits from its nearness to London, which is 78 miles away and reached by train in $1\frac{1}{4}$ hours. The cargo trade is in part somewhat specialised, although, with 16 million people living within a radius of 100 miles, the port is busy with trade of a general nature. Perishable imports handled at Southampton include foodstuffs and fruit, which are received in increasing quantities. South Africa sends fruit, eggs, wool, hides and skins; among other leading suppliers of cargo are the West Indies, the Canary Islands, the Channel Islands, France, and West Africa.

The shipbuilding industry of Southampton produces small and moderate-sized craft, and is overshadowed by the maintenance, repair, and refitting of ships of all sizes. Industries encouraged to develop around the New Docks include flour-milling, timber-milling, and the manufacture of radio equipment and rubber. The railway works at Eastleigh and the local aircraft industry represent 19th-century and 20th-century engineering, while the great oil refinery at Fawley has an output of some 7 million tons a year, supplying about a quarter of the country's need of motor spirit and sending large quantities for export. A pipeline from Fawley to a depot near London Airport has been built.

THE CHANNEL ISLANDS

Area: 75 square miles.
Population: about 104,250.
Largest towns: St. Helier (Jersey) (about 22,500 in built-up area).
　　　　　　　St. Peter Port (Guernsey) (about 14,000 in built-up area).
　Some 53% of the total land area is in farms and market-gardens. Tillage is one-and-a-third times as extensive as grassland.
Numbers of livestock: cattle, 14,000; pigs, 5,000.

About 70 square miles of the combined extent of the Channel Islands, and nearly all the inhabitants, are accounted for by Jersey and Guernsey. Other islands are Alderney, Sark, Herm, Jethou, and Lihou.

Lying off the Cotentin Peninsula, well within sight of the French coast on clear days, the Channel Islands have been attached to the

English Crown since 1066. They rank politically as Crown Dependencies. They are outside the limits of the regulations on customs and excise which apply in the United Kingdom, and, unless they are specified in Acts of Parliament, are unaffected by British law. Feudal powers are enforced in Sark; government in the remaining islands, although revised to some extent in recent years, is distinctly late-medieval in structure.

FIG. 150. The Channel Islands: physique and main settlements

Physique, Climate, and Agriculture

Physically, the Islands (Fig. 150) constitute detached fragments of the Armorican massif of France. They are based mainly upon ancient metamorphic, plutonic, and extrusive rocks, rising abruptly from the sea in lines of indented cliffs. Sweeping bays and and numerous small inlets variegate their shores (Plate 66). Only in the north of Guernsey is there any considerable extent of low ground; elsewhere the terrain is of the plateau type, composed of old beach-platforms which approach 450 feet in Jersey and 350 feet in Guernsey. These two islands are considerably dissected by young valleys. The plateau-tops are widely mantled with loess, while raised-beach deposits occur up to heights of a hundred feet above present sea-level. Climate is markedly maritime, with very mild winters—mean temperatures for February, the coldest month, are above 40°F; frost and snow are infrequent, and the growing season is very long. Mean annual rainfall varies from 40 inches on the highest ground to below 30 inches in the drier parts, and sunshine is more abundant than it is anywhere in the British Isles proper.

Except in Alderney, where the field-pattern has been influenced by the holding of land in common, farmland on the Islands is minutely subdivided—partly because of the operation of complex laws of inheritance. Fragmentation is emphasised by the stout earthen banks, some of them topped by hedges, which divide the tiny fields from one another. Dairy-farming, stock-breeding, and market-gardening are well established. The native breeds of Jersey and Guernsey cattle are famous for high-grade milk, and breeding-stock is exported. Farming and market-gardening combined take one-fifth of the labour force; in Guernsey, more than four-fifths of the workers on the land are employed in market-gardening, and fewer than one-fifth in farming; the proportions are exactly reversed in Jersey.

This striking contrast is due mainly to the great development in Guernsey of cultivation under glass. With rather poor light land in the north, and with a slightly unfavourable aspect, Guernsey has concentrated on glasshouse working, with an acreage of glass among the greatest in the world. Most of the glasshouses are heated by anthracite-fired boilers, the leading crop being early tomatoes. Jersey, with its plateau sloping towards the south, is noted mainly for early potatoes and for tomatoes grown in the open. Market-garden produce, including cut flowers, is shipped to England from the Channel Islands, competing in London and the West Midlands with the produce of Southwest England, the Netherlands, and Italy.

Economic Change

Market-gardening and farming, although both need much labour, cannot possibly support the dense populations of the Channel Islands, where overcrowding and underemployment have formed a constant threat for some centuries past. The 17th-century production of hand-knitted clothes failed with the industrial revolution. During the 18th century, about a third of the cropped area was under orchards of cider-apple trees, a large surplus of cider being exported to France. Numbers of Channel Islanders were employed at this time in home fisheries, the Newfoundland fisheries, and in the carrying trade, but there was still persistent emigration. Both Jersey and Guernsey did well for a time in shipbuilding during the 19th century, and in its later part profited by stone-quarrying—some London streets are still paved with Channel Island stone. But technical developments elsewhere ruined the local shipyards, just as changes in the techniques of road-making and building caused most quarries to be abandoned, and highly intensive cultivation for export developed in the late 19th century, with the aid of increasingly fast sea-transport.

A vigorous tourist trade has grown up during the 20th century; some half-a-million visitors from Britain go to the Channel Islands each year. The air journey from London to the Islands takes less time than the rail journey from London to the resorts of Southwest England, while sea passages from Southampton or Weymouth take half a day. The Channel Islands have climatic attractions fully equal

66. Part of north Guernsey, with extensive glasshouses.

67. View across the northern tip of Romney Marsh, to the Chalk cliffs beyond Folkestone.

68. Brighton beach in summer.

to those of the Southwest, possess the same kind of indefinable charm, and are sufficiently distant from England to give the illusion of foreign travel. This illusion is heightened by the distinctive style of native domestic architecture, by the abundance of local surnames on shop-fronts, by the use of patois by some islanders, and by the freedom from British customs and excise. Economic depression apart, the tourist trade promises to continue to flourish, in common with the specialised cultivation of these heavily-settled and intensively-worked islands.

Settlement

The largest nucleated settlements are St. Helier, St. Peter Port, St. Sampson's—Guernsey's second port—and St. Anne's on Alderney. Houses on the two largest islands are scattered in little groups throughout the interior. With increase in population the best sites are becoming well built-up, and small concentrations of dwellings are newly emerging. Broadly speaking, however, the Islands succeed in retaining their rural character, even though the acreage of cultivated land has been declining for more than 50 years. The Channel Islands are notably free from that peculiar brashness which typifies some of the resort towns of England.

CHAPTER 27

Southeast England

Area: about 3,000 square miles.
Population: about 2,250,000.
Largest towns: Brighton (162,750).
  Gillingham (72,750).
  Hove (72,750).
  Hastings (66,250).
  Eastbourne (61,000).
  Maidstone (59,750).
  Guildford (54,000).
  Reigate (53,750) (includes Redhill).
  Rochester (50,250).
  Chatham (49,000).
  Margate (45,750).
  Folkestone (44,000).
  Tunbridge Wells (39,750).
  Ramsgate (37,000).
  Dover (35,250).
  Canterbury (30,500).
  Ashford (28,000).
  Some 50% of this region is in improved farmland, with tillage
more extensive than grassland.
Numbers of livestock: cattle, 300,000; sheep, 550,000; pigs, 225,000.

About half of Surrey and most of Kent and Sussex are included
in Southeast England. The regional boundary, drawn from the estuary
of the Thames near Gravesend, along the crest of the Chalk hills
which face into the Weald, and thence to the Channel coast near
Shoreham, separates it from the London and Hampshire Basins.
The whole coastal belt of North Kent is included in Southeast
England, but the Coastal Plain of Sussex is excluded (Figs. 83, 151).

On a small-scale map such a boundary is clear and well-defined,
but when the scale is large enough to give the appreciable width to the
Chalk cuestas a problem immediately arises. A cuesta is a distinctive
physical unit, which a boundary fixed on the scarp-crest divides
artificially into two parts. For many purposes it is convenient to
refer to the whole of the North and South Downs in describing
Southeast England, just as the backslopes of the North Downs and

Alluvial and raised-beach deposits, with expanses of London Clay in North Kent

Belt of Tertiary rocks and brickearth in North Kent, bearing warm soils

Chalk downland, flat-topped and dissected by dry valleys

Cuestas of Lower Greensand with soils loose and podsolic, rising above 800 ft. in the west

The Weald Clay belt

Hills of the High Weald, based mainly on sandstones of the Hastings Beds well wooded and cut by deep narrow valleys

Concealed coalfield   ◆ Colliery

FIG. 151. Southeast England: physique and main settlements

of the Chilterns may suitably be included in an account of the London Basin.

Structure and Drainage

Southeast England contrasts very strongly indeed with the regions which adjoin it. Structurally it is an area of uplift, while the London and Hampshire Basins are areas of structural depression. Whereas the land of these two basins slopes down towards large inlets on which the two regional capitals are located, Southeast England is a region of infacing scarps and concentric vales which encircle a hilly core. Most of the Southeast is taken up by the Weald, where the pattern of relief delicately reflects the strength and attitude of the underlying rocks. The Weald was not glaciated, its rocks vary greatly in resistance to erosion, and its trunk rivers have cut deeply into weak strata. The Wealden landforms are therefore boldly carved. As the structural pattern is fairly simple, the groups of relief-elements are few in number.

Many fine examples of two classes of stream are to be found in Southeast England. The vales eroded along the strike of weak outcrops have been excavated, in the main, by subsequent streams, but the rock-waste has been, and is still being, carried away by streams which flow on consequent lines and break through the encircling hills in deep gaps. They cross the broken belt of Lower Greensand

and the more continuous Chalk downland because they have been superimposed across the geological grain. The gaps of the Stour, Medway, Darent, Mole and Wey on the north, and those of the Arun, Adur, Ouse and Cuckmere on the south bear witness to a former pattern of consequents draining more-or-less directly outwards from the central part of the Weald. The consequents were initiated by upwarping during Tertiary times; as they have cut down they have thrown out subsequents along the clay-belts, and these subsequents have taken over most of the drainage-system. The longest subsequents naturally belong to the most powerful streams—the Medway, the Wey, and the Arun. Some of the wind-gaps in the Chalk mark the lines of former streams which have been dismembered; the latest known capture is that of the Blackwater, which used to flow through the Farnham Gap but has lost its headwaters to the piractical Wey.

The Forest Ridges

The centrally hilly portion of this region goes under various names—the High Weald, the Forest Ridges, and Ashdown Forest. It is based on the Hastings Beds, which were laid down in a subsiding basin where continuous sedimentation bridged the gap of time between the Jurassic and Cretaceous periods. The Hastings Beds consist mostly of sandstones separated by thin formations of clay; being rather poorly cemented, they weather freely into a deep soil, and being permeable, they are little affected by surface wash. The Forest Ridges rise to more than 600 ft. between sharply-cut young valleys, many of which run east-west along the lines of the folds and faults produced by Tertiary earth-movement. In the natural state the Forest Ridges were covered in woodland dominated by durmast oak, for their soils are not coarse and permeable enough to be podsolised.

Large numbers of pigs were pastured in the forests of the Central Weald during the Dark Ages and the early Middle Ages, each manor on the outskirts of the region having customary rights over a certain portion of the woodland. The area became slowly more accessible as small settlements were established in clearings, and place-names significantly ending in *hurst* and *den* were widely applied, but the main attack on the trees came from the iron-workers who exploited the ore of the Hastings Beds and used the local trees in making charcoal; abandoned hammer-ponds which supplied water-power to the medieval and post-medieval forges can still be seen. Oak timber was also cut for shipbuilding, particularly during the 18th century. Despite the concern already felt during Tudor times over the depletion of the Wealden forests, the Forest Ridges are quite heavily wooded at the present day—indeed, this area and the vale

which surrounds it are richer in hardwood trees than any other part of
the British Isles. Individual woods are small and well-managed, the
post-war shortage of timber having made them attractive prospects
for investment. Oak-hazel and chestnut coppices yield small timber,
including hop-poles.

The Low Weald

Surrounding the Forest Ridges is a great horseshoe-shaped belt of
vale country, eroded in the thick and weak Weald Clay which dips
off the Hastings Beds on all sides. This is the Low Weald, where the
ground stands well below the levels of the Forest Ridges and where
the surface is gently undulating. The Weald Clay cannot sustain
steep slopes such as occur on the Hastings Beds. As it is impermeable,
there are many surface streams. Where gradients are gentle it is
liable to develop meadow soils, and the broad flood-plains along the
larger rivers were formerly very ill-drained indeed. The Weald Clay is
siliceous, so that it becomes very sticky in wet weather, and travel
in the vale was difficult before the days of well-surfaced roads. The
forests, dominated by the stalked oak, long resisted clearing.

Inner Cuestas

The belt of lowland is overlooked on the north and west by scarps
based on the Lower Greensand, a generally sandy formation which
varies in strength and in thickness from place to place. At the eastern
end it is much eroded and the scarp is discontinuous, but the ground
rises in a ridge west of the Medway and reaches 965 ft. on Leith Hill
between the Mole and the Wey. At the western end of the Weald
comes a whole block of high ground, culminating in Blackdown
(918 ft.), but, as the outcrop swings round towards the southeast, the
formation thins out and the line of hills tails away. The Lower
Greensand is typically very permeable, and the soils formed on its
coarse sandstones have been heavily leached, tending strongly to
form podsols. Left to themselves, they would probably carry heather,
bracken, bramble, birch and occasional oaks, and heathland and
scrubby woods do indeed occur in places, but conifers which may
originally have been introduced by man have spread far and wide.

Along the northern rim of the Weald, the hills eroded in the Lower
Greensand are separated from the Chalk downs by a narrow but
continuous vale eroded in the Gault. The largest development of this
vale occurs in the basins of the Medway and the Darent, where it is
called the Vale of Holmesdale. On its northern side there may be a
minor scarp formed on the Upper Greensand, but the Gault vale is
everywhere overlooked by the infacing Chalk scarps which enclose
the Weald.

The Chalk Rim

Seen from a distance, the Chalk scarps appear to rise in continuous walls, and they are in actuality continuous for long distances, having retreated as a whole instead of being dissected into fragments. The Chalk forms high ground because it is thick, permeable, and much stronger than the Gault beneath it or the Tertiary rocks above. Water easily passes through its many joints, so that the valleys of the backslopes are streamless (Plate 2).

The width of the Chalk downland varies according to the dip. In the South Downs the dip changes little, but in the North Downs it ranges from very steep in the Hog's Back to very gentle in the area south of Canterbury. Consequently the Hog's Back is narrow and slopes steeply down on either side, whereas in East Kent the block of Chalkland is wide. In the Isle of Thanet the Chalk rises in a small anticline beyond the floodplain of the Stour.

The soils of the Chalk scarps are of the shallow, humified and lime-rich group called rendzina. Soil-creep on the steep scarps keeps the rendzinas shallow, but thickens and enriches the soils of the scarp-foot belt. Soils on the crests of the Downs are quite varied, the reddish, stony soils of the Clay-with-Flints attaining considerable depth on the highest summits, bare Chalk soils occurring on old marine benches at about 600 ft., and sandy patches complicating the pattern in places. Bare Chalk soils are most widespread on the South Downs, where in the natural state they would probably be covered by scrub and coarse grass; soils of the Clay-with-Flints can support thick woodland, while the loose sands, restricted in extent, tend to be under heath. If short grassland exists on the Downs, it is the product of centuries of burning, clearing, and grazing (cf. Fig. 152).

North Kent

The backslope of the Chalk in North Kent passes under a broad strip of Tertiary rocks, where warm sandy loams have developed on friable parent materials, and where soils formed on patches of loess (brickearth) are also loamy and warm. These warm soils are the physical basis of the market-gardening and fruit-growing of North Kent. Cultivation of the same kind is carried on within the Weald near Maidstone, where warm soils occur on brickearth, river terraces, and a lime-rich development of the Lower Greensand.

The Seaward End

The several belts of contrasted terrain in Southeast England are all truncated by the sea in the east. The tip of the Weald lies beyond the Channel in the Boulonnais. Resistant formations project in headlands: the North Foreland is the cliffed extremity of the Chalk in

FIG. 152. Land-use sample for the northern rim of the Weald, in Kent. The rough grazing occurs on the scarp of the North Downs

Thanet, the South Foreland and the cliffs of Dover mark the end of the North Downs, the sandy Hastings Beds reach the sea in cliffs at the town of Hastings, and the South Downs terminate in the Seven Sisters and Beachy Head. But the greatest projection of the land occurs in Romney Marsh, a depositional feature, with its tip at Dungeness. Constructive waves have been adding shingle ridges on the eastern side for at least two thousand years, and floodwater has covered the shingle with alluvium. The fact that Romney Marsh abuts directly on to the Weald Clay belt is accidental, for old cliffs cut in the Weald Clay rise sharply from the levels of the Marsh (Plate 67). The Pevensey Levels at the other end of the Weald Clay outcrop have a different origin, being due to the impounding of a lagoon by a bar and to subsequent infilling by sediment.

Climate and Agriculture

The rural aspect of the Wealden scene is enhanced by the effects of climate on growing plants. By comparison with, say, the Midland Triangle, the Weald looks lush. Rainfall is not heavy—from 25 inches in the northeast to something more than 30 in the west—and the rather low mean January temperature of about 39°F is adequately compensated by warm summers in which the July mean rises to 62° or more. Summers are very sunny for the British Isles, and the countryside wears a genial aspect in all but the worst years. Standing crops in the rather small fields are set off by their background of woods and flourishing hedgerow trees.

Tillage is widespread in Southeast England, especially since it has greatly increased in extent since 1939 in response to wartime and post-war conditions. This region was certain to share in the conversion of permanent grass to rotation grass or tillage, for it lies on the drier side of England and is well suited climatically to arable farming. Its farmers, however, are less heavily committed to arable working than are those of Holderness, Lincolnshire, the Fenlands and East Anglia, so that much land was put to grass in the depressed 1930s and land was available for ploughing-up when conditions changed.

There are differences between the northeast and the southwest parts of the region. The former is drier, sunnier, more highly tilled and more involved in cash-cropping than is the latter, which has the higher proportion of grassland, fodder crops, and cattle. It contains much bare Chalkland in the South Downs, and has the heavier rainfall. The several terrains of the region also differ from one to another, quite apart from the general transition across the region. The sandy soils of the Forest Ridges are much tilled, while the heavy clays of the Low Weald are largely in permanent grass. Parts of the Lower Greensand belt and of the Gault vale are under the plough today, and cropland, extending on to the flanks of the North Downs, is also well in evidence on the summits wherever the Chalk is mantled by some other deposit.

Grain crops take more than half the tilled acreage in the region. Wheat is the leading grain on the farms of the northeast, oats on those of the southwest. Similarly, potatoes are grown the more widely in the northeast and fodder crops in the southwest, but wheat, oats, potatoes, and fodder crops, like barley and mixed corn, are common to all parts.

Dairy cattle everywhere outnumber beefstock, for farms are well within reach either of London or of the coastal towns. The large number of pigs corresponds to the high development of dairy-farming. There are nearly twice as many sheep as cattle in this region, which records one of the three concentrations of sheep outside Highland Britain (Fig. 41). The main areas of sheep pasture lie on the North Downs and on Romney Marsh, but the sheep do not live always on permanent grassland—they are not very numerous on the South Downs, having been displaced by dairy cattle, and have been partly displaced from Romney Marsh by arable farming.

The most extensive single crop in Kent is orchard fruit, which takes nearly a quarter of all cropland. The combined acreage of orchard fruit, small fruits, hops, flowers, and vegetables other than potatoes amounts in Kent to more than a third of the land in crops. Much of the fruit-growing and market-gardening is concentrated in the two belts of warm soils in the Medway valley and in North Kent, but specialised cultivation is well represented in most parts of the county. The orchard lands of Kent are unrivalled in the British Isles (Fig. 40), and Kentish hopfields produce more than half the British crop of hops.

The highly specialised production of fruit and vegetables, depending largely on London for its market and for its enormous force of seasonal labour, has been greatly helped by the development of road transport. London itself consumes much of the produce, but some is sold in London for redistribution.

Fruit-farming is a highly competitive undertaking, with very highly-developed techniques. The orchards are planted on ground where slopes ensure that cold air will drain away during still nights in spring; in the Medway valley they line the face and crest of the Lowei Greensand scarp, in North Kent they lie on the slopes of the gently-dissected belt of Tertiary rocks. Apples and cherries are the most common orchard fruits; on the best farms, the varieties of a single fruit are planted in accordance with subtle differences in the properties of the soils.

The production of soft fruits and of market-garden vegetables relies still more heavily upon rapid transport than does the growing of hard fruit. Kent is particularly successful with strawberries, raspberries, currants, gooseberries, cabbages, beans and peas. Market-gardens are, however, to be found throughout the region, and hopfields are common in all eastern parts. Hop-growing is carried on under contract for the large breweries—including those of Burton-upon-Trent—which also take much of the barley crop for malting.

Distribution of People

Very intensive cultivation helps to account for the quite dense population of the region, which averages 350 p.s.m. outside the towns listed above. Although the true figure of rural population is somewhat lower than this, the largest towns contain under half the total population.

A wide scatter of small rural settlements is one of the outstanding characteristics of Southeast England, where a dispersed pattern has been inherited from the array of settlement established by the Jutes (Chap. 4). Some of the Wealden settlements have inevitably become larger in the course of the centuries, emerging as compact villages or growing into small towns, but nucleation is not typical of the region as a whole. Strings of spring-line villages are absent from the feet of some scarps.

Good building-stone is rare in most of the region, and the traditional building-materials are lath-and-plaster or brick, except in Northeast Kent where ragstone from the Lower Greensand is used. Half-timbered or palely coloured houses, set among abundant trees,

ⅢⅢ *Woodland*   ▓▓ *Orchards*   ☐ *Improved Farmland*   ⁚⁚ *Buildings*

FIG. 153. Farmland, woodland, orchards, and scattered settlement in the central Weald contrast strongly with the suburban dwellings on the southern outskirts of the metropolis, and farmland interlocks with woodland in a countryside where large settlements are rare (Fig. 153).

The deep gaps through the Chalk make Southeast England accessible from the London Basin, roads and railways leading to the interior and to the Channel coast. Parts of the northern Weald are well within the limits of daily commuting to London, and some towns have been stimulated into expansion by functioning as dormitories. Only two of the 17 largest towns are located in the interior of the region, however, while nearly a quarter of the regional population lives in one of the seven largest coastal towns, and one in nine lives either in Brighton or in Hove. Coastal situation obviously favours town growth. Only along the shore is the effect of the metropolis fully expressed, in a chain of resorts and cross-Channel termini.

Resorts and Packet-Stations

Hove, Brighton, Eastbourne, Hastings, Ramsgate, and Margate, located in that order along the coast, function chiefly as resorts. Among them, they receive anything up to 12 million visitors a year. Their resort trade relied originally on the fashion for sea-bathing which developed in the late 18th and early 19th centuries, on their shelving beaches, and on their sunny climate. Brighton enjoyed royal favour in the late 1700s, but it was the railways which made all the resorts accessible to large numbers of visitors. Transport by road and rail, the impetus of success, the custom of taking holidays by the seaside, and vigorous publicity lend powerful support to the modern resort trade (Plate 68).

The large resorts of Southeast England, located on continuous beaches, are ill-equipped to take part in seafaring, except for the inshore fishing which they practised when they were still no more than villages. Seaborne traffic has, indeed, been handicapped in some way along the whole coast throughout historical times. Rye and Winchelsea are among the ancient ports which have had their harbours blocked by marine deposition; Folkestone suffers from erosion, which has removed the original harbour and part of the early site of the town, and which continues to endanger the railway to Dover.

London is able to receive shipping in the broad Thames, and Southeast England gets its imported produce by way of London Docks; passenger services, however, demand speed, and great numbers of travellers to and from the Continent pass through the packet stations of Dover, Folkestone, and Newhaven (8,000), with their chief respective links to Calais, Boulogne, and Dieppe. All there have long histories as ports engaged in coasting trade, Continental trade, and fishing; their harbours are all served by railway, and are protected by breakwaters. Folkestone has a share in the resort trade, and both it and Dover have engineering industries.

To the sea routes across the Channel with termini in Southeast England has been added the post-war air ferry which operates from Lydd, on Romney Marsh. The airfield first used was at Lympne, at the top of the old cliffs which fringe the lowlying Marsh, but low cloud coming in from the sea frequently interrupted services and led to the transfer to Lydd. The ferry service, which has greatly increased in frequency with booming demand, takes cars and their passengers to Le Touquet in 20 minutes.

Dormitory Towns and Metropolitan Invasion

Guildford, Reigate, Tunbridge Wells, Dorking (22,500) and Sevenoaks (17,500) are members of the group of dormitory towns which lie on routes radiating from London. Tunbridge Wells, located—exceptionally for a large town—in the heart of the region, gained fame as a watering-place in the 18th century. Numbers of the most-used dormitories, however, are situated at one end of the gaps through the North Downs.

Where the Downs are wide, towns occur in pairs—for instance, Dorking and Leatherhead on the Mole Gap. Guildford, at the eastern end of the Hog's Back, occupies a very short gap and spreads up the slopes on to the adjacent hilltops; but even Guildford incorporates the sites of two early settlements, and belongs both to the scarp-foot and to the dip-foot lines. In former times, Guildford controlled routes running not through but across the gap; for many centuries travel along the valley-bottom was difficult because of poor drainage, and Guildford arose where the dry route coming in from the west diverged to pass along the dip-foot to London and beneath the scarp to Canterbury. Dorking, Reigate and Redhill, Sevenoaks, and Maidstone are all on the Canterbury road.

London's grip on the northern and central parts of Southeast England is tightening. The new airport at Gatwick (p.453) and the new town at Crawley (Plate 23, Chap. 28) lie well within the Weald.

Maidstone and the North Coastal Belt

At Maidstone (Fig. 151), the navigable Medway is approached from the west by a road on the flank of the Lower Greensand cuesta. Maidstone, the county town of Kent, is the urban focus of an intensively-cultivated district. Its industries include the making of agricultural machinery, paper, beer, and cement, but cement-manufacture is concentrated chiefly in the Medway Gap through the North Downs.

At the other end of the Medway Gap, the Medway towns of Gillingham, Chatham, and Rochester stand on the tidal estuary where it is crossed by Watling Street. Rochester is well known for its manufacture of agricultural implements and road-rollers; it formerly made flying-boats and other aircraft, but its aircraft industry has been transferred to Belfast. Cement is manufactured here from chalk and estuarine mud. Chatham, the site of a naval dockyard which was founded by Elizabeth I, has a long record of naval construction. Its growth has stimulated the growth of Gillingham, which is also heavily dependent on naval orders, and, with more room to expand, has become larger than Chatham. The occupational census of 1951 recorded one in six of the working inhabitants of the two towns as members of the armed forces.

Sittingbourne (23,500) and Faversham (13,000) are at the heads of creeks, where tongues of firm rock exposed by river-erosion project towards the muddy shores of the estuary. Around them extend the orchards and market-gardens of North Kent, through them passes Watling Street on its way to Canterbury. Herne Bay and Whitstable on the coast demonstrate that a muddy sea-bed can favour an oyster fishery, without preventing a resort trade so long as there is a rapid rail connection with London.

Canterbury and Ashford

Canterbury and Ashford are at opposite ends of the long gap made by the Stour through the widening Downs. It would be difficult to find a more strongly-contrasting pair of towns. Canterbury, successively a British, Roman, and Jutish town, had its cathedral founded by St. Augustine in A.D. 597, and the city became a centre of pilgrimage after the murder of Thomas à Becket. It did not grow very large, however, and had spread very little beyond its stout walls by the end of the 18th century. The system of roads converging on Canterbury has evolved in part from the Roman ways leading inland from Lympne, Dover, Richborough and Reculver.

Whereas Canterbury is exceptionally well nucleated, Ashford (Fig. 154) is tripartite. The old centre of the town is cramped by the buildings which occupy part of the former market-square, and displays many of the typical alterations of the form and function of buildings which accompany the town growth. The railway town with its locomotive shops lies apart, beyond the flood-plain of the Stour. It offers a striking example of 19th-century town-planning, with its houses arranged in a triangle and built in accordance with the rank in the railway service of their intended occupants.

FIG. 154. Ashford, Kent:
internal structure and
nearby surroundings

The third element of Ashford consists of the suburbs growing
haphazardly along the roads to the south. A fourth element will
consist of a second new town (p. 455).

The Kent Coalfield

Like the railway works at Ashford, the coalmines of Kent needed
workers brought from outside the region. The exploration of the
coalfield was intertwined with the extension of railways in east Kent,
both developments showing private enterprise at its least effective.
Coal was proved in 1886 in a boring near Dover; the borehole was
made, when work on the Channel Tunnel project was halted by
Government order, in the bottom of the shaft. After a long, involved,
and deplorable series of technical and financial failures, coal-winding
started in 1918. Annual production reached 2 million tons in 1935, and
future production is forecast at $2\frac{1}{2}$ million tons. Four collieries exist,
at Chislet, Snowdon, Betteshanger and Tilmanstone (Fig. 151). Post-
war reconstruction of overground buildings and machinery should
reduce costs; there may also be a new colliery. The seams are preserved
in an eroded syncline in the Palaeozoic block which underlies the
Cretaceous and Jurassic strata of the region, and shafts are deep.
The friable coal, suited to the domestic rather than to the industrial
market, can be sold over a wide area in competition with seaborne
coal from the Northeast and railborne coal from the Midlands.

70. The West India Docks, looking upstream.

69. Wet gravel-workings in the Lea Valley, where the water-table is always high.

71. Crowds at Waterloo Station—one of the great terminals for commuter traffic.

72. The beginnings of vertical expansion—post-war flats at Roehampton.

CHAPTER 28

The London Basin

Area: about 3,000 square miles.
Population: about 10,750,000.
Largest towns: (*a*) The Greater London Conurbation (8,172,000).
        (*b*) Towns near the Conurbation but not included in
            it:—
            Hornchurch (128,250).
            Romford (114,500).
            Thurrock (114,250).
            Woking (67,500).
            Gravesend (51,500).
            Dartford (45,750).
            Leatherhead (35,500).
        (*c*) Outlying towns:—
            Southend (165,000).
            Reading (120,000).
            Slough (80,500).
            Watford (75,750).
            High Wycombe (50,250).
            St. Albans (50,250).
            Staines (49,250).
            Aldershot (31,250).
        The following are new towns; the figures given in
        brackets are those of planned totals of popula-
        tion:—
            Basildon (106,000).
            Bracknell (60,000).
            Crawley (75,000).
            Harlow (80,000).
            Hatfield (28,000).
            Hemel Hempstead (80,000).
            Stevenage (80,000).
            Welwyn Garden City (50,000).
    Some 60% of this region is in improved farmland; tillage is half as
extensive again as grassland.
Numbers of livestock: cattle, 280,000; sheep, 120,000; pigs, 270,000.

The London Basin is broadly synclinal in structure. The Chalk
which forms the upstanding Chilterns sinks gently underground
towards the southeast, passing beneath the younger rocks which

P

Boulder clay and glacial sand and gravel

Gravel-capped South Herts. Plateau, rising to 400 ft.

Crags and sandy drift of East Anglia

Low plainland based on London Clay, with terrace near river

Tertiary sands W. of London, capping London Clay in low tabular plateaus, with podsolic soils and much heath

Tertiary sands and gravels east of London, appearing from beneath London Clay

Chalk downlands, extensively mantled with Clay- with Flints in the Chilterns, where the crest overtops 800 ft.

FIG. 155. The London Basin: physique and main settlements

occupy the central parts of the Basin and reappearing in the North Downs. The syncline widens and deepens eastward, so that the Chalk outcrops diverge in this direction; it becomes narrower and shallower towards the west, so that the topographical basin narrows westward and the two belts of Chalkland finally unite beyond Newbury (Fig. 155).

Physical Evolution

The whole area has been affected by alternating submergence and emergence. At times of submergence the sea invaded the basin from the east, and marine and estuarine deposits accumulated above the downwarped Chalk. Such deposits are represented by the Thanet Beds, Woolwich Beds, and Blackheath Beds, all of which are mainly sandy or pebbly. Fairly deep submergence in a muddy sea is recorded in the overlying London Clay, which is widely preserved throughout the Basin. Upstream of London are found extensive remains of the Bagshot Beds, a sandy and permeable deposit which rests on the London Clay and forms blocks of low plateau.

A great deal is known of the erosional history of the London Basin. At heights above 800 ft. O.D. are preserved remnants of a peneplain, in the form of subdued Chalk summits capped with Clay-with-Flints. Between 550 and 650 ft. O.D. come the remains of a marine bench, appearing as broad flat-topped spurs on the back-slope of the Chilterns and in places cutting right across the North

Downs. At a little over 400 ft. O.D. are the relics of a gravel spread laid down by the ancestral Thames when sea-level stood at about the 400-ft. mark; these gravels are well in evidence on the South Herts. Plateau, a dissected block based on London Clay but much obscured by younger material.

The ancestral Thames flowed from west-southwest to east-northeast, well to the north of the present line. Part of the old track is indicated by the reach between Henley and Marlow, where the Thames is incised into the Chiltern Chalk. The river was diverted to the south by ice, which overrode the Chalkland as far west as the Hitchin gap and sent prongs up the river-valleys which it invaded. The full story of the diversion is long and complex, but the net effect is that the Thames now flows round the south of the South Herts. Plateau. Thick deposits of sand and gravel washed out from the melting ice line the bottom of the Vale of St. Albans, where they are partly covered by boulder clay, and boulder clay becomes thick and widespread east of the river Lea.

Intermittent falls of sea-level caused the Thames and its tributaries to be rejuvenated and to cut down anew. The deposits of their old valley-floors remain as terraces, covered in places by brickearth, which line the inner valley of the main river throughout the whole length of the Basin, but are most widely developed in the reach from Slough downstream, where they form wide, gravel-strewn flats above the level of the flood-plain.

The last recorded movement was one of submergence, which flooded the river-mouths at the eastern end of the Basin and converted them into wide, shallow estuaries. This submergence was due in part to the post-glacial rise in sea-level which has affected all the coasts of the British Isles, but in the very east of the London Basin the crust itself sagged gently downwards, increasing the extent of submergence and encouraging the development of muddy creeks and coastal marshes.

THE REGION OUTSIDE THE METROPOLIS

The West

Much of the London Basin beyond the bounds of Greater London is still rural. Slough is the last big metropolitan outpost on the upstream side, although Maidenhead (35,500) functions as a dormitory for London as well as a riverside resort. The western part of the London Basin has an urban focus of its own in Reading, with Newbury (20,500) and Hungerford (3,000) as lesser centres.

Newbury is located on the Kennet, in the middle of a valley-basin four or five miles in radius, while Reading has spread on both sides of the Kennet just above the confluence with the Thames, and lies near the edge of a piece of vale country some 20 miles across. Thus the immediate hinterland of Reading is about five times as large as that of Newbury. Here is one reason for the difference in the sizes of the two towns; another lies in the situation of Reading on the route through Goring Gap and close to the navigable Thames.

The industrial history of Newbury illustrates the detachment of manufacture from its original dependence on farming. The story includes the decline of the weaving for which Newbury was famous in the late 15th and early 16th centuries, when Jack of Newbury set up the first real factory in England; but if weaving went, brewing and flour-milling were retained. The town mills date from Saxon times. Engineering began with a local millwright in the late 1700s, who became an agricultural engineer and produced a plough of improved design, and the firm which he founded now makes marine engines. The making of oak furniture—an industry rooted in the local countryside—has been succeeded by the production of light aircraft and gliders. Newbury remains a small town, however, with all the charm of a southern English market centre. Even the Kennet-Avon Canal, from which so much was hoped in the way of trade and industry, is now obsolete after less than 150 years of use, and ranks as an antiquity of civil engineering.

Similar trends to those epitomised in Newbury are traceable in the more complex case of Reading. Successively a British, Romano-British, and Saxon settlement, the centre of Reading is based on a

FIG. 156. Reading and its local setting

patch of terrace above the fordable Kennet (Fig. 156). Reading as a royal burgh was second in Berkshire only to Wallingford at the time of the Domesday Survey, and became, like Newbury, a medieval centre of textile-making. The cloth trade was destroyed by the Civil War, but the corn and cattle markets continued to operate, as they still do. Reading became a considerable centre of commerce, but its industrial days did not reopen until the late 18th century. Brewing, the manufacture of farm equipment and horticultural machinery, seed-growing and biscuit-making were all more or less closely related, at the outset, to the activities of the neighbouring farms and gardens, but the last two activities in particular have far outgrown their origins. The largest single manufacturing concern in Reading today is a biscuit factory, the largest single industry is engineering. Weighing machines, pumps, electrical equipment, metal boxes and windows are among the engineering products; for none of the relevant trades can any obvious locating factor be given. Industrial Reading was greatly stimulated by the railway, which reached the town in 1840. In these present days of heavy road traffic, Reading is a centre of bus routes—a sign of its importance in retail trade, which amounts to £30 million a year.

The rural environs of Newbury and Reading are largely in farmland. The general character of local farming is indicated by figures for Berkshire, even though the county—extending over the Chalk belt into the Vale of White Horse—does not give a wholly satisfactory sample. Eighty per cent of Berkshire is in farmland, with half the farmland in grass and half in tillage. The main tillage crops are cereals, with wheat leading; permanent grass is more extensive than rotation grass, and dairying and the growing of cereals for sale are the principal farming interests. Since 1939 there has been a marked increase in tillage, both for cash and for fodder crops, in the whole western part of the London Basin, but at the same time the number of cattle—both beef and dairy—has risen.

The Bagshot Plateau and its Surroundings

Rural settlement is quite thickly scattered throughout the upper part of the London Basin, avoiding the broad flood-plains but being well represented on the adjoining river-terraces. Villages are more typical of the lower levels than of the modest hills, where signs of piecemeal reclamation appear in scattered dwellings. There is still woodland and near-heath on the podsols developed on the Bagshot sand on either side of the Kennet, and country of the same kind extends across the Blackwater in the southeast.

Here, however, the countryside begins to appear either military or residential. Part of the former block of dry heathland between the Blackwater and the Wey has been taken for training-grounds, on which lie Aldershot, Farnborough, Camberley and Bisley. A criss-cross of electrified suburban railways denotes the nearness of London, with Virginia Water, the climax of dormitory settlement, still building detached houses amid mature coniferous trees. Between the steep-sided Bagshot Plateau and the southward extension of London on to the North Downs lie the broad lower valleys of the Wey and Mole, containing Guildford and Leatherhead at the mouths of gaps through the Chalk, and the dormitory town of Woking between Guildford and the congested Thames crossing at Staines.

The Chilterns

Northeast of Reading the Thames enters the Chilterns, which are highly dissected by systems of dry valleys running between tabular divides. The water-table lies far beneath most of the surface, and rural settlement is rather sparse. Elongated towns are wedged into the valleys, most of them on roads leading to gaps in the crest of the cuesta—High Wycombe on the Wye, Amersham on the Misbourne, Chesham on the Chess, Hemel Hempstead on the Gade and Berkhampstead on the tributary Bulbourne, Harpenden in a dry valley. Stevenage lies in the broad, drift-encumbered corridor at the northeast end of the Chiltern plateau, Dunstable on Watling Street.

The past fortunes of Chiltern towns have been as varied as their predictable futures are dissimilar. Most of them serve to some extent as dormitories for London. High Wycombe, possessing a manufacture of furniture, was able to attract engineering; Dunstable, engaged like its larger neighbour Luton (Chap. 23) in the motor industry, has more than trebled its population since the 1931 census, while Hemel Hempstead and Stevenage have expanded with the addition of new towns, their modern factories and houses spreading rapidly across country. Much of Hemel Hempstead New Town stands on the top of the Chiltern Plateau, but the older towns are mainly confined in their narrow valleys, out of sight from the flat summits. The typical Chiltern scene consists of farmland diversified by woods and belts of ornamental timber.

Most of the Chiltern timber is deciduous. Beech—the original basis of furniture-making at High Wycombe—is quite prominent still, although oakwoods are the most characteristic. In some places the woods deteriorate into tangled hawthorn scrub, which can grow thickly on the widely-developed soils of the Clay-with-Flints; these explain the one-time presence of almost continuous forest on the Chiltern Plateau, and favour tillage where the land is farmed.

At the present time there is far more tillage on the Chilterns than there was in 1939. The Chilterns lie in that belt which, stretching from Kent to Nottinghamshire, has experienced a marked wartime and post-war extension of tillage, especially for cash crops. The figures for Hertfordshire give a very rough guide to the land-use of the district; about 70% of the county is in farmland, with 60% of the farmland in tillage and 40% in grass. Cereals are by far the most extensive tillage crops, occupying nearly four-fifths of the cropland, with barley leading.

The perceptible difference between the farming of the Chiltern Plateau and that of the environs of Newbury and Reading corresponds to difference of soils and of climate. The second of the two areas includes quite extensive heavy soils developed on the London Clay, while the soils of the Chiltern Plateau are, in general, of lighter kinds. Hertfordshire is slightly less rainy than Berkshire, with some 26 inches of rain a year against 28, and is slightly the more extreme in range of temperature. Thus the northeastern part of the London Basin falls within the area where the growing of cereals and potatoes is apt to increase in times of increasing demand for these crops, whereas Berkshire has some affinities with the grazing-lands of the Midlands and the Borders of the West Country.

The Vale of St. Albans, the Lea Valley, the South Herts Plateau, the Thames Valley above and below London

South of the Chilterns comes the drift-filled Vale of St. Albans, with Hertford and Ware, two small country towns of great antiquity, at the eastern end. These two towns have not developed industry on the scale displayed by Hatfield, St. Albans, and Watford, which lie on routes between London and the industrial Midlands, and where engineering is well established, with products including aircraft, aircraft components, and tractors.

Many gravel pits in the glacial outwash of the Vale of St. Albans supply building-sand and aggregate to the metropolis, and other pits are at work in the river-laid gravels west of London, in the valleys of the Thames and the Colne. Here, on the upstream side of the capital, is a stretch of low-lying vale, where flood-plains and wide, flat terraces line gently-sloping valleys cut in London Clay. For a very long time the clayland was thickly wooded, and even after it had been cleared it carried little settlement. Drainage works begun in the 19th century, however, have enabled building to spread far beyond the limits of the well-drained terraces, and the outlying settlements of former times have been joined to London. Mechanical engineering is well developed in this part of the region, and there are many factories producing foodstuffs, clothing, light electrical goods and plastics. Slough lies at the western end of the industrial ribbon, on the opposite side of the river to the royal seat of Windsor.

Parts of the floodplains above London have been taken for use as reservoirs. Parts of the terraces are under market-gardens, which have been pushed westwards and have expanded as London grew. In places the terrace gravels are covered by loess (brickearth), and on the brickearth soils market-gardening is especially prominent. In the natural state the brickearth soils were infertile, being seriously deficient in humus and potash, liable to dry out in summer, and becoming soggy in winter; they were avoided by early settlement, which was generally located on the water-bearing terrace gravels. As raw material for intensive cultivation, however, the brickearth soils are good. The demands of the London market made it profitable to fertilise them heavily, and their warmth promotes rapid growth of vegetable crops.

Similar developments have occurred in the Lea Valley downstream of Ware (Fig. 157). The Lea flows southwards, on the western side of the South Herts. Plateau, in a broad trench floored with alluvium, below terraces widely mantled with loess. As in the Thames valley above London, Dark-Age settlement avoided the brickearth, which came under intensive cultivation only as metropolitan demands enforced themselves. Here too the market-gardens were pushed

Arable
M Meadow (permanent grass)
h Heath (all rough grazing)
f Forest (all woodland)
9 Gardens
Glasshouses
P Inland water waste (non-agricultural land)

0   ¼   ½ MILE

FIG. 157. Land-use sample for the Lea Valley. The railway in the centre follows the boundary between the flood-plain on the east and terrace on the west. The terrace is widely covered with brickearth, the flood-plain has been exploited for gravel

farther and farther up the valley as London spread. During the 19th century and in the early part of the 20th century, many glasshouses were built in the Lea Valley, despite the drainage of cold air into the valley on still nights, and despite the increasing pollution of the atmosphere by London smoke. The greatest single concentration of glasshouses in the world is located in the Lea Valley, but growing under glass in this locality has passed its peak. Market-gardens are disappearing under buildings. Where the brickearth has been used in brickworks, the shallow worked-out pits are commonly occupied by factories. Light industry—especially electrical industry—lines the main roads to the north, but heavy metalwork is confined to the floodplain. Gravel-pits and reservoirs recur in the valley-bottom (Plate 69).

West of the Lea Valley, north of London, and south of the Vale of St. Albans lies the South Herts. Plateau, still in part well wooded, with sparse hamlets and single settlements. Its southern flank, however, is within the suburban limits of London, and land which produced hay and milk fifty or a hundred years ago is now heavily built-up.

North London has spread more widely on the western side of the Lea Valley than on the eastern. On the east the metropolis ends rather abruptly against the farmland of Essex. Epping Forest has been in part saved from destruction, and remains a bastion of country against spreading town. Farther east still, Romford has not yet lost its character of market town, although it is growing fast by virtue of its tightening links with London. Southend is a resort whose nearness to London offsets the disadvantage of a muddy foreshore.

On the Thames itself, Tilbury is an outport of London. Thurrock, Gravesend, and Dartford have been reduced almost to annexes of the metropolis, and Dartford is not far from being physically incorporated in the sprawl of London building. The segment of country between Dartford and Croydon resembles the triangle defined by Staines, Guildford and Kingston in being bound to London by electrified suburban railways.

THE METROPOLIS

So huge has London become that it inevitably overshadows every other town of the British Isles. Its size becomes still more impressive in a comparison with other towns of its region. Reading is the only town very largely independent of London which has reached a total of 100,000 inhabitants, and few of the other independent towns exceed 50,000. London apart, the London basin has not done a great deal to encourage urban growth. Some allowance must be made for the centripetal pull of the capital, but a comparison of the London Basin with, say, East Anglia or the South Midlands, suggests that the other towns are normal and London the phenomenal exception.

No single factor or small group of factors can be held to account for the remarkable growth of the town, either in medieval or in modern times. Even when every possible allowance has been made for a location on an estuary facing the mouths of the Rhine delta, it is still clear that the urban strength of London has diverse and ancient origins. Its size and urban force made it the object of jealousy and mistrust in medieval days, when the citizens of other towns regarded London much as some inhabitants of northern England are apt to regard it today.

The difficulties of explaining—or even of describing—the growth of London may be illustrated by a few statements of fact. Unlike Liverpool, Hull and Glasgow, it serves no near coalfield. It has an enormous hinterland today, serving as an inlet and outlet for much of the country's external trade, but the chief hinterland of the Port of London is Greater London itself, and in earlier times the London Basin was much more rural than most of it is now. As an ecclesiastical centre London ranks below Canterbury and York. It became a university town only in the 19th century, and even then its university was partly a paper organisation. Admittedly it is the centre of national and Commonwealth government; but it was already the greatest town in England before a powerful Parliament was seated at Westminster, and long before colonies were founded overseas.

Complex though its origins have been, London is a geographical reality. The expanding town has survived repeated epidemics—including epidemics of plague and cholera—and has recovered from the devastating fires of 1666 and 1940. The Greater London Conurbation holds nearly one in five of the total population of England and Wales, and one in six of the total of industrial workers. More people live in Greater London than in Austria, Ceylon, Chile, Peru, Sweden or Venezuela, and almost as many as in Australia, Belgium, or Portugal. The Conurbation sprawls across the London Basin, reaching from the North Downs to the South Herts. Plateau, laying a tight grip on settlements upstream in the Thames valley and downstream on the estuary.

Setting and Early Growth

The distribution of rock-types illuminates the study of the setting and early growth of London. Thick forests and unproductive heaths survived in this region well into the Middle Ages, and have not yet entirely vanished. Their general effect was to isolate London from remote parts of the Basin and, even more strongly, from places outside the region. Extensive woods covered much of Essex during Roman times and the Dark Ages, the trees growing thickly on the soils developed on bare London Clay or glacial deposits, while the bottom of the Lea Valley was under a mile-wide strip of marsh, and forest came in again on the clay and gravel soils of the South Herts.

Plateau. The notoriously sticky soils of lowlands based on London Clay also supported trees, while the podsols developed on the Blackheath and Bagshot Beds were under oak-birch heath, gorse, and broom. Even on parts of the Chilterns there was much natural wood, for the soils of the Clay-with-Flints could retain ample moisture to sustain trees. The environs of early London, therefore, consisted of lightly-vegetated spreads of terrace, encircled on three sides by abundant forest. The fourth side, however, lay open to the sea. There was a land-route leading eastwards along the flank of the North Downs, across the belt of light soils which lies between the tabular crest of the Chalk and the indented, muddy shore of Kent (Chap. 4). It was when Roman invaders approached by this route that certain advantages of the site of London were made clear.

In Roman days it was possible to ford the river close to the present site of London Bridge. There was an alternative crossing at Brentford, but as soon as the lower route had been secured it became the more frequented, and the ford was replaced by a bridge. The mouths of the Walbrook and the Fleet provided harbours adequate for the limited needs of Roman times, for most cross-Channel shipping then made for Lympne, Dover, Richborough or Reculver. Roads from these ports converged on Canterbury, whence Watling Street ran to London. A town was laid out inside defensive walls, including the hills on which the Tower and St. Paul's now stand, and coinciding roughly with the eastern two-thirds of the City.

Legions were detailed to construct roads radiating west, northwest, north and northeast from London, and the Roman Londinium became the effective focus of civil government in the province of Britannia, but it was by no means as pre-eminent at that time as it is today. St. Albans, for instance, remained an autonomous town—a political experiment of the emperor Claudius. The municipal independence of St. Albans was, in some degree, a measure of the strength of the forest barrier between that town and London.

Significantly enough, the Roman town at St. Albans adjoined a conquered British capital, which had formerly been located at nearby Wheathampstead. Both British sites lie in the Chalkland belt, along which the Icknield Way, avoiding the forests both of the London Basin and of the clay vales to the northwest, ran to Salisbury Plain. It was on the margin of Salisbury Plain that Winchester emerged, towards the end of the Dark Ages, as the capital of Wessex.

London's rise to the status of national capital could scarcely have been foretold in the Dark Ages. For a long period there was no English nation: separate kingdoms—Kent, Wessex, East Anglia, Northumbria, Mercia and others—rose, expanded, and engaged in war. Some were extinguished by absorption, some by conquest, and some by Viking and Danish invasion. In the long run the most successful was Wessex, whose kings were able to recover the Danelaw in the 10th century and to reign over a united England, but, even in Wessex, the king and the court moved from place to place, so that the centre of legislature and administration shifted from one royal estate to another. Similar practices were followed by the Danish kings who ruled from 1016 to 1042, and the names of several towns appear in the records of the time as temporary centres of royal power.

There is little in the obscure Dark-Age history of London to suggest a conscious rivalry with Winchester. Even with the help of Domesday Book, it is impossible to make satisfactory comparisons of the sizes, urban strength, and urban consciousness of 11th-century English towns.[1] Judged by the number of moneyers, however, London, Winchester and York were among the principal towns at the time of the Conquest, and London was a busy port carrying on a vigorous trade with nearby ports of the Continental mainland. Its history during the Dark Ages had not been wholly one of stagnation.

Although so little is known of pre-Domesday London, it is clear that civic administration had developed in the town to a most unusual degree. The burgesses were so powerful that William I concluded a treaty with them as a means of securing control of the flourishing town, which gained still more in importance from the building of the Tower, Montfichet's Tower and Bayard's Castle. The political connection with the Continent doubtless did much for London under the Normans: the significance of the situation of the town, on the nearest large estuary to Europe, was beginning to reveal itself. London never had merchant gilds, presumably because civic affairs were regulated strongly enough to make controls on trade unnecessary, and the already cosmopolitan town presumably profited from its commercial freedom. Its supremacy as a port appears in the tax records of 1204, when London merchants paid more than the merchants of any other English port.

The strongly centralised government of the Tudors was based on Westminster, the ancient royal centre eventually to be engulfed by London. London itself, with 75,000 inhabitants by 1500, had long been growing under the impetus of its own size, and by 1550 had secured 80% of the country's external trade. The momentum which had carried it so far had already become independent of any advantages derived from its site or from its situation in its region. As the capital of a united country, and later of a united empire, it was to

---

[1] Domesday Book lists about 70 places with borough status, additional to boroughs on royal, ecclesiastical, and aristocratic estates, but is known to omit mention of certain towns which existed at the time of the survey.

experience growth unaffected by its regional or by its national situation.

Physical Expansion and Functional Change

Within the Metropolis, however, qualities of site continued to be influential. When the growth of London is mapped by stages (Fig. 158), an immediate connection can be perceived between form and quality of the ground on the one hand, and mode and direction of growth on the other. Physical extension has been accompanied by functional change, the various early Londons indicated in Fig. 158 corresponding roughly to the distinctive functional areas of today.

FIG. 158. Stages in the growth of London

The population of 75,000 in 1500 had become 150,000 or more by Elizabethan times; a century had sufficed to double the number of inhabitants. As the map shows, late-Tudor London was spreading along the north bank of the river, reaching out both to the east and to the west. Bankside settlement stretched from the Tower through Wapping to Shadwell. The Inns of Court already existed west of the City, and the area between the Strand and Holborn had been built-up. That is to say, late Tudor London included those areas which at the present time contain concentrations of business houses and news-paper offices, as well as parts of the existing West End. Buildings on Whitehall linked the Strand with the immediate surroundings of Westminster Abbey.

On the south bank, Southwark lay at the far end of London Bridge, still the only bridge over the Thames at London, and a ribbon of building ran along the south bank of the river as far as Rotherhithe. The flood-plain alluvium further downstream had been empoldered and was in use as cattle pasture, but both London and Southwark stood on patches of terrace above the level of floods.

By the early 1700s, the ribbon-building reaching out from the City had become continuous town. Southwark was consolidating itself in between the roads which radiated southward, and Lambeth marshes were being drained, but the most marked extension had taken place towards the west, on the north bank, where building had reached the Tyburn, and Westminster Bridge built in 1738 testified to the growth of London on the upstream side. The whole of the area which is now called the West End had been built over by 1725, but the site of Hyde Park remained in pasture.

By 1800 London had a population of a million. Hyde Park, Green Park and St. James's Park indented the fringe of a London which had caused to swell, and was fast uniting with, Chelsea, Paddington, Somers Town, Islington, and Bethnal Green. Streets and buildings extended continuously from Watling Street to the lower end of the Lea. Building by this time was clearly associated with gravel terraces, for London was large enough to abut on land of varying quality. The terraces had been first settled, for they alone could supply ground-water, and it was across the terraces that continuous building kept on spreading. By the end of the Napoleonic Wars, the settlement of Southwark was merging with Walworth and Kennington, and Blackfriars bridge linked the western end of the City with the South Bank. The main port area remained below London Bridge, which set a limit to shipping by its narrow arches. Early 19th-century London thus included what are now recognised as the central districts. Tottenham Court Road, Oxford Street, Piccadilly, Whitehall, Shoreditch, and Whitechapel Road were all built-up; Soho, Mayfair, Westminster and Spitalfields had emerged as recognisable divisions.

The pace of growth and of internal change increased as the 19th century drew on. The specialised functional areas of today could not have emerged unless houses had been converted to, or replaced by, shops and offices, and conversion and replacement could not have occurred if residents had not moved out. Large numbers of people could not have slept in the suburbs and worked in the centre without the aid of public transport. The huge 19th-century extension of London was, therefore, made practicable by advances in engineering.

Steam railways built during the 19th century do not cross inner London: the termini at Paddington, Marylebone, Euston, St.

Pancras and King's Cross lie roughly on the edge of London as it was in 1800. Lines from the east were able to penetrate the City, and four lines from the south cross the Thames to north-bank termini. Since the radial lines belonged to competing companies, no ring-railway was constructed, and, in any case, the suburban services were needed mainly to move people inwards and outwards to and from the centre, which acquired omnibus services and electric railways. The earliest electrified lines were partly exposed and partly underground, but the later tube railways run wholly through tunnels beneath central London, emerging to the surface only on the out-skirts. Tunnelling continued well into the present century, its costs being kept down by the character of the London Clay, which allowed tunnels to be cut accurately and quickly.

Land drains, installed—or at least begun—in the 19th century, enabled dense building to invade the outcrops of London Clay. But even when surface water is drained off, the clay is still liable to shrink when dry and to swell when wet; it makes a poor foundation for buildings, and numbers of the houses constructed upon it are liable to cracking. The extending tentacles of London spread preferentially across sandy and gravelly deposits, along the roads which themselves kept as far as possible to dry ground, but the spaces between the roads were built over as the fringing suburbs struck deeper and deeper into the country. Thus by 1900 the Greater London Conurbation had come into being, containing some 6 million inhabitants.

The achievements of 19th-century civil engineering in London included great improvements to the systems of water supply and sewage disposal, without which London could scarcely have grown so large. In a sense, the installations were the outcome of the needs of the time, but in another sense they were typical products of new industrial techniques. Piped water greatly speeded the settlement of clayland. On the terraces it superseded supplies from shallow wells, which were much contaminated and great spreaders of disease. Only in the 19th century did London shake itself free of the epidemics by which it had been troubled for so long.

The rise of consolidated authorities was almost inevitable in the circumstances of the 19th century, but was also a sign of character-istic changes in public service and administration. The Metropolitan Water Board was not actually established until 1902, when the century had turned, and the Port of London Authority came into being in 1908. Their formation amounted to a recognition of the unity of the port and of the Conurbation. By 1900, the sprawling town was consolidating itself by infilling many of its vacant spaces. In the early years of the 20th century, the population of Greater

London increased no more rapidly than that of England and Wales as a whole. But although the impetus which had produced an enormous conurbation, with an enormous number of inhabitants, was dying away, people were still moving out from the centre, and the town continued to spread physically. The functional characteristics of its inner districts became more and more strongly defined. During the inter-war period there was another spell of rapid increase in numbers, due mainly to migration, which helped to bring about the spread of suburbs. Very many estates of semi-detached houses came into being at this time, setting an architectural pattern which is now typical of many residential districts throughout the country.

Five main divisions of the Conurbation have separated themselves out from one another (Fig. 159). The metropolitan centre of commerce, finance and government—the City, the West End and Westminster—has a very low density of resident population. The old residential, industrial, and dockside areas, developed in the late 18th and early 19th centuries, and corresponding in part to the East End, tend to suffer from urban blight, their houses sliding into disrepair and whole districts declining in social esteem. The third division includes high-density housing built in the late 19th and early 20th centuries.

central commercial and administrative districts

old residential and industrial districts

dense residential building dating from before 1914

newer residential and surburban industrial districts

outer residential fringe, rural in some places

0   5   10   15   20 MILES

Fig. 159. Structure of the Greater London Conurbation

Some parts of this division have also gone downhill—Victorian and Edwardian houses, designed for large families and their servants, have commonly been subdivided into flats or simply let by rooms. The suburban ring includes the homes of half the people of the Conurbation, besides patches of older building where former outlying settlements have been engulfed, and belts of industry, especially of light industry located alongside trunk roads. Finally there comes the outer fringe, distinguished by low-density housing. Like the main suburban ring, this division experienced invasion by housing in the inter-war period, and in the post-war years some of its open spaces have been taken for estates of council houses. The 20th-century pattern of development has followed that of former times. London has thrust vigorously outwards on the outgoing routes, and after some delay the intervening gaps have been filled in.

Docks, Port Trade, and External Passenger Traffic

The dock system is largely the product of 19th-century engineering, although the 20th century has brought some notable additions and improvements. The need for docks arose from the high tidal range of the estuarine Thames, and from the congestion prevailing on the wharf-lined river. Each group of docks is located on the inside of a bend in the channel—that is, on the lobe of a meander, on flat ground underlain by alluvium and London Clay, and not greatly built-over (Fig. 160). Dock entrances could be made both on the upstream and the downstream sides of the systems (Plate 70). Two expectable tendencies can be noted in the development of the docks— the extension of docks farther and farther down the river, and a downstream increase in the size of basins. A certain specialisation in types of cargo is also detectable.

FIG. 160. The dock systems of London

The London and St. Katharine Docks, on the north bank adjoining the Pool, adjoin the City. Dating mainly from the first half of the 9th century, they specialise in handling cargoes of tea, fruit, wine and wool; large quantities of general cargo are also dealt with. The site of this group of docks was already enclosed by continuous building when construction took place, and the quays are not rail-served. The Surrey Commercial Docks, on the opposite side of the Lower Pool, are scarcely better placed in relation to railways. This group, the outcome of 250 years of piecemeal development, handles much imported timber, especially from the Baltic, in addition to general cargo.

The West India and Millwall Docks are located on the Isle of Dogs, and the East India Dock by the confluence of the Lea. The elements of this group were completed at dates ranging from 1802 to 1870. The system is rail-served, is well equipped to handle bulk imports of grain, sugar, and hardwood, and shares in the import trade in fruit. The East India Dock has lost the site of its Export Basin to a power station, and now concentrates on coaster-borne traffic.

The Victoria and Albert Docks were opened in 1885 and 1880, and the King George V Dock was added to the group in 1921. The combined group of Royal Docks, occupying an extensive site between Gallions Reach and the mouth of the Lea, includes the largest collective sheet of impounded dock water in the world. The rail-served quays and transit sheds receive meat, grain, tobacco and fruit among the cargoes imported from Commonwealth countries, the Americas, and the Far East. It is mainly by traffic through the Royal Docks that the Port of London acts as an inlet and outlet for the whole country.

Tilbury Docks were opened in 1886. Rail services were generously provided, but road access was limited, all road transport at the time of construction being horse-drawn. In later years the road system has been improved, and more than half the import tonnage is now distributed by road. Enlargements have been carried out to allow Tilbury Docks to accommodate big ships, and trade is bound to increase with the completion of the Dartford-Purfleet tunnel under the Thames and a future new dock. Tilbury Docks are designed for transit, providing no warehouses. Export cargoes include a wide range of manufactures; among the imports are the products of Australasia, the Indian sub-continent, and the oilfields which export from the Persian Gulf. Tilbury became London's nearest passenger port when the floating landing-stage was built in 1930; vehicle ferries connect it with termini on the European mainland.

The airports of London compete very strongly for passenger traffic, not only with Tilbury, but also with Harwich, Southampton, and packet stations on the Channel coast. London Airport is located on a wide expanse of flat terrace, east of the lower Colne and between the diverging roads to Staines and Slough. The new terminal at Gatwick, within the Weald, is further from the capital but adjoins a main railway.

London as an Industrial Region

Of the $4\frac{1}{2}$ million workers in Greater London, fewer than 1 million are employed in manufacturing industry, but the proportion so employed is not much less than that in England and Wales as a whole. London takes its proportionate share in the metal and engineering trades, in timber-milling, in woodworking, and in the processing of foodstuffs, and has a high proportion of workers in garment-making, paper-milling, and printing and publishing. There is a great attraction to light industry in the huge local market offered by London, and London's industrial development in the inter-war period took place partly at the expense of the depressed industrial regions of the coalfields.

The downstream spread of docks was accompanied by the location on the lower river of industry which needs raw material in bulk—oil refining, sugar refining, timber-milling, and cement-making. In the Conurbation generally, however, industry is very widely scattered. Certain concentrations can be identified—the clothing and furniture industries in the East End, the modern electrical industries on radiating trunk roads and on the North Circular Road—but industry has not become as strongly localised as have service functions.

Present Status and Future Prospects of the Metropolis

The Greater London Conurbation, as officially defined for census purposes, is remarkably self-contained. Of its 8 million people, fewer than 100,000 live in the Conurbation and work outside it; some 250,000 live outside it but come in to work. Most of the daily movement takes place within the limits of the Conurbation, with more than 1 million travelling daily between the central districts and the suburbs (Plate 71).

While Greater London has great advantages as a market, port town, and supplier of labour, it suffers undeniably from serious congestion. Attempts to build suburban houses on the edge of the surrounding country have defeated their own object, by converting country to suburb, and the definition of a Green Belt round the metropolis has not entirely arrested expansion (Plate 23). The building of new towns—at Stevenage, Crawley, Hemel Hempstead, Harlow, Welwyn Garden City, Hatfield, Basildon, and Bracknell—constitutes a kind of leapfrogging of London over the Green Belt. London County Council estates are in existence, or are planned, at a dozen places, including a number well outside the London Basin (Fig. 161). Thus, even if the physical spread of London be stopped, the metropolis is fast colonising the region in which it lies, and is setting up outposts beyond the rim of Chalkland which forms the regional boundary. The urban pattern of the whole of southeastern England is fast being modified. Electric power and road transport

FIG. 161. Colonisation of southeastern England by outposts
of Metropolitan London

assist in the modification, as they do in the development of trading estates in regions where heavy industry is concentrated.

The rapid post-war changes in the environs of London have been accompanied by reconstruction and improvement in the Port, for there is every reason to expect that the near hinterland will continue to become more and more populous. There have also been marked changes in the appearance of the central parts of the Conurbation. The process of reconstruction which affects all large towns has probably been speeded, rather than retarded, by wartime bombing, which cleared sites where tall new buildings of austere design, some elegant and some merely slabby, are rising in many places (Plate 72). It seems possible that London is at last to begin vertical instead of horizontal expansion, but the time still seems distant when sky-scrapers of the North American kind will be a familiar feature of the London scene. It appears most unlikely that the boundaries of the Conurbation will be drawn inwards except by some truly catastrophic event. London continues to attract its migrants, both from overseas and from other parts of the British Isles, and to become greater simply by reason of its existing urban strength.

APPENDIX

NEW TOWNS IN THE LONDON BASIN AND ADJACENT REGIONS: LONDON COUNTY COUNCIL OVERSPILL SCHEMES

New Towns	Planned Populations	Populations in 1964
Basildon	106,000	61,500
Bracknell	60,000	24,100
Crawley	75,000	60,300
Harlow	80,000	66,100
Hatfield	28,000	22,500
Hemel Hempstead	80,000	64,700
Stevenage	80,000	52,000
Welwyn Garden City	50,000	39,000

London County Council Overspill Schemes

Town	Additional Population[1]
Ashford (Kent)	not yet decided
Aylesbury	15,000
Basingstoke	10,500
Bletchley	7,000
Bury St. Edmunds	7,000
Haverhill	7,000
Huntingdon	5,000
Letchworth	7,500
Luton (Borough)	5,000
Luton (Rural District)	7,000
Swindon	30,000
Thetford	7,500

[1] The figures given under this head are estimated at 5 people per new dwelling; numbers of new dwellings relate to periods of expansion up to 15 years in length.

CHAPTER 29

Conclusion

DRASTIC change in national and local economy and land-use, with associated change in the visible landscape, have been described in the foregoing chapters. Although the pace of change seems greater now than it has ever been before, the appearance of speed may be due in part to the difference between the limited perspective of the present day and the long, leisured vistas of history. It is difficult from this distance to appreciate the feelings aroused by Dark-Age invasions, by the Conquest, by the Black Death, by depopulation of medieval villages, by the Civil War, by parliamentary enclosure, by the French Revolutionary and Napoleonic Wars, by early industrialisation, by the Great Famine of Ireland, or by the agricultural depression of the late 19th century. To the people directly involved, and to many contemporary observers, these events must have seemed as vital and urgent as anything occurring today. On the other hand, very many of the processes which affected the geography of the British Isles before 1914 were initiated, and carried out, at some level lower than the national. Economic activity and its geographical distribution, the relationship between the people and the land, evolved for many centuries by natural selection. Only with the emergence of numerous nation-states in the 19th and 20th centuries, and with their involvement in world war, did national influence, control, and direction come to be thought necessary, useful, and inevitable.

In its external relations, the United Kingdom today is a single unit—affected as a whole by the interplay of world politics, by the political development of the Commonwealth, and by halting and dubious advance towards some kind of European unity. For many internal purposes, also, it is a single unit, and the trend towards a strongly centralised government has, during the inter-war and post-war periods, been very marked. Internal stresses, however, have not been entirely resolved. Among the former Celtic lands of the north and west, most of Ireland has detached itself from the United Kingdom. Movements of independence in Cornwall, the Orkneys, and the Shetlands—variously complicated by appeals for union with Brittany, Denmark, the Faroes, Iceland, and Norway—are small symptoms of the sort of feeling which is quite powerfully expressed by demands for increased control by Wales and Scotland over their own affairs. Whatever may happen in the future, it can at least be said that the past has not sufficed to anglicise the uplands of the west and north.

On the regional scale, as on the national, an historical view tends to minimise the swift drama of past change. The rapid rise—and equally rapid decline—of iron-manufacture in the Black Country and in South Wales lose their immediacy by belonging to the past. Region-wide conversion of agriculture in Southwest England and in East Anglia, having been accomplished, are accepted with scarcely a question. Scarcely a region, however, fails to record some mode of transformation during the last hundred, fifty, or even twenty years. The market-gardening and resort trade of coastlands in the south, the tourist industry of North Wales, the Lake District, and the Scottish Highlands, the threat to Scottish coal-mining, the decline in exports of coal and cotton, the rise of mechanical engineering— all, on the historical time-scale, are recent developments, separated by very few years from the establishment of industrial estates, the building of nuclear power stations, and the driving of motorways across the Midlands.

The most recent changes, and changes now in progress, loom large because they are close, and seem uncertain because their outcome is still not fully known. Without some scale of measurement, it is impossible to make a direct comparison between present and former rates of change. Every age of rapid technical development has been acclaimed as a climax—usually as a climax of progress, whatever that may mean—but it is undeniable that, during the 20th century, thermal, mechanical, and electrical power have been applied more widely and more effectively than ever before.

A direct result has been to increase mobility. Despite difficulties of congestion, travel is easier and swifter than in previous centuries. Increased real incomes make travel possible for a large fraction of the community, and daily journeys to work and annual journeys on holiday are now customary. Personal mobility for purposes of business and pleasure has increased. Internal migration, however, has been somewhat handicapped in the post-war period by the housing shortage; it is a sign of the times that successive national governments have made themselves responsible for the promotion and control of building-campaigns.

Social mobility—the possibility of moving on the social scale— has increased during the 20th century. However greatly the ethics of social classification may be deplored, people in practice apply their own criteria, often basing them on occupation. The increase in social mobility therefore amounts to increased occupational mobility—an increased chance for children to lose or gain occupational and social status by choosing—or being forced into— occupations different from those of their parents.

Although internal migration is beset by difficulty, occupational change is in practice often accompanied by a change of residence. The resulting redistribution of people, and the nation-wide effects of national newspapers and broadcasting, might be expected to reduce the contrasts between one region and another. Additional factors likely to work in the same direction are the dispersion of industry and of administration—a dispersion made possible by road transport and electric power. Dispersion of industry is already reflected in the new life injected into old towns, in the construction of new towns, and in the variety introduced into areas where industry has hitherto been uniform. The very fact of dispersion, however, demonstrates that centralising tendencies do not operate unopposed. The industrial pull of the coalfields, already weakened, can be expected to weaken further in the future. Moreover, new industries— such as the overlapping groups of petro-chemical and synthetic fibre industries—set whole new series of problems in location. Rising industrial output, rising consumption, and increase of population all encourage deliberate planning; for purposes of planning, large parts of the country, or even the whole country in some contexts, are taken as the fundamental unit. Southeast England, for instance, is calculated to increase its population from $17\frac{3}{4}$ million to $21\frac{1}{4}$ million by 1980. Greater London has its own Council; Southampton-Portsmouth, Bletchley, and Newbury are all intended to undergo massive expansion, and Ashford, Ipswich, Northampton, Peterborough, Swindon, and Stansted are all to grow fast.

It need not be concluded, however, that differences among regions will become so blurred as to disappear. Quite apart from enduring physical contrasts, there are local loyalties, and some regional loyalties, which are dynamic enough not merely to persist but also to grow stronger. Local consciousness, if not regional consciousness, seems likely to continue in full force.

Although traditional dialects, with their distinctive vocabularies, are dying out it is quite possible that local and regional accents are becoming more and more specialised and distinctive with the passage of time. Broadcasting not only makes allowance for regional accents, but also demonstrates their great variety. It may well be significant that Lancashire and Yorkshire speech are distinguishable by accent, that the Liverpool area has developed its own accent within Lancashire, and that the Black Country, in the course of industrialisation, produced an accent all of its own. The pace and direction of the growth of local accents is impossible to gauge, but general observation reinforces the historical study of language in suggesting that regional developments on diverging lines are likely to take place. In this way, at least, contrasts between regions may well be enhanced. Customs, like speech, are slow to change, and can also display divergent trends. The southern limit of Rugby League football or of the custom of taking high tea are real social boundaries. Only detailed anthropological study could show where such boundaries should be drawn, to what extent they coincide with boundaries of other kinds, where lie the limits between contrasted accents, and where regions are thought, by their inhabitants, to end.

It may be doubted if people in general have any strong regional consciousness, beyond a vague sense of loyalty to their home town, their home area, or their home county. In any event, regional consciousness is very difficult to assess because of its subjective, subconscious, and emotional nature. In direct contrast, a very clear result emerges from recent studies—namely, that large towns tend to secure for themselves a service area, which is quite well marked-off from the adjacent service areas of neighbouring towns. The greatest towns, however, serve areas which include their smaller neighbours, some becoming regional capitals. It has repeatedly been suggested that the present administrative subdivision of the United Kingdom— a product of the Dark Ages and the Norman Conquest—should be revised on regional lines, giving practical expression in the work of administration to the effective status of regional capitals. Here, again, is a tendency opposed to centralisation on the national level.

In the towns themselves, as in the surrounding countryside, old and new are intermingled. It is fashionable with some today to show sentimental regard for railways and for Victorian architecture; but fascinating as these works of the 19th century may be, they form no more than one group of the products of the past. In every town and in every region, structures of diverse periods are to be seen. New in their day, and the expression of change in progress, they have been preserved by the forces of anti-change. Wherever old and new alike are combined in a unified scene—even when the unity is one of repeated variety—and wherever the activities of the people are subject to some localised influences, there a distinctive geographical character can be identified. So long as such a character can be perceived on a regional scale, regional geography will continue to serve its purpose of description, definition, assessment and inter-pretation.

Bibliography

THE works listed below range widely in character, scope, and purpose. The statistical publications have provided much of the source-material for the foregoing chapters. Some of the text-books contain detailed accounts of single topics; others—particularly those intended for the general reader—are both wider in scope and generally lighter in treatment. Ease of reading, however, need imply neither deficiency of content nor over-simplification; slight and discursive books of a topographical kind have been rigidly excluded, and the works named are recommended as being both sound and up-to-date. Some of them provide most useful reviews of subjects linked with, but distinct from, geography.

The articles listed for the regional chapters have been selected to give recent accounts of varying aspects of regional life. With few exceptions, they have appeared in the *Advancement of Science*, the handbooks published by the British Association for annual meetings, *Economic Geography*, *Geography*, the *Geographical Journal*, *Geographical Studies*, the *Geographical Review*, the *Proceedings of the Geologists' Association*, the *Scottish Geographical Magazine*, or the *Transactions of the Institute of British Geographers*. Numerous works on Ireland appear in *Irish Geography*; the *East Midland Geographer* is among the university publications dealing with a particular area.

As far as possible, given works are cited under one head only, in order to keep the lists down to reasonable length. The main exceptions are those books or articles which deal with a certain subject in relation to more than one region. On the other side, statistics of agriculture, population, employment, and industry do not appear under the regional heads, although part of the regional text relies heavily upon them.

The recommended maps are either on the scale of 1: 63,360 or on that of 1: 25,000. Sheet-numbers for the 1: 63,360 maps of Great Britain refer to the Seventh Series. Sheets of the 1: 25,000 map are not named by the Ordnance Survey, but names have been added below in order to help identification. Generally speaking, the recommended 1: 63,360 sheets provide as typical a sample as possible of a whole region, while the 1: 25,000 sheets illustrate single important aspects.

PART ONE

1. LIVELIHOOD AND LAND USE

Central Statistical Office: *Annual Abstract of Statistics*. London: H.M.S.O.
Central Statistics Office: *Statistical Abstract of Ireland (annual)*. Dublin: Stationery Office.
Statesman's Yearbook.
Ulster Yearbook. Belfast: H.M.S.O.
Whitaker's Almanack.

2. The Nature of the Land

E. H. Brown, 'The Physique of Wales'. *Geogr. Journ.* 123, 1957.

G. H. Dury, *The Face of the Earth.* Penguin Books.

G. H. Dury, 'Diversion of Drainage by Ice'. *Science News* 38, 1955.

W. G. Fearnsides and O. M. B. Bulman, *Geology in the Service of Man.* Penguin Books.

J. F. Kirkcaldy, *General Principles of Geology.* London: Hutchinson.

D. L. Linton, 'The Delimitation of Morphological Regions'; in *London Essays in Geography* (ed. L. D. Stamp and S. W. Wooldridge). London: Longmans, Green.

D. L. Linton, 'Problems of Scottish Scenery'. *Scot. Geogr. Mag.* 47, 1951.

C. R. Longwell and R. F. Flint, *Introduction to Physical Geology.* New York: Wiley.

J. A. Steers, *The Sea Coast.* London: Collins.

J. A. Steers, *The Coastline of England and Wales.* Cambridge: University Press.

J. A. Steers, *The Coastline of Scotland.* Cambridge: University Press.

A. E. Trueman, *Geology and Scenery.* Penguin Books.

A. K. Wells and J. F. Kirkaldy, *Outline of Historical Geology.* London: Murby.

3. Climate, Vegetation and Soils

Air Ministry, Meteorological Office, *Climatological Atlas of the British Isles.* London: H.M.S.O.

S. R. Badmin, *Trees in Britain.* Penguin Books.

W. G. V. Balchin, 'The Nation's Water Supply'. *Geog.* 42, 1957.

British Forestry Commission: reports and other publications. London: H.M.S.O.

T. J. Chandler, 'London's Urban Climate'. *Geogr. Journ.* 128, 1962.

'Climatology Applied in the Service of Man: A Symposium'. *Adv. Sci.* 13, 1957.

G. H. Dury, 'Weather, Climate, and River Erosion in the Ice Age'. *Science News* 33, 1954.

H. L. Edlin, *Trees, Woods, and Man.* London: Collins.

R. Geiger, *The Climate Near The Ground.* Harvard: U.P.

S. Gregory, 'Accumulated Temperature Maps of the British Isles'. *Trans. Inst. Brit. Geog.* 1954.

S. Gregory, 'Regional Variations in the Trend of Annual Rainfall over the British Isles'. *Geogr. Journ.* 122, 1956.

S. Gregory, 'The Contribution of Uplands to the Public Water Supply of England and Wales'. *Trans. Inst. Brit. Geog.* 1954.

F. K. Hare, *The Restless Atmosphere.* London: Hutchinson.

C. E. Hubbard, *Grasses.* Penguin Books.

G. Kimble and R. Bush, *The Weather.* Penguin Books.

G. Manley, *Climate and the British Scene.* London: Collins.

A. A. Miller, 'The Use and Misuse of Climatic Resources'. *Adv. Sci.* 13, 1956.

W. H. Pearsall, *Mountains and Moorlands*. London: Collins.
Sir John E. Russell, *The World of the Soil*. London: Collins.
A. G. Tansley, *Britain's Green Mantle*. London: Allen & Unwin.
W. B. Turrill, *British Plant Life*. London: Collins.

4. THE PATTERN OF PEOPLING

J. H. Andrews, 'Some Statistical Maps of Defoe's England'. *Geog. Studies* 3, 1956.
M. Ashley, *England in the Seventeenth Century*. Penguin Books.
M. Beresford, *History on the Ground*. London: Lutterworth Press.
M. Beresford, *The Lost Villages of England*. London: Lutterworth Press.
S. T. Bindoff, *Tudor England*. Penguin Books.
V. G. Childe, *Prehistoric Communities of the British Isles*. Edinburgh: Chambers.
G. Clark, *Prehistoric England*. London: Batsford.
R. G. Collingwood, *Roman Britain*. Oxford: U.P.
H. C. Darby, 'The Clearing of the English Woodlands'. *Geog.* 36, 1951.
H. C. Darby (ed.), *An Historical Geography of England and Wales before 1800*. Cambridge: U.P.
E. Ekwall, *The Concise Oxford Dictionary of English Place-names*. Oxford: Clarendon Press.
H. J. Fleure, *A Natural History of Man in Britain*. London: Collins.
H. L. Gray, *English Field Systems*. Harvard: U.P.
J. and C. Hawkes, *Prehistoric Britain*. London: Chatto and Windus.
W. G. Hoskins, *The Making of the English Landscape*. London: Hodder & Stoughton.
A. R. Myers, *England in the Late Middle Ages*. Penguin Books.
S. Piggott, *British Prehistory*. Oxford: U.P.
S. Piggott and K. Henderson, *Scotland Before History*. Edinburgh: Nelson.
J. K. St. Joseph, 'Air Photographs and Archaeology'. *Geog. Journ.* 105, 1945.
D. M. Stenton, *English Society in the Early Middle Ages*. Penguin Books.
D. Whitelock, *The Beginnings of English Society*. Penguin Books.

5. AGRICULTURE FROM 1700

F. A. Barnes, The Evolution of Salient Patterns of Milk Production and Distribution in England and Wales'. *Trans. Inst. Brit. Geog.* 1958.
Central Statistics Office: *Statistical Abstract of Ireland (annual)*. Dublin: Stationery Office.
H. C. Chew, 'Changes in Land Use, and Stock over England and Wales, 1939 to 1951'. *Geogr. Journ.* 122, 1956.
H. C. Chew, 'Fifteen Years of Agricultural Change'. *Geog.* 43, 1958.
J. T. Coppock, *An Agricultural Atlas of England and Wales*. London: Faber & Faber.
Department of Agriculture for Scotland: *Agricultural Statistics, Scotland (annual)*. Edinburgh, H.M.S.O.
Lord Ernle, *English Farming Past and Present*. London: Heinemann.
H. L. Gray, *English Field Systems*. Harvard: U.P.

J. F. Hart, 'The Changing Distribution of Sheep in Britain'. *Econ. Geog.* 32, 1956.

D. A. Hill, *The Land of Ulster.* Belfast: H.M.S.O.

S. R. Jones, *English Village Homes.* London: Batsford.

Land Utilisation Survey of Great Britain: *County Reports.* (These Reports, dealing chiefly with the inter-war period, are now mainly of historical interest. Numbers of them, however, contain useful summaries of geology, climate, landform, and agricultural history).

Ministry of Agriculture and Fisheries: *Agricultural Statistics, England and Wales* (*annual*). London: H.M.S.O.

C. S. Orwin, *A History of English Farming.* Edinburgh: Nelson.

H. Pakington, *English Villages and Hamlets.* London: Batsford.

J. H. Plumb, *England in the Eighteenth Century.* Penguin Books.

L. D. Stamp, *Man and the Land.* London: Collins.

L. D. Stamp, 'Wartime Changes in British Agriculture'. *Geogr. Journ.* 109, 1947.

L. D. Stamp, *The Land of Britain: its Use and Misuse.* London: Longmans, Green.

6. THE RISE OF INDUSTRY

T. S. Ashton, *Iron and Steel in the Industrial Revolution.* Manchester: U.P.

H. L. Beales, *The Industrial Revolution, 1750–1850.* London: Frank Cass.

G. D. H. Cole, *Introduction to Economic History, 1750–1950.* London: Macmillan.

W. H. B. Court, *A Concise Economic History of Britain.* Cambridge: U.P.

H. C. Darby (ed.), *An Historical Geography of England and Wales before 1800.* Cambridge: U.P.

K. G. T. McDonnell, D. C. Coleman, and S. Pollard, *A Survey of English Economic History.* London and Glasgow: Blackie.

P. Matoux, *The Industrial Revolution in the Eighteenth Century.* London: Jonathan Cape.

J. U. Nef, *Cultural Foundations of Industrial Civilisation.* Cambridge: U.P.

J. H. Plumb, *England in the Eighteenth Century.* Penguin Books.

A. Redford, *Labour and Migration in England, 1800–1850.* Manchester. U.P.

Wilfred Smith, *An Economic Geography of Great Britain.* London: Methuen.

L. D. Stamp and S. H. Beaver, *The British Isles.* London: Longmans, Green.

D. Thomson, *England in the Nineteenth Century.* Penguin Books.

7. COAL AND INDUSTRIAL POWER

British Iron and Steel Federation: *Annual Statistics.*

Central Electricity Authority: *Reports and Accounts* (*annual*). London: H.M.S.O.

Central Statistical Office: *Annual Abstract of Statistics.* London: H.M.S.O.

Central Statistics Office: *Statistical Abstract of Ireland* (*annual*). Dublin: Stationery Office.

Colliery Yearbook.

W. H. B. Court, *Coal—History of the Second World War.* London: H.M.S.O. and Longmans, Green.

J. H. Dunning and C. J. Thomas, *British Industry, Change and Development in the Twentieth Century.* London: Hutchinson.

P. R. Mounfield, 'The Location of Nuclear Power Stations, &c.' *Geog.* 46, 1961.

R. C. Estall, 'The Problem of Power in the United Kingdom'. *Econ. Geog.* 34, 1958.

N. Lansdell, *The Atom and the Energy Revolution.* Penguin Books.

National Coal Board: *Annual Report and Statement of Accounts.* London: H.M.S.O.

J. E. Nef, *The Rise of the British Coal Industry.* London: Routledge.

North of Scotland Hydro-electric Board: *Annual Report and Accounts.* Edinburgh: H.M.S.O.

E. M. Rawstron, 'Changes in the Geography of Electricity Production in Great Britain'. *Geog.* 40, 1955.

T. M. Thomas, 'Recent Trends and Developments in the British Coal Mining Industry'. *Econ. Geog.* 34, 1958.

Sir Arthur Trueman (ed.), *The Coalfields of Great Britain.* London: Edward Arnold.

Ulster Yearbook, Belfast, H.M.S.O.

8. THE AGE OF STEEL

G. C. Allen, *British Industries and their Organization.* London: Longmans, Green.

British Iron and Steel Federation: *Alloy Steels and their Uses.*

British Iron and Steel Federation: *Annual Statistics.*

British Iron and Steel Federation: *A Simple Guide to Basic Processes in the Iron and Steel Industry.*

British Iron and Steel Federation: *A Simple Guide to Finishing Processes in the Iron and Steel Industry.*

British Iron and Steel Federation: *Britain's Iron Ore Resources.*

British Iron and Steel Federation: *The Location of the British Steel Industry.*

British Iron and Steel Federation: *The World's Iron Ore Supplies.*

K. Hutton, *Chemistry.* Penguin Books.

Iron and Steel Board: *Development in the Iron and Steel Industry.* London: H.M.S.O.

W. R. Jones, *Minerals in Industry.* Penguin Books.

J. E. Martin, 'Location Factors in the Iron and Steel Industry'. *Trans. Inst. Brit. Geog.* 1957.

E. M. Rawstron, 'Three Principles of Industrial Location'. *Trans. Inst. Brit. Geog.* 1958.

H. C. Roepke, 'Movements of the British Iron and Steel Industry, 1720 to 1951. *Urbana*, Ill.: U. of Illinois Press.

Statistical Summary of the Mineral Industry (annual). London: H.M.S.O.

A. Street and W. Alexander, *Metals in the Service of Man*. Penguin Books.
T. I. Williams, *The Chemical Industry*. Penguin Books.

9. TRADE, TRANSPORT AND COMMUNICATION

Board of Trade: *Annual Statement of the Trade of the United Kingdom*. London: H.M.S.O.
British Transport Commission: Reports. London: H.M.S.O.
Central Statistical Office: *Annual Abstract of Statistics*. London: H.M.S.O.
Central Statistics Office: *Statistical Abstract of Ireland (annual)*. Dublin: Stationery Office.
C. A. Fisher, 'Britain and the Common Market—I'. *Geog.* 48, 1963.
F. H. W. Green, 'Bus Services in the British Isles'. *Geog. Review* 41, 1951.
C. Hadfield, *British Canals*. London: Phoenix House.
Lloyd's Register of Shipping: *Annual Summary of Merchant Ships Launched*.
Ministry of Transport and Civil Aviation: *Report of the Committee of Inquiry into Inland Waterways* (Cmnd. 486, 1956). London: H.M.S.O.
F. W. Morgan, *Ports and Harbours*. London: Hutchinson.
A. C. O'Dell, *Railways and Geography*. London: Hutchinson.
K. R. Sealy, *The Geography of Air Transport*. London: Hutchinson.
Statesman's Yearbook.
Ulster Yearbook. Belfast: H.M.S.O.
Whitaker's Almanack.
M. J. Wise, 'Britain and the Common Market—I'. *Geog.* 48, 1963.

10. POPULATION

I. Carruthers, 'A Classification of Service Centres in England and Wales'. *Geog. Journ.* 123, 1957.
Census Reports for England and Wales, Ireland, Northern Ireland, Scotland.
J. B. Fleming and F. H. W. Green, 'Some Relations between Country and Town in Scotland'. *Scot. Geog. Mag.* 68, 1952.
F. H. W. Green, 'Community of Interest Areas'. *Econ. Geog.* 34, 1958.
E. M. Hubback, *The Population of Britain*. Penguin Books.
R. H. Osborne, 'Internal Migration in England and Wales, 1951'. *Adv. Sci.* 48, 1956.
P.E.P. Report: *World Population and Resources*. Distributed by Allen & Unwin.
A. E. Smailes, 'The Geography of Towns'. London: Hutchinson.
G. P. Wibberley, 'Some Aspects of Problem Rural Areas in Britain'. *Geogr. Journ.* 120, 1954.

PART TWO

11. INTRODUCTION TO PART TWO

H. E. Bracey, 'A Rural Component of Centrality Applied to Six Southern Counties in the United Kingdom' *Econ. Geog.* 32, 1956.

Central Statistics Office: *Statistical Abstract of Ireland (annual)*. Dublin: Stationery Office.

J. T. Coppock, 'The Relationship of Farm and Parish Boundaries'. *Geog. Studies* 2, 1955.

Department of Agriculture for Scotland: *Agricultural Statistics, Scotland (annual)*. Edinburgh: H.M.S.O.

G. H. Dury, *Map Interpretation*. London: Pitman.

G. H. Dury and J. A. Morris, *The Land from the Air*. London: Harrap.

F. H. W. Green, 'Community of Interest Areas in Western Europe'. *Econ. Geog.* 29, 1953.

G. H. T. Kimble, 'The Inadequacy of the Regional Concept'. In *London Essays in Geography* (ed. L. D. Stamp and S. W. Wooldridge). London: Longmans, Green.

D. L. Linton, 'The Delimitation of Morphological Regions'. In *London Essays in Geography* (ed. L. D. Stamp and S. W. Wooldridge). London: Longmans, Green.

Ministry of Agriculture and Fisheries: *Agricultural Statistics, England and Wales (annual)*. London: H.M.S.O.

A. C. Montefiore and W. M. Williams, 'Determinism and Possibilism'. *Geog. Studies* 2, 1955.

O. H. K. Spate, 'How Determined is Possibilism?' *Geog. Studies* 4, 1957.

12. THE REGIONS OF IRELAND

A View of Ireland. British Association.

Belfast in its Regional Setting. British Association.

Central Statistics Office: *Statistical Abstract of Ireland*. Dublin: Stationery Office.

J. K. Charlesworth, *The Geology of Ireland*. Oliver & Boyd: Edinburgh and London.

D. J. Dwyer, 'The Peat Bogs of the Irish Republic'. *Geogr. Journ.* 128, 1962.

E. Estyn Evans, *Irish Heritage*. Dundalk: Tempest.

T. W. Freeman, *Ireland: its Physical, Historical, Social and Economic Geography*. London: Methuen.

T. W. Freeman, 'The Prospect for Irish Agriculture'. *Geogr. Journ.* 120, 1954.

J. N. Greene, 'A Survey of Irish Agriculture'. *Adv. Sci.* 14, 1958.

J. P. Haughton, 'The Social Geography of Dublin'. *Geog. Review* 47, 1957.

J. H. Johnson, 'Studies of Irish Rural Settlement'. *Geog. Review* 48, 1958.

J. H. Johnson, 'Population Changes in Ireland, 1951–61'. *Geogr. Journ.* 129, 1963.

A. J. P. McCarthy, 'The Irish National Electrification Scheme'. *Geog. Review* 47, 1957.

T. McEvoy, 'Forestry in Ireland'. *Adv. Sci.* 14, 1958.

Sean O'Faolain, *The Irish*. Penguin Books.

L. Symons (ed.), *Land Use in Northern Ireland*. London: University of London Press.

Ulster Yearbook. Belfast: H.M.S.O.

Recommended maps: Ordnance Map of Ireland, 1 : 63,360.
Sheets 43 (with parts of sheets 31 and 42) (Manor Hamilton), 105 (with part of sheet 114) (Galway), 110 (Edenderry), 139 (Arklow), 145 (Limerick), 166 (Clonmel), 188 (Youghal), 192 (Glengarriff).
Ordnance Survey of Northern Ireland, 1 : 63,360, Popular.
Sheets 7 (Belfast), 11 (The Mourne Mountains).

13. WALES AND THE WELSH BORDER

J. A. Andrews, 'Chepstow: a Defunct Seaport of the Severn Estuary'. *Geog.* 40, 1955.

E. G. Bowen (ed.), *Wales: A Physical, Historical, and Regional Geography.* London: Methuen.

E. G. Bowen, *The Settlement of the Celtic Saints in Wales.* Cardiff: U. of Wales Press.

British Regional Geology: *The Welsh Borderland.* London: H.M.S.O.

H. Carter, 'Aberystwyth: the Modern Development of a Medieval Castle Town in Wales'. *Trans. Inst. Brit. Geog.* 1958.

H. C. Chew, 'Fifteen Years of Agricultural Change'. *Geog.* 43, 1958.

H. W. E. Davies, 'The Development of the Industrial Landscape of Llanelly'. *Geog. Studies* 4, 1957.

H. W. E. Davies and D. F. Hagger, 'Recent Industrial Changes in South Wales'. *Adv. Sci.* 18, 1961.

M. Davies, *Wales in Maps.* Cardiff: U. of Wales Press.

M. Davis, 'The Open Fields of Laugharne'. *Geog.* 40, 1955.

Wyn Griffiths, *The Welsh.* Penguin Books.

G. M. Howe, *Wales from the Air.* Cardiff: U. of Wales Press.

G. M. Howe and P. Thomas, *Welsh Landforms and Scenery.* London: Macmillan.

E. Jones, 'Tregaron, a Welsh Market Town'. *Geog.* 35, 1950.

G. R. Jones, 'Some Medieval Rural Settlements in North Wales'. *Trans. Inst. Brit. Geog.* 1953.

J. Oliver, 'The Wetness of Wales. Rainfall as a Factor in the Geography of Wales'. *Geog.* 43, 1958.

W. H. Pearsall, *Mountains and Moorlands.* London: Collins.

J. G. Thomas, 'Some Enclosure Patterns in Central Wales'. *Geog.* 42, 1957.

J. G. Thomas, 'The Geographical Distribution of the Welsh Language'. *Geogr. Journ.* 122, 1956.

T. M. Thomas, 'Wales: Land of Mines and Quarries'. *Geog. Review* 46, 1956.

Recommended maps: Seventh Series sheets 116, 129, 154.
1 : 25,000 sheets SH48 [part of Anglesey], SO53 [Hereford], SS69 [Swansea].

14. THE SCOTTISH HIGHLANDS

British Regional Geology: *The Grampian Highlands.* Edinburgh: H.M.S.O.

British Regional Geology: *The Northern Highlands.* Edinburgh: H.S.M.O.

Department of Agriculture for Scotland: *Types of Farming in Scotland.* Edinburgh: H.M.S.O.

Q

F. Fraser Darling, *Natural History in the Highlands and Islands*. London: Collins.

W. A. Hance, 'Crofting in the Outer Hebrides'. *Econ. Geog.* 28, 1952.

W. A. Hance, 'The Fishing Industry of the Outer Hebrides'. *Econ. Geog.* 29, 1953.

P. M. Hobson, 'Assynt Parish'. *Scot. Geog. Mag.* 65, 1949.

D. L. Linton, 'Watershed Breaching by Ice in Scotland'. *Trans. Inst. Brit. Geog.* 1951.

Moray McLaren, *The Scots*. Penguin Books.

North of Scotland Hydro-electric Board: *Report and Accounts* (annual) Edinburgh: H.M.S.O.

A. C. O'Dell and J. Mackintosh (eds.), *The North-east of Scotland*. Aberdeen: Central Press.

W. H. Pearsall, *Mountains and Moorlands*. London: Collins.

I. M. L. Robertson, 'The Head-dyke: a Fundamental Line in Scottish Geography'. *Scot. Geog. Mag.* 65, 1949.

H. Walton, 'Climate and Famine in Northeast Scotland'. *Scot. Geog. Mag.* 68, 1952.

Recommended maps: Seventh Series sheets 19, 37, 40.
1 : 25,000 sheet NS26 [Elgin].

15. CENTRAL SCOTLAND

British Regional Geology: *The Midland Valley of Scotland*. Edinburgh: H.M.S.O.

Department of Agriculture for Scotland: *Types of Farming in Scotland*. Edinburgh: H.M.S.O.

C. J. Robertson, 'Locational and Structural Aspects of Industry in Edinburgh'. *Scot. Geog. Mag.* 74, 1958.

D. Semple, 'The Growth of Grangemouth'. *Scot. Geog. Mag.* 74, 1958.

Scientific Survey of Southeastern Scotland: British Association handbook.

J. M. Soons, 'Landscape Evolution in the Ochil Hills'. *Scot. Geog. Mag.* 74, 1958.

The Glasgow Region: British Association handbook.

W. H. K. Turner, 'The Evolution of the Pattern of the Textile Industry within Dundee'. *Trans. Inst. Brit. Geog.* 1955.

Recommended maps: Seventh Series sheet 60.
1 : 25,000 sheet NS98 [Grangemouth].

16. THE SOUTHERN UPLANDS AND THE BORDER COUNTRY

British Regional Geology: *Northern England*. London: H.M.S.O.

British Regional Geology: *The South of Scotland*. Edinburgh: H.M.S.O.

R. Common, 'The Geomorphology of the East Cheviot Area'. *Scot. Geog. Mag.* 70, 1954.

Department of Agriculture for Scotland: *Types of Farming in Scotland*. Edinburgh: H.M.S.O.

J. B. Fleming and F. H. W. Green, 'Some Relations between Country and Town in Scotland'. *Scot. Geog. Mag.* 68, 1952.

W. H. Pearsall, *Mountains and Moorlands*. London: Collins.
Scientific Survey of Southeastern Scotland: British Association handbook.
J. Tivy, 'Reconnaissance Survey of Certain Hill Grazings in the Southern Uplands'. *Scot. Geog. Mag.* 70, 1954.

Recommended maps: Seventh Series sheet 69.
    1: 25,000 sheet NU00 [Rothbury].

17. THE LAKE DISTRICT, THE ISLE OF MAN AND THE PENNINES
T. H. Bainbridge, 'Population Changes over the West Cumberland Coalfield'. *Econ. Geog.* 25, 1949.
British Regional Geology: *Northern England*. London: H.M.S.O.
British Regional Geology: *The Pennines and Adjacent Areas*. London: H.M.S.O.
E. Davies, 'Treens and Quarterlands. A Study of the Land System of the Isle of Man'. *Trans. Inst. Brit. Geog.* 1956.
R. H. Kinvig, 'The Isle of Man and Atlantic Britain: a study in historical geography'. *Trans. Inst. Brit. Geog.* 1958.
R. Lawton, 'The Economic Geography of Craven in the Early Nineteenth Century'. *Trans. Inst. Brit. Geog.* 1954.
W. H. Pearsall, *Mountains and Moorlands*. London: Collins.
W. E. Richardson, 'Temperature-differences in the South Tyne Valley, near Alston, Cumberland'. *Weather*, 9, 1954.
A. E. Smailes, 'The Lead Dales of the Northern Pennines'. *Geog.* 21, 1936.
M. M. Sweeting, 'Erosion Cycles and Limestone Caverns in the Ingleborough District'. *Geogr. Journ.* 115, 1950.

Recommended maps: Seventh Series sheets 82, 84, 111.
    1: 25,000 sheets NY45 [Carlisle], NY63 [North Pennines], SK05 [South Pennines].

18. THE LANCS.-CHESHIRE PLAIN AND ITS INDUSTRIAL BORDERS
British Regional Geology: *The Pennines and Adjacent Areas*. London: H.M.S.O.
R. C. Estall, 'Industrial Change in Lancashire and Merseyside'. *Geog.* 46, 1961.
R. K. Gresswell, *Sandy Shores in South Lancashire*. Liverpool: U.P.
G. Mercer, 'Speke as a New Town'. *Town Planning Review*, 24, 1953.
Merseyside: British Association handbook.
R. Millward, *Lancashire: The History of the Landscape*. London: Hodder & Stoughton.
E. S. Simpson, 'The Cheshire Grass-Dairying Region'. *Trans. Inst. Brit. Geog.* 1957.
A. Taylor, 'The Relation of Crop-distribution to the Drift Pattern in Southwest Lancashire'. *Trans. Inst. Brit. Geog.* 1955.
K. L. Wallwork, 'The Cotton Industry in North West England: 1941–61.' *Geog.* 47, 1962.

Recommended maps: Seventh Series sheets 101, 109.
    1: 25,000 sheet SJ52 [Wem].

19. THE INDUSTRIAL NORTHEAST OF ENGLAND

A Physical Land Classification of Northumberland, Durham, and Part of the North Riding of Yorkshire. Newcastle-upon-Tyne: The North East Development Association.

British Regional Geology: *Northern England.* London: H.M.S.O.

A. A. L. Caesar, *A Survey of Industrial Facilities of the North East Region.* Newcastle-upon-Tyne: Reid & Co.

G. H. Daysh and J. S. Symonds, *West Durham. A Study of a Problem Area in North Eastern England.* Oxford: Basil Blackwell.

Industrial Estates. Cheltenham and London: J. Burrow, for North Eastern Trading Estates.

Scientific Survey of Northeastern England: British Association handbook.

Recommended maps: Seventh Series sheet 78.
1:25,000 sheet NZ52 [Tees Estuary].

20. THE INDUSTRIAL REGION OF THE WEST RIDING

J. H. Appleton, 'The Railway Network of Southern Yorkshire'. *Trans. Inst. Brit. Geog.* 1956.

British Regional Geology: *The Pennines and Adjacent Areas.* London: H.M.S.O.

G. B. D. Gray, 'The South-Yorkshire Coalfield'. *Geog.* 32, 1947.

E. Lipson, *A Short History of Wool and Its Manufacture.* London: Heinemann.

H. Rees, 'Leeds and the Yorkshire Woollen Industry'. *Econ. Geog.* 24, 1948.

Sheffield and Its Region: British Association handbook.

Recommended maps: Seventh Series sheet 96. 1:25,000 sheet SK49 [Rotherham].

21. THE SCARPLANDS OF EASTERN ENGLAND

British Regional Geology: *East Yorkshire and Lincolnshire.* London: H.M.S.O.

British Regional Geology: *The Pennines and Adjacent Areas.* London: H.M.S.O.

H. C. Chew, 'Fifteen Years of Agricultural Change'. *Geog.* 43, 1958.

K. C. Edwards, 'Changing Geographical Patterns in Lincolnshire'. *Geog.* 39, 1954.

G. E. Fussell, ' "High Farming" in the North of England, 1840–1880'. *Econ. Geog.* 24, 1948.

M. Kirk, 'The Vale of York: The Evolution of a Landscape'. *Geog.* 40, 1955.

D. L. Linton, 'The Landforms of Lincolnshire'. *Geog.* 39, 1954.

R. F. Peel and J. Palmer, 'The Physiography of the Vale of York'. *Geog.* 40, 1955.

H. Thorpe, 'Some Aspects of Settlement in County Durham'. *Geog.* 35, 1950.

Recommended maps: Seventh Series sheet 105.
1:25,000 sheet SE97 [Vale of Pickering].

22. THE MIDLAND TRIANGLE AND ITS NORTHERN BORDERS

Birmingham and Its Regional Setting: British Association handbook.

British Regional Geology: *The Central England District.* London: H.M.S.O.

British Regional Geology: *The Pennines and Adjacent Areas.* London: H.M.S.O.

K. Buchanan, 'Modern Farming in the Vale of Evesham'. *Econ. Geog.* 24, 1948.

T. J. Chandler, 'Communications and a Coalfield: a study in the Leicestershire and South Derbyshire Coalfield'. *Trans. Inst. Brit. Geog.* 1957.

G. H. Dury, 'Drainage Diversion by Ice'. *Science News* 38, 1955.

W. G. Hoskins, *Leicestershire: the History of the Landscape.* London: Hodder & Stoughton.

B. L. C. Johnson, 'The Distribution of Factory Population in the West Midland Conurbation'. *Trans. Inst. Brit. Geog.* 1958.

H. A. Moisley, 'The Industrial and Urban Development of the North Staffordshire Conurbation'. *Trans. Inst. Brit. Geog.* 1951.

E. R. Rawstron, 'Some Aspects of the Location of Hosiery and Lace Manufacture in Great Britain'. *East Midland Geographer,* no. 9, 1954.

M. J. Wise, 'Some Factors Influencing the Growth of Birmingham'. *Geog.* 33, 1948.

Recommended maps: Seventh Series sheet 131.
1: 25,000 sheet SK51 [Loughborough].

23. SCARPLANDS OF THE SOUTH MIDLANDS

S. H. Beaver, 'The Development of the Northamptonshire Iron Industry, 1881–1930'. In *London Essays in Geography* (ed. L. D. Stamp and S. W. Wooldridge). London: Longmans, Green.

British Regional Geology: *Bristol and Gloucester District.* London: H.M.S.O.

British Regional Geology: *East Anglia and Adjoining Areas.* London: H.M.S.O.

British Regional Geology: *London and Thames Valley.* London: H.M.S.O

British Regional Geology: *The Central England District.* London: H.M.S.O.

H. P. R. Finberg, *Gloucestershire.* London: Hodder & Stoughton.

E. W. Gilbert, 'The Industrialisation of Oxford'. *Geogr. Journ.* 109, 1947.

W. R. Mead, 'Ridge and Furrow in Buckinghamshire'. *Geogr. Journ.* 120, 1954.

W. L. Sargant, 'The Pattern of the Anglo-Saxon Settlement of Rutland'. *Geog.* 31, 1946.

The Oxford Region: British Association handbook.

Recommended maps: Seventh Series sheet 144.
1: 25,000 sheet SP81 [Aylesbury].

24. EAST ANGLIA AND THE FENLANDS

M. A. Arber, 'Dust-storms in the Fenland around Ely'. *Geog.* 31, 1946.

British Regional Geology: *East Anglia and Adjoining Areas.* London: H.M.S.O.

H. C. Darby, *The Draining of the Fens*. Cambridge: U.P.

R. E. Dickinson, 'The Town Plans of East Anglia. A Study in Urban Morphology'. *Geog.* 19, 1934.

G. J. Fuller, 'Geographical Aspects of the Development of Boston (Lincs.) between 1700 and 1900'. *East Midland Geographer*, 2, 1954.

G. E. Fussell, ' "High Farming" in the East Midlands and East Anglia'. *Econ. Geog.* 27, 1951.

W. W. Williams, 'An East Coast Survey: Some Recent Changes in the Coast of East Anglia'. *Geogr. Journ.* 122, 1956.

Recommended maps: Seventh Series sheets 124, 125.
1 : 25,000 sheets TF22 [Spalding], TM45 [Aldeburgh].

25. SOUTHWEST ENGLAND

British Regional Geology: *Southwest England*. London: H.M.S.O.

H. C. Chew, 'Fifteen Years of Agricultural Change'. *Geog.* 43, 1958.

A. Downes, 'Farming the Fortunate Isles'. *Geog.* 42, 1957.

G. E. Fussell, ' "High Farming" in Southwestern England, 1840–1880'. *Econ. Geog.* 24, 1948.

E. Johns, 'The Surveying and Mapping of Vegetation on some Dartmoor Pastures'. *Geog. Studies* 4, 1957.

W. L. D. Ravenhill, 'The Settlement of Cornwall during the Celtic Period'. *Geog.* 40, 1955.

A. H. Shorter, 'The Site, Situation, and Functions of Exeter'. *Geog.* 39, 1954.

Recommended maps: Seventh Series sheet 186.
1 : 25,000 sheet SX97 [Teignmouth].

26. THE BORDERS OF THE WEST COUNTRY, THE HAMPSHIRE BASIN AND ITS BORDERS, THE CHANNEL ISLANDS

Bristol and its Adjoining Counties: British Association handbook.

British Regional Geology: *Bristol and Gloucester District*. London: H.M.S.O.

British Regional Geology: *The Hampshire Basin and Adjoining Areas*. London: H.M.S.O.

Channel Islands: Committees for Horticulture and for Agriculture and Fisheries in Jersey and Guernsey. Reports and Special Publications.

G. M. Davies, *The Dorset Coast*. London: Adam & Charles Black.

G. H. Dury, *The Channel Islands* (Report of the Land Utilisation Survey of Great Britain).

S. J. Jones, 'The Growth of Bristol'. *Trans. Inst. Brit. Geog.* 1946.

L. E. Taverner, 'The Port of Southampton'. *Econ. Geog.* 26, 1950.

L. E. Taverner, 'Changes in the Agricultural Geography of Dorset, 1929–1949'. *Trans. Inst. Brit. Geog.* 1955.

M. J. Williams, 'Drainage Activity in the Somerset Levels Since 1939', *Geog.* 49, 1964.

Recommended maps: Seventh Series sheets 165, 179.
1 : 25,000 sheets ST95 [Vale of Pewsey], SU11 [Fordingbridge].

27. SOUTHEAST ENGLAND

J. A. Andrews, 'The Development of the Passenger Ports of Southeast England'. *Geog.* 35, 1950.

British Regional Geology: *The Wealden District*. London: H.M.S.O.

E. W. Gilbert, 'The Growth of Brighton'. *Geog. Journ.* 114, 1949.

I. D. Margary, *Roman Ways in the Weald*. London: Phoenix House.

W. H. Parker, 'Settlement in Sussex, 1840–1940'. *Geog.* 35, 1950.

B. W. Sparks, 'The Denudation-chronology of the Dip-slope of the South Downs'. *Proc. Geol. Assoc.* 60, 1949.

G. S. Sweeting, 'Wealden Iron Ore and the History of its Industry'. *Proc. Geol. Assoc.* 55, 1944.

S. W. Wooldridge and F. Golding, *The Weald*. London: Collins.

Recommended maps: Seventh Series sheet 172.
 1 : 25,000 sheet TQ72 [Rye].

28. THE LONDON BASIN

J. Bird, *The Geography of the Port of London*. London: Hutchinson.

J. Bird, 'The Industrial Development of Lower Thames-side'. *Geog.* 37. 1952.

British Regional Geology: *London and Thames Valley*. London: H.M.S.O.

H. C. Chew, 'Fifteen Years of Agricultural Change'. *Geog.* 43, 1958.

K. M. Clayton and J. Brown, 'The Glacial Deposits around Hertford'. *Proc. Geol. Assoc.* 69, 1958.

R. Clayton (ed.), *The Geography of Greater London.* London: George Philip.

J. T. Coppock, 'Changing Arable in the Chilterns, 1875–1951'. *Geog.* 42, 1957.

J. T. Coppock, 'Land-use Changes in the Chilterns, 1931–1951'. *Trans. Inst. Brit. Geog.* 1954.

R. C. Estall, 'The London Coal Trade'. *Geog.* 43, 1958.

P. Hall, *London 2000*. London: Faber & Faber.

F. K. Hare, 'The Geomorphology of a part of the Middle Thames'. *Proc. Geol. Assoc.* 58, 1947.

D. M. J. Hooson, 'The Recent Growth of Population and Industry in Hertfordshire'. *Trans. Inst. Brit. Geog.* 1958.

Port of London Authority (Port of London Authority handbook).

K. R. Sealy, 'London's Airports and the Geography of Airport Location'. *Geog.* 40, 1955.

M. J. Wise, 'The Role of London in the Industrial Geography of Great Britain'. *Geog.* 41, 1956.

S. W. Wooldridge and G. E. Hutchings, *London's Countryside*. London: Methuen.

Recommended maps: Seventh Series sheet 160.
 1 : 25,000 sheet SU86 [Aldershot].

29. CONCLUSION

P. Archer (ed.). *Social Welfare and the Citizen*. Penguin Books.

Britain and Europe: Economist Intelligence Unit Ltd., London.

J. A. C. Brown, *The Social Psychology of Industry.* Penguin Books.

M. Chisholm, 'Must We All Live in South-east England?' *Geog.* 49, 1964.

G. D. H. Cole, *Local and Regional Government.* London: Cassell.

G. Connell-Smith, *Pattern of the Post-war World.* Penguin Books.

J. H. Dunning and C. J. Thomas, *British Industry, Change and Development in the Twentieth Century.* London: Hutchinson.

P. S. Florence, *Industry and the State.* London: Hutchinson.

T. W. Freeman, *Geography and Planning.* London: Hutchinson.

L. L. Goodman, *Man and Automation.* Penguin Books.

C. D. Harbury, *The Industrial Efficiency of Rural Labour.* Cardiff: U. of Wales Press.

Ministry of Housing and Local Government, *The South East Study 1961–81.* London: H.M.S.O.

A. E. Moodie, *The Geography Behind Politics.* London: Hutchinson.

P.E.P. Report: *Growth in the British Economy.* London: Allen & Unwin.

W. J. H. Sprott, *Human Groups.* Penguin Books.

G. Williams, *Economics of Everyday Life.* Penguin Books.

M. J. Wise and others (13 articles), 'This Changing Britain'. *Geog.* 49, 1964.

FURTHER TEXTS

J. B. Mitchell (ed.), *Great Britain: Geographical Essays.* Cambridge University Press.

Nelson's *Regions of the British Isles* (in progress: various authors).

L. D. Stamp and S. H. Beaver, *The British Isles.* London: Longmans Green.

J. A. Wreford Watson and J. B. Sissons (eds.), *The British Isles.* London. Nelson.

Index

475

equilibrium, of air masses, 34
Erewash, 345, 359
Erica (heather), 48
Ermine Street, 338
Erne, river, 185, 191
    h.e.p. on, 186
erosion, 12, 16, 345
erosional platforms, 19–20, 176, 182, 187, 246, 392, 394
Erribol, Loch, 233
Escrick, 338
Esk (N. and/or S.), 246, 247
eskers, 171, 175
Essex, 56, 377, *379*, 443–4
    estuaries of, 381, 437
estuarine clays, 250, 433, 436
estuarine flats, 267
estuary-head settlements, 174, 385
Ettrick, 268
European Coal and Steel Community, 138
European Common Market, 138
evaporation, 31, 380
evaporites, 15, 278
Evenlode, 364
Evesham, 224, 345, 346–7
excavating plant, 337
exchange, rates of, 130
Exe, 15, 393, 394, 399, 406
Exeter, 392, 396, 397, 399–401
Exmoor, 16, 392, 393, 395
explosives, 300
exports, 4, 133–4, 146
express goods trains, 338
external trade, 2, 4, 72, 130, *137*, 140, 146–7

F

factories, 91
factory towns, 71, 91
fairs, medieval, 67
Falkirk, 242, 254, 260–1
falling sea-levels, 19, 20, 437
fallow, 58, 59, 61, 64
Falmouth, 27, 394, 397, 401
family labour, in industry, 319
famine, of 1845, 72, 77, 152, 154
Fareham, 412, 415, 416
farmhouses, erection of, 70
farming, customs of, 50
    mechanisation of, 155, 250, 415
    part-time, 230
farm labour supply, 168
farmland, proportion of, *81*
farmsteads, 278, 365
Farnborough, 440
Farnham, 424
fat cattle, 366
faulted depressions, 16

faulting, 10, 16, 405
fault-angle valley, 276
fault-line scarp, 284
fault-line valleys, 12, 228
Faversham, 433
Fawley, 418
Felixstowe, 386
fenland, 39, 338
Fenlands, 17, 21, 48, 83, 329, 342, 369, 372, 377–8, 381, 387, 428
    borders of, 369–70
    climate of, 390
    drainage of, 69, 387–9
    embankments in, 389
    'islands' of, 390
    settlement of peat Fen, *389*
    soils of, 387–9, 390
    town sites of, 391
    wheat in, 85
fen peat, 46, 48, 172, 388
    shrinking of, 388
Fenton, 355
Fermanagh, 190
ferries, 261, 416, 452
fertilisers, 45, 49, 75, 175, 236, 247, 309, 370, 387, 442
fescue-agrostis grassland, 43, 45, 233
fescue moor, 268
Feudalism, decay of, 67, 69
feudal system, 61
field boundaries, 70
Fife, 248, 261
    coalfields of, 246, 251–2, 260–1
filtration plant, 286
Finchingfield, 383
fine-grained sediments, 12, 45
fine steel products, 128
Finnart, 261
fiords, 228
fireclay, 327, 348
Firth of Clyde, 247, *257*
Firth of Forth, 31, 246, 248
Firth of Tay, 246
fishermen, decline in numbers of, 240
Fishguard, 178, 206, 208
fishing ports, 141, 208, 232, 304, 337, 386, 420, 430–1
fishing vessels, 145, 240, 337
fishing villages, 398
fishing, in Highlands, 240
fishmeal, 189
Flamborough Head, 17
flax, 91, 192, 193, 293, 366, 408
Fleet, The, 445
Fleetwood, 289, 304
flights, passenger, 145
flints, 354
flood plains, 48, 87, 331, 346, 368, 380–381, 425, 437, 441, 448
flooding, prevention of, 48, 388

LIVERPOOL
UNIVERSITY